PEARSON CUSTOM
ELECTRONICS TECHNOLOGY

Compiled by: Dr. Wael Ibrahim
ECPI College of Technology
Electronics Engineering Technology
Lab Manual

Pearson Custom Publishing

New York   Boston   San Francisco
London   Toronto   Sydney   Tokyo   Singapore   Madrid
Mexico City   Munich   Paris   Cape Town   Hong Kong   Montreal

Senior Vice President, Editorial and Marketing: Patrick F. Boles
Sponsoring Editor: Debbie Coniglio
Development Editor: Amy Galvin
Editorial Assistant: Jeanne Martin
Marketing Manager: Kathleen Kourian
Operations Manager: Eric M. Kenney
Database Product Manager: Jennifer Berry
Rights Editor: Francesca Marcantonio
Art Director: Renée Sartell
Cover Designer: Kristen Kiley

Cover Art: "Air Traffic Controller at Work, Radar in Foreground," courtesy of Roger Tully / Getty Images; "Young Man Enjoying Music with Headphones," courtesy of Geni Corwin / iStockphoto; "Rov Ventana Submersible is Lowered by Crane from MBARI Ship, Point Lobos, Monterey Bay, California," courtesy of Norbert Wu / Getty Images; "Air Traffic Control Room, Two Men Studying with Radar Screen, Rear View," courtesy of Paul Chesley / Getty Images; "Autonomous Submersible," courtesy of Norbert Wu / Getty Images.

Please visit our website at *www.pearsoncustom.com*.

Attention bookstores: For permission to return any unsold stock, contact us at *pe-uscustomreturns@pearson.com*.

**Pearson
Custom Publishing**
is a division of

www.pearsonhighered.com

ISBN 10: 053699384x
ISBN 13: 9780536993847

Attention Students!
Important Information Regarding Supplemental Materials for Your Customized Book

Your custom book may come with additional student resources designed to aid you in further understanding material covered in your text. These supplements are available to you via the following website, searchable by author last name and title:

http://www.pearsoned.com/electronics

When you encounter a text reference to the website above, simply follow these instructions to access the supplemental materials.

Accessing the Student Data Files in the Pearson Custom Publishing Program in Electronics Technology:

1. **From an open Web browser go to:** http://www.pearsoned.com/electronics. **Note:** You should consider bookmarking this URL, as it may contain links to additional supplements that you will be using in your class.

2. **Select the book from which your custom chapter is derived.** In order to determine this, go to the first page of the chapter in which you are currently working. At the bottom of the first page you will see a credit line that includes a book title and author name. On the website, click on the first letter of the author's last name. **Note:** If the author has written more than one text, all titles will be listed. Simply select the appropriate book title for your chapter.

3. **Select the corresponding chapter to access supplemental materials.** Since you have a custom book, refer only to chapter titles – not the original chapter numbers which appear in parentheses. This is because your instructor may have re-ordered the sequence of chapters for your customized book. Simply browse through the chapter titles to locate the one that matches the title of the chapter you are reading. **Note:** If unsure of your chapter title, again refer to the first page of the chapter in which you are currently working.

4. **Locate the file that you need.** You may open to view it immediately, or you may save the file to a specific location on your hard drive. We recommend saving the files to your desktop to find them easily. **Note:** Student data file names may have numbers that differ from your custom book's chapter numbers. Again, this will occur if your instructor re-ordered the chapters when creating your custom book.

Contents

ELECTRONIC SYSTEMS

DIGITAL LOGIC

CIRCUIT ANALYSIS

To the Student...

Safety

Like most technologies, electronics can be hazardous if approached carelessly or without proper training. Although the circuits in this manual are designed for relatively low currents, you should be aware that even low-current circuits can harm you under certain circumstances. To keep the lab environment as safe as possible, always follow these guidelines:

1. Always ask your instructor for help when you are unsure of how to proceed or how to use a specific piece of equipment.

2. Always read the exercise *before* coming to lab. By doing so, you can identify any concerns before beginning.

3. Unless directed otherwise, have your instructor inspect your circuits prior to applying power.

4. Use only equipment that is approved by your instructor.

5. Always disconnect circuits before leaving your work station. (This holds true for soldering irons as well.)

6. Unless directed otherwise by your instructor, perform all of the steps in each exercise in their proper order.

7. *Never try to defeat any safety feature on your equipment or in your circuit.*

8. Never touch the components in a live circuit unless specifically told to do so.
Even when power is disconnected, some components (such as capacitors) can store a significant charge.

9. Never bring food or liquids into your work area.

10. Avoid wearing jewelry, such as rings and watches, when working on live circuits.

11. Never work alone.

12. Don't make the mistake of believing that safety rules are written for everyone *else* to follow. They were written for *you*.

Getting the Most from the Exercises

Here are some suggestions that will help you to have a positive learning experience in lab:

1. Come prepared. Lab time is limited, so the more prepared you are, the less lab time you will spend trying to get ready.

2. Review the text material identified under the LAB PREPARATION heading before coming to lab.

3. Perform any relevant calculations before coming to lab. That way, you'll have an idea of the results you should expect before performing the exercise.

4. Make certain that you have all of the needed components and equipment before starting the exercise.

5. Work in a neat and organized manner. Whenever possible, build your circuits so that they are laid out exactly like the schematic. That way, you'll never have trouble identifying the component of interest for a specific step.

6. Record your results at the time a measurement is taken. Don't rely on memory to "fill in the blanks" later.

7. Use your own words to answer the questions in each exercise, making your answers as complete as possible. Here's a simple guideline to answering questions: Answer them as if you were trying to explain the operating principle, measurement, or calculation to someone.

If you follow these suggestions and the safety rules presented earlier, your experience in the lab will be beneficial and educational, rather than a source of frustration.

Resistor Color Coding

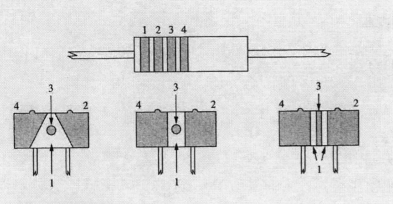

1 First significant digit
2 Second significant digit
3 Multiplying value
4 Tolerance (percent)

FIG. I.1

TABLE I.1   RETMA color code for resistors

Color	1 First Significant Digit	2 Second Significant Digit	3 Multiplier	4 Percent Tolerance
Silver			0.01	10
Gold			0.1	5
Black	(not used)	0	1.0	
Brown	1	1	10	1
Red	2	2	100	2
Orange	3	3	1000	3
Yellow	4	4	10,000	4
Green	5	5	100,000	
Blue	6	6	1,000,000	
Purple	7	7	10,000,000	
Gray	8	8	100,000,000	
White	9	9	1,000,000,000	
No color				20

EXAMPLE I.1   Application of resistor color code

Nominal Value	Percent Tolerance	Band				Tolerance	Range
		1	2	3	4		
22,000 Ω	±20	Red	Red	Orange	No Band	±4400 Ω	17,600–26,400 Ω
100 Ω	±5	Brown	Black	Brown	Gold	±5 Ω	95–105 Ω
10 Ω	±10	Brown	Black	Black	Silver	±1 Ω	9–11 Ω
1.2 kΩ	±5	Brown	Red	Red	Gold	±60 Ω	1140–1260 Ω
6.8 MΩ	±20	Blue	Gray	Green	No Band	±1.36 MΩ	5.44–8.16 MΩ

Capacitor Color Coding

MOLDED CERAMIC CAPACITORS

FIG. II.1

G A B C D

A First significant digit
B Second significant digit
C Multiplying value
D Tolerance
G Temperature coefficient

TABLE II.1 Color code for molded ceramic capacitors

Color	A First Significant Digit	B Second Significant Digit	C Multiplier	D TOLERANCE Value Greater Than 10 pF (%)	Value 10 pF or Less (pF)	G Temperature Coefficient (parts per million per °C)
Black	(not used)	0	1	20	2.0	0
Brown	1	1	10	1		−30
Red	1	1	100	2		−80
Orange	3	3	1000			−150
Yellow	4	4	10,000			−220
Green	5	5	100,000	5	0.5	−330
Blue	6	6	1,000,000			−470
Violet	7	7	10,000,000			−750
Gray	8	8	0.01		0.25	+30
White	9	9	0.1	10	1.0	+550

Resistance Measurements (VOM)

Never Make Resistance Measurements on a Live Circuit!

Select the two leads used for resistance measurements. (Consult the instruction manual.) Set the function selector switch to the ohms position. Select the proper range with the range switch. The ranges are usually marked as multiples of R. For example,

$$R \times 1 \qquad R \times 10 \qquad R \times 100 \qquad R \times 1 \text{k}\_$$

The value of the resistor can be found by multiplying the reading by the range setting. For example, a reading of 11 on the $R \times 1$ kΩ range is $11 \times I$ kΩ $= 11$ kΩ, or 11,000 Ω. Note that the ohms scale (usually the topmost scale) reads from right to left, opposite to the other scales on the meter face.

Before you attach the unknown resistance to the test leads, short the leads together and observe the reading. If the meter does not read zero ohms, adjust the ZERO ADJUST control until it does. Disconnect the leads. The meter should now read infinite resistance (the extreme left-hand index of the scale). If the meter does not read infinite ohms, an adjustment will be required, using the OHMS ADJUST control. On the YOM, the control is a mechanical adjustment which requires the use of a screwdriver. Do not attempt this adjustment on the YOM without first consulting your instructor. The zero and infinite ohm adjustments must be checked each time the range of the ohmmeter is changed. Otherwise the readings will be incorrect.

Proper Use of

the VOM Multimeter

1. Always start with the highest range of the instrument and switch down to the proper range successively.
2. Use the range in which the deflection falls in the upper half of the meter scale.
3. Whenever possible, choose a voltmeter range such that the total voltmeter resistance (ohms/volt X FSD) is at least 100 times the resistance of the circuit under test. This rule will prevent erroneous readings due to the loading of the circuit under test.
4. Use an ohmmeter range so that the deflection falls in the uncrowded portion of the scale.
5. Exercise extreme caution when measuring voltages and currents in high-voltage circuits. A safe procedure is to shut down the power, connect the meter, turn the power on, read the meter, and again shut down to disconnect.
6. Try to ascertain the polarity of dc voltages before making the measurement.
7. Never measure resistances in a live circuit. Always shut down before making resistance measurements.
8. Whenever measuring the resistance of a resistor in a circuit, note whether there are any other resistive elements that could cause an error in the reading. It may be necessary to disconnect one side of the resistor before measuring.
9. Check the zero and ohms adjustments each time the range is changed. For proper procedure, see Appendix III.
10. When making measurements, grip the test prods by the handles as close to the lead end as possible. *Do not allow the fingers to touch the prod tips while measuring.*
11. When the instrument is not being used, do not leave it in the ohmmeter function. If the instrument has an OFF position, use it; otherwise, switch to its highest dc voltage range.
12. *Keep the instruments away from the edge of the workbench, and away from heat and dangerous fumes.*

Scientific Notation
and Trigonometric Identities

Scientific Notation

Scientific Notation

The positive exponent of 10 is equal to one less than the number of places to the left of the decimal point:	The negative exponent of 10 is equal to the number of places to the right of the decimal point:

$$10^0 = \quad 1.0$$
$$10^1 = \quad 10.0$$
$$10^2 = \quad 100.0$$
$$10^3 = \quad 1000.0$$
$$10^4 = \quad 10000.0$$
$$10^5 = 100000.0$$
etc.

$$10^0 \quad = 1.0$$
$$10^{-1} = 0.1$$
$$10^{-2} = 0.01$$
$$10^{-3} = 0.001$$
$$10^{-4} = 0.0001$$
$$10^{-5} = 0.00001$$
etc.

Dimensional Prefixes

Prefix	Multiplier
tera	10^{12}
giga	10^{9}
mega	10^{6}
kilo	10^{3}
hecto	10^{2}
deka	10^{1}
deci	10^{-1}
centi	10^{-2}
milli	10^{-3}
micro	10^{-6}
nano	10^{-9}
pico	10^{-12}

Trigonometric Identities

$$\sin(-\theta) = -\sin\theta$$
$$\cos(-\theta) = \cos\theta$$
$$\tan(-\theta) = -\tan\theta$$
$$\sin(\theta + 90°) = \cos\theta$$
$$\cos(\theta - 90°) = \sin\theta$$
$$\sin^2\theta + \cos^2\theta = 1$$
$$\cos(A + B) = \cos A \cos B - \sin A \sin B$$
$$\cos(A - B) = \cos A \cos B + \sin A \sin B$$
$$\sin(A + B) = \sin A \cos B + \cos A \sin B$$
$$\sin(A - B) = \sin A \cos B - \cos A \sin B$$

Oscilloscope Guide
Analog and Digital Storage Oscilloscopes

The oscilloscope is the most widely used general-purpose measuring instrument because it allows you to see a graph of the voltage as a function of time in a circuit. Many circuits have specific timing requirements or phase relationships that can be readily measured with a two-channel oscilloscope. The voltage to be measured is converted into a visible display that is presented on a screen.

There are two basic types of oscilloscope: analog and digital. In general, they each have specific characteristics. Analog scopes are the classic "real-time" instruments that show the waveform on a cathode-ray tube (CRT). Digital oscilloscopes are rapidly replacing analog scopes because of their ability to store waveforms and because of measurement automation and many other features such as connections for computers. The storage function is so important that it is usually incorporated in the name as a Digital Storage Oscilloscope (DSO). Some higher-end DSOs can emulate an analog scope in a manner that blurs the distinction between the two types. Tektronix, for example, has a line of scopes called DPOs (Digital Phosphor Oscilloscopes) that can characterize a waveform with intensity gradients like an analog scope and gives the benefits of a digital oscilloscope for measurement automation.

Analog and digital scopes have similar functions, and the basic controls are essentially the same for both types (although certain enhanced features are not). In the descriptions that follow, the analog scope is introduced first to familiarize you with basic controls, then a specific digital storage oscilloscope is described (the Tektronix TDS220).

ANALOG OSCILLOSCOPES
Block Diagram
The analog oscilloscope contains four functional blocks, as illustrated in Figure I-2. Shown within these blocks are the most important typical controls found on nearly all oscilloscopes.

Each of two input channels is connected to the vertical section, which can be set to attenuate or amplify the input signals to provide the proper voltage level to the vertical deflection plates of the CRT. In a dual-trace oscilloscope (the most common type), an electronic switch rapidly switches between channels to send one or the other to the display section.

The trigger section samples the input waveform and sends a synchronizing trigger signal at the proper time to the horizontal section. The trigger occurs at the same relative time, thus superimposing each succeeding trace on the previous trace. This action causes a repetitive signal to stop, allowing you to examine it.

The horizontal section contains the time-base (or sweep) generator, which produces a linear ramp, or "sweep," waveform that controls the rate the beam moves across the screen. The horizontal position of the beam is proportional to the time that elapsed from the start of the sweep, allowing the horizontal axis to be calibrated in units of time. The output of the horizontal section is applied to the horizontal deflection plates of the CRT.

Finally, the display section contains the CRT and beam controls. It enables the user to obtain a sharp presentation with the proper intensity. The display section usually contains other features such as a probe compensation jack and a beam finder.

Controls
Generally, controls for each section of the oscilloscope are grouped together according to function. Frequently, there are color clues to help you identify groups of controls. Details of these controls are

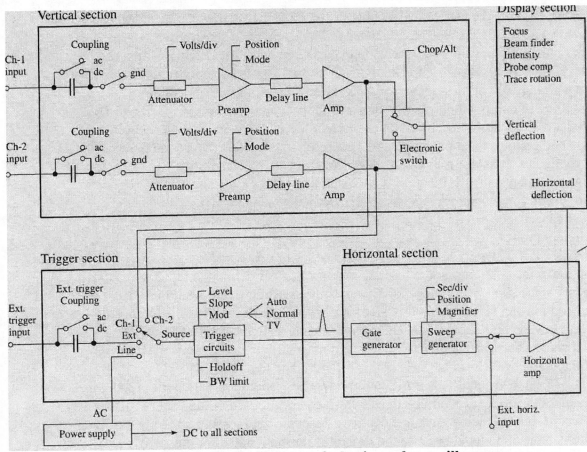

Figure I-2 Block diagram of a basic analog oscilloscope.

explained in the operator's manual for the oscilloscope; however, a brief description of frequently used controls is given in the following paragraphs. The important controls are shown on the block diagram of Figure I-2.

Display Controls The display system contains controls for adjusting the electron beam, including FOCUS and INTENSITY controls. FOCUS and INTENSITY are adjusted for a comfortable viewing level with a sharp focus. The display section may also contain the BEAM FINDER, a control used in combination with the horizontal and vertical POSITION controls to bring the trace on the screen. Another control over the beam intensity is the z-axis input. A control voltage on the z-axis input can be used to turn the beam on or off or adjust its brightness. Some oscilloscopes also include the TRACE ROTATION control in the display section. TRACE ROTATION is used to align the sweep with a horizontal graticule line. This control is usually adjusted with a screwdriver to avoid accidental adjustment. Usually a PROBE COMP connection point is included in the display group of controls. Its purpose is to allow a quick qualitative check on the frequency response of the probe-scope system.

Vertical Controls The vertical controls include the VOLTS/DIV (vertical sensitivity) control and its vernier, the input COUPLING switch, and the vertical POSITION control. There is a duplicate set of these controls for each channel and various switches for selecting channels or other vertical operating modes. The vertical inputs are connected through a selectable attenuator to a high input impedance dc amplifier. The VOLTSIDIV control on each channel selects a combination *of* attenuation/gain to determine the vertical sensitivity. For example, a low-level signal will need more gain and less attenuation than a higher level signal. The vertical sensitivity is adjusted in fixed

9

VOLTSIDIV increments to allow the user to make calibrated voltage measurements. In addition, a concentric vernier control is usually provided to allow a continuous range of sensitivity. This knob must be in the detent (calibrated) position to make voltage measurements. The detent position can be felt by the user as the knob is turned because the knob tends to "lock" in the detent position. Some oscilloscopes have a warning light or message when the vernier is not in its detent position.

The input coupling switch is a multiple-position switch that can be set for AC, GND, or DC and sometimes includes a 50 Ω. position. The GND position of the switch internally disconnects the signal from the scope and grounds the input amplifier. This position is useful if you want to set a ground reference level on the screen for measuring the dc component of a waveform. The AC and DC positions are high-impedance inputs, typically 1 MΩ shunted by 15 pF of capacitance. High-impedance inputs are useful for general probing at frequencies below about I MHz. At higher frequencies, the shunt capacitance can load the signal source excessively, causing measurement error. Attenuating divider probes are good for high-frequency probing because they have very high impedance (typically 10 MΩ) with very low shunt capacitance (as low as 2.5 pF).

The AC position of the coupling switch inserts a series capacitor before the input attenuator, causing dc components of the signal to be blocked. This position is useful if you want to measure a small ac signal riding on top of a large dc signal-power supply ripple, for example. The DC position is used when you want to view both the AC and DC components of a signal. This position is best when viewing digital signals because the input *RC* circuit forms a differentiating network. The AC position can distort the digital waveform because of this differentiating circuit. The 50 Ω position places an accurate 50 Ω load to ground. This position provides the proper termination for probing in 50 Ω systems and reduces the effect of a variable load, which can occur in high-impedance termination. The effect of source loading must be taken into account when using a 50 Ω input. It is important not to overload the 50 Ω input because the resistor is normally rated for only 2 W, implying a maximum of 10 V of signal can be applied to the input.

The vertical POSITION control varies the dc voltage on the vertical deflection plates, allowing you to position the trace anywhere on the screen. Each channel has its own vertical POSITION control, enabling you to separate the two channels on the screen. You can use vertical POSITION when the coupling switch is in the GND position to set an arbitrary level on the screen as ground reference.

There are two types of dual-channel oscilloscope: dual beam and dual trace. A dual-beam oscilloscope has two independent beams in the CRT and independent vertical deflection systems, allowing both signals to be viewed at the same time. A dual-trace oscilloscope has only one beam and one deflection system; it uses electronic switching to show the two signals. Dual-beam oscilloscopes are generally restricted to high-performance research instruments and are much more expensive than dual-trace oscilloscopes. The block diagram in Figure I-2 is for a typical dual-trace oscilloscope.

A dual-trace oscilloscope has user controls labeled CHOP or ALTERNATE to switch the beam between the channels so that the signals appear to occur simultaneously. The CHOP mode rapidly switches the beam between the two channels at a fixed high speed rate, so the two channels appear to be displayed at the same time. The ALTERNATE mode first completes the sweep for one of the channels and then displays the other channel on the next (or alternate) sweep. When viewing slow signals, the CHOP mode is best because it reduces the flicker that would otherwise be observed. High-speed signals can usually be observed best in ALTERNATE mode to avoid seeing the chop frequency.

Another feature on most dual-trace oscilloscopes is the ability to show the algebraic sum and difference of the two channels. For most measurements, you should have the vertical sensitivity (VOLTS/DIV) on the same setting for both channels. You can use the algebraic sum if you want to compare the balance on push-pull amplifiers, for example. Each amplifier should have identical out-of-phase signals. When the signals are added, the resulting display should be a straight line, indicating balance. You can use the algebraic difference when you want to measure the waveform across an ungrounded component. The probes are connected across the ungrounded component with probe ground connected to circuit ground. Again, the vertical sensitivity (VOLTS/DIV) setting should be the same for each channel. The display will show the algebraic difference in the two signals. The algebraic difference mode also allows you to cancel any unwanted signal that is equal in amplitude and phase and is common to both channels.

Dual-trace oscilloscopes also have an X - Y mode, which causes one of the channels to be graphed on the X-axis and the other channel to be graphed on the Y-axis. This is necessary if you want to change the oscilloscope base line to represent a quantity other than time. Applications include viewing a transfer characteristic (output voltage as a function of input voltage), swept frequency measurements, or showing Lissajous figures for phase measurements. Lissajous figures are patterns formed when sinusoidal waves drive both channels.

Horizontal Controls The horizontal controls include the SEC/DIV control and its vernier, the horizontal magnifier, and the horizontal POSITION control. In addition, the horizontal section may include delayed sweep controls. The SEC/DIV control sets the sweep speed, which controls how fast the electron beam is moved across the screen. The control has a number of calibrated positions divided into steps of 1-2-5 multiples, which allow you to set the exact time interval at which you view the input signal. For example, if the graticule has 10 horizontal divisions and the SEC/DIV control is set to 1.0 ms/div, then the screen will show a total time of 10 ms. The SEC/DIV control usually has a concentric vernier control that allows you to adjust the sweep speed continuously between the calibrated steps. This control must be in the detent position in order to make calibrated time measurements. Many scopes are also equipped with a horizontal magnifier that affects the time base. The magnifier increases the sweep time by the magnification factor, giving you increased resolution of signal details. Any portion of the original sweep can be viewed using the horizontal POSITION control in conjunction with the magnifier. This control actually speeds the sweep time by the magnification factor and therefore affects the calibration of the time base set on the SEC/DIV control. For example, if you are using a 10X magnifier, the SEC/DIV dial setting must be divided by 10.

Trigger Controls The trigger section is the source of most difficulties when learning to operate an oscilloscope. These controls determine the proper time for the sweep to begin in order to produce a stable display. The trigger controls include the MODE switch, SOURCE switch, trigger LEVEL, SLOPE, COUPLING, and variable HOLDOFF controls. In addition, the trigger section includes a connector for applying an EXTERNAL trigger to start the sweep. Trigger controls may also include HIGH or LOW FREQUENCY REJECT switches and BANDWIDTH LIMITING.

The MODE switch is a multiple-position switch that selects either AUTO or NORMAL (sometimes called TRIGGERED) and may have other positions, such as TV or SINGLE sweep. In the AUTO position, the trigger generator selects an internal oscillator that will trigger the sweep generator as long as no other trigger is available. This mode ensures that a sweep will occur even in the absence of a signal because the trigger circuits will "free run" in this mode. This allows you to obtain a baseline for adjusting ground reference level or for adjusting the display controls. In the NORMAL or TRIGGERED mode, a trigger is generated from one of three sources selected by the SOURCE switch—the INTERNAL signal, an EXTERNAL trigger source, or the AC LINE. If you are using the internal signal to obtain a trigger, the normal mode will provide a trigger only if a signal is present and other trigger conditions (level, slope) are met. This mode is more versatile than AUTO as it can provide stable triggering for very low to very high frequency signals. The TV position is used for synchronizing either television fields or lines and SINGLE is used primarily for photographing the display.

The trigger LEVEL and SLOPE controls are used to select a specific point on either the rising or falling edge of the input signal for generating a trigger. The trigger SLOPE control determines which edge will generate a trigger, whereas the LEVEL control allows the user to determine the voltage level on the input signal that will start the sweep circuits.

The SOURCE switch selects the trigger source—either from the CH-1 signal, the CH-2 signal, an EXTERNAL trigger source, or the AC LINE. In the CH-1 position, a sample of the signal from channel-1 is used to start the sweep. In the EXTERNAL position, a time-related external signal is used for triggering. The external trigger can be coupled with either AC or DC COUPLING. The trigger signal can be coupled with AC COUPLING if the trigger signal is riding on a dc voltage. DC COUPLING is used if the triggers occur at a frequency of less than about 20 Hz. The LINE position causes the trigger to be derived from the ac power source. This synchronizes the sweep with signals that are related to the power line frequency.

The variable HOLDOFF control allows you to exclude otherwise valid triggers until the holdoff time has elapsed. For some signals, particularly complex waveforms or digital pulse trains, obtaining a stable trigger can be a problem. This can occur when one or more valid trigger points occurs before the signal repetition time. If every event that the trigger circuits qualified as a trigger were allowed to start a sweep, the display could appear to be unsynchronized. By adjusting the variable HOLDOFF control, the trigger point can be made to coincide with the signal-repetition point.

OSCILLOSCOPE PROBES

Signals should always be coupled into an oscilloscope through a probe. A probe is used to pick off a signal and couple it to the input with a minimum loading effect on the circuit under test. Various types of probes are provided by manufacturers but the most common type is a 10: 1 attenuating probe that is shipped with most general-purpose oscilloscopes. These probes have a short ground lead that should be connected to a nearby circuit ground point to avoid oscillation and power line interference. The ground lead makes a mechanical connection to the test circuit and passes the signal through a flexible, shielded cable to the oscilloscope. The shielding helps protect the signal from external noise pickup.

Begin any session with the oscilloscope by checking the probe compensation on each channel. Adjust the probe for a flat-topped square wave while observing the scope's calibrator output. This is a good signal to check the focus and intensity and verify trace alignment. Check the front-panel controls for the type of measurement you are going to make. Normally, the variable controls (VOLTS/DIV and SEC/DIV) should be in the calibrated (detent) position. The vertical coupling switch is usually placed in the DC position unless the waveform you are interested in has a large dc offset. Trigger holdoff should be in the minimum position unless it is necessary to delay the trigger to obtain a stable sweep.

DIGITAL STORAGE OSCILLOSCOPES
Block Diagram

The digital storage oscilloscope (DSO) uses a fast analog-to-digital converter (ADC) on each channel (typically two or four channels) to convert the input voltage into numbers that can be stored in a memory. The digitizer samples the input at a uniform rate called the sample rate; the optimum sample rate depends on the speed of the signal. The process of digitizing the waveform has many advantages for accuracy, triggering, viewing hard-to-see events, and for waveform analysis. Although the method of acquiring and displaying the waveform is quite different than analog scopes, the basic controls on the instrument are similar.

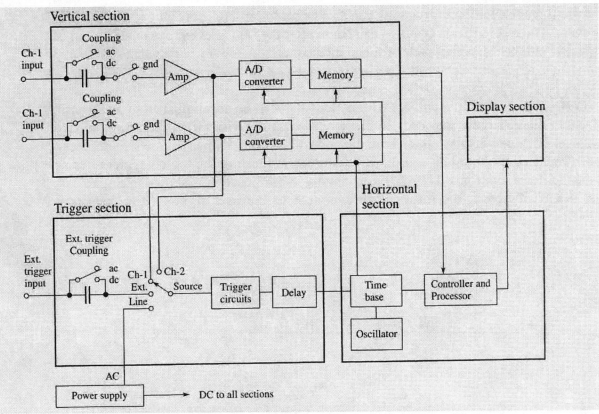

Figure I-3 Block diagram of a basic digital storage oscilloscope.

A block diagram of the basic DSO is shown in Figure I-3. As you can see, functionally, the block diagram is similar to the analog scope. As in the analog oscilloscope, the vertical and horizontal controls include position and sensitivity, which are used to set up the display for the proper scaling.

Specifications   Important parameters with DSOs include the resolution, maximum digitizing rate, and the size of the acquisition memory as well as the available analysis options. The resolution is determined by the number of bits digitized by the ADC. A low-resolution DSO may use only six bits (one part in 64). A typical DSO may use 8 bits, with each channel sampled simultaneously. High-end DSOs may use 12 bits. The maximum digitizing rate is important to capture rapidly changing signals; typically the maximum rate is 1 Gsample/s. The size of the memory determines the length of time the sample can be taken; it is also important in certain waveform measurement functions.

Triggering   One useful feature of digital storage oscilloscopes is their ability to capture waveforms either before or after the trigger event. Any segment of the waveform, either before or after the trigger event, can be captured for analysis. **Pretrigger capture** refers to acquisition of data that occurs *before* a trigger event. This is possible because the data are digitized continuously, and a trigger event can be selected to stop the data collection at some point in the sample window. With pre trigger capture, the scope can be triggered on the fault condition, and the signals that preceded the fault condition can be observed. For example, troubleshooting an occasional glitch in a system is one of the most difficult troubleshooting jobs; by employing pretrigger capture, trouble leading to the fault can be analyzed. A similar application of pre trigger capture is in material failure studies where the events leading to failure are most interesting but the failure itself causes the scope triggering.

Besides pretrigger capture, posttriggering can also be set to capture data that occur some time after a trigger event. The record that is acquired can begin after the trigger event by some amount of time or by a specific number of events as determined by a counter. A low-level response to a strong stimulus signal is an example of when posttriggering is useful.

A Specific DSO Because of the large number of functions that can be accomplished by even basic DSOs, manufacturers have largely replaced the plethora of controls with menu options, similar to computer menus and detailed displays that show the controls as well as measurement parameters. CRTs have been replaced by liquid crystal displays, similar to those on laptop computers. As an example, the display for a Tektronix TDS 220 digital storage oscilloscope is shown in Figure 1-4. Although this is a basic scope, the information available to the user right on the display is impressive.

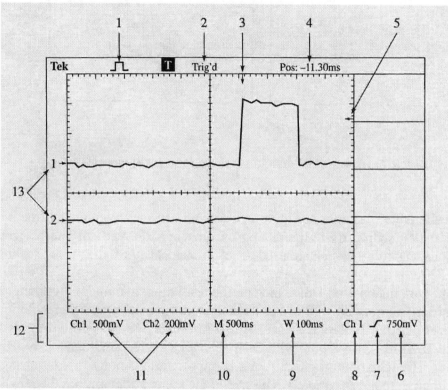

Figure I-4 The display area for a Tektronix TDS 220 Oscilloscope (courtesy of Tektronix, Inc.)

The numbers on the display in Figure I-4 refer to the following parameters:
1. Icon display shows acquisition mode.

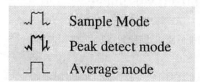

    Sample Mode
    Peak detect mode
    Average mode

2. Trigger status shows if there is an adequate trigger source or if the acquisition is stopped.
3. Marker shows horizontal trigger position. This also indicates the horizontal position since the Horizontal Position control actually moves the trigger position horizontally.

4. Trigger position display shows the difference (in time) between the center graticule and the trigger position. Center screen equals zero.
5. Marker shows trigger level.
6. Readout shows numeric value of the trigger level.
7. Icon shows selected trigger slope for edge triggering.
8. Readout shows trigger source used for triggering.
9. Readout shows window zone time-base setting.
10. Readout shows main time-base setting.
11. Readout shows channels 1 and 2 vertical scale factors.
12. Display area shows on-line messages momentarily.
13. On-screen markers show the ground reference points of the displayed waveforms. No marker indicates the channel is not displayed.

A front view of the TDS220 is shown in Figure I-5. Operation is similar to that of an analog scope except more of the functions are menu controlled; in the TDS220, 12 different menus are accessed to select various controls and options. For example, the MEASURE function brings up a menu that the user can select from five automated measurements including voltage, frequency, period, and averaging to name a few.

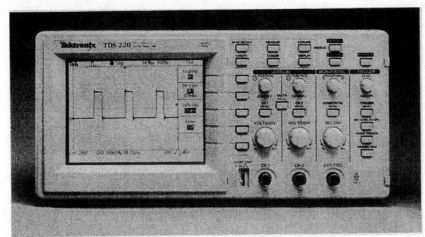

Figure I-5 The Tektronix TDS220 oscilloscope (courtesy of Tektronix, Inc.).

The Technical Report

EFFECTIVE WRITING

The purpose of technical reports is to communicate technical information in a way that is easy for the reader to understand. Effective writing requires that you know your reader's background. You must be able to put yourself in the reader's place and anticipate what information you must convey to have the reader understand what you are trying to say. When you are writing experimental results for a person working in your field, such as an engineer, your writing style may contain words or ideas that are unfamiliar to a layperson. If your report is intended for persons outside your field, you will need to provide background information.

WORDS AND SENTENCES

You need to choose words that have clear meaning to a general audience or define every term, including acronyms, that does not have a well-established meaning. Keep sentences short and to the point. Short sentences are easier for the reader to comprehend. Avoid stringing a series of adjectives or modifiers together. For example, the meaning of this figure caption is unclear:

Operational amplifier constant-current source schematic

The noun *schematic* is described by two modifiers, each of which has its own modifier. By changing the order and adding natural connectors such as *of, using,* and *an,* the meaning can be clarified:

Schematic of a constant-current source using an operational amplifier

PARAGRAPHS

Paragraphs need to contain a unit of thought. Excessively long paragraphs suffer from the same weakness that afflict overly long sentences. The reader is asked to digest too much material at once, causing comprehension to diminish. Paragraphs should organize your thoughts in a logical format. Look for natural breaks in your ideas. Each paragraph should have one central idea and contribute to the development of the entire report.

Good organization is the key to a well-written report. Outlining in advance will help organize your ideas. The use of headings and subheadings for paragraphs or sections can help steer the reader through the report. Subheadings also prepare the reader for what is ahead and make the report easier to understand.

FIGURES AND TABLES

Figures and tables are effective ways to present information. Figures should be kept simple and to the point. Often a graph can make clear the relationship of data. Comparisons of different data drawn on the same graph make the results more obvious to the reader. Figures should be labeled with a figure number and a brief label. Don't forget to label both axes of graphs.

Data tables are useful for presenting data. Usually data presented in a graph or figure should not also be included in a data table. Data tables should be labeled with a table number and short title. The data table should contain enough information that its meaning is clear to the reader without having to refer to the text. If the purpose of the table is to compare information, then form the data in columns rather than rows. Information in columns is easier for people to compare. Table footnotes are a useful method of clarifying some point about the data. Footnotes should appear at the bottom of the table with a key to where the footnote applies.

Data should appear throughout your report in consistent units of measurement. Most sciences use the metric system; however, the English (or customary) system is still sometimes used. The metric system uses derived units that are cgs (centimeter-gram-second) or mks (meter-kilogram-second). It is best to use consistent metric units throughout your report.

Tabular data should be shown with a number of significant digits consistent with the precision of the measurement.

Reporting numbers using powers of 10 can be a sticky point with reference to tables. Table I-2 shows four methods of abbreviating numbers in tabular form. The first column is unambiguous; the number is presented in conventional form. This requires more space than if the information is presented in scientific notation. In column 2, the same data are shown with a metric prefix used for the unit. In column 3, the power of 10 is shown. Each of the first three columns shows the measurement unit and is not subject to misinterpretation. Column 4, on the other hand, is wrong. In this case, the author is trying to tell us what operation was performed on the numbers to obtain the values in the column. This is incorrect because the column heading should contain the unit of measurement for the numbers in the column.

Table I-2 Reporting numbers in tabular data.

Column 1	Column 2	Column 3	Column 4
Resistance ohms	Resistance $k\Omega$	Resistance $\times 10^3$ ohms	Resistance ohms $\times 10^{-3}$
470,000	470	470	470
8,200	8.2	8.2	8.2
1,200,000	1,200	1,200	1,200
330	0.33	0.33	0.33
	Correct		Wrong

SUGGESTED FORMAT

1. *Title.* A good title needs to convey the substance of your report by using key words that provide the reader with enough information to decide if the report should be investigated further.
2. *Contents.* Key headings throughout the report are listed with page numbers.
3. *Abstract.* The abstract is a brief summary of the work with principal facts and results stated in concentrated form. It is a key factor in helping a reader to determine if he or she should read further.
4. *Introduction.* The introduction orients a reader. It should briefly state what you did and give the reader a sense of the purpose of the report. It may tell the reader what to expect and briefly describe the report's organization.
5. *Body of the report.* The report can be made clearer to the reader if you use headings and subheadings to mark major divisions through your report. The headings and subheadings can be generated from the outline of your report. Figures and tables should be labeled and referenced in the body of the report.
6. *Conclusion.* The conclusion summarizes important points or results. It may refer to figures or tables previously discussed in the body of the report to add emphasis to significant points. In some cases, the primary reasons for the report are contained within the body and a conclusion is deemed to be unnecessary.

7. *References.* References are cited to enable the reader to find information used in developing your report or work that supports your report. The references should include names of all authors, in the order shown in the original document. Use quotation marks around portions of a complete document such as a journal article or a chapter of a book. Books, journals, or other complete documents should be underlined. Finally, list the publisher, city, date, and page numbers.

Introduction to the Student

Preparing for Laboratory Work

The purpose of experimental work is to help you gain a better understanding of the principles of electronics and to give you experience with instruments and methods used by technicians and electronic engineers. You should begin each experiment with a clear idea of the purpose of the experiment and the theory behind the experiment. Each experiment requires you to use electronic instruments to measure various quantities. The measured data will be recorded and you will need to interpret the measurements and draw conclusions about your work. The ability to measure, interpret, and communicate results is basic to electronic work.

Preparation before coming to the laboratory is an important part of experimental work. You should prepare in advance for every experiment by reading the *Reading, Objectives,* and the *Summary of Theory* sections before coming to class. *The Summary of Theory* is *not* intended to replace the theory presented in the text—it is meant only as a short review to jog your memory of key concepts and to provide some insight to the experiment. You should also look over the *Procedure* for the experiment. This prelab preparation will enable you to work efficiently in the laboratory and enhance the value of the laboratory time.

This laboratory manual is designed to help you measure and record data as efficiently as possible. Techniques for using instruments are described in many experiments. Data tables are prepared and properly labeled to facilitate the recording of data. Plots are provided where necessary. You will need to interpret and discuss the results in the *Conclusion* section and answer the *Evaluation and Review Questions.* The *Conclusion* to an experiment is a concise statement of your key findings from the experiment. Be careful of generalizations that are not supported by the data. The conclusion should be a specific statement that includes important findings with a brief discussion of problems, revisions, or suggestions you may have for improving the circuit. It should directly relate to the objectives of the experiment. For example, if the objective of the experiment is to measure VOS(Oft) and *loss* for a JFET, the conclusion should indicate these values as determined in the experiment. Then add a statement in which you discuss experimental error and a comparison to theory or specified value.

The Laboratory Notebook

Your instructor may assign a formal laboratory report or a report may be assigned in the section titled *For Further Investigation.* A suggested format for formal reports is as follows:

1. *Title and date.*
2. *Purpose:* Give a statement of what you intend to determine as a result of the investigation.
3. *Equipment and materials:* Include a list of equipment model and serial numbers which can allow retracing if a defective or uncalibrated piece of equipment was used.
4. *Procedure:* Give a brief description of what you did and what measurements you made. A diagram or schematic is often useful.
5. *Data:* Tabulate raw (unprocessed) data; data may be presented in graph form.
6. *Sample calculations:* Give the formulas that you applied to the raw data to transform it to processed data.

7. *Conclusion:* The conclusion is a specific statement supported by the experimental data. It should relate to the objectives for the experiment. For example, if the purpose of the experiment was to determine the frequency response of a filter, the conclusion should describe the frequency response or contain a reference to an illustration of the response.

Graphing

A graph is a pictorial representation of data that enables you to see the effect of one variable on another. Graphs are widely used in experimental work to present information because they enable the reader to discern variations in magnitude, slope, and direction between two quantities. In this manual, you will graph data in many experiments. You should be aware of the following terms that are used with graphs:

abscissa: the horizontal or x-axis of a graph. Normally the independent variable is plotted along the abscissa.

dependent variable: a quantity that is influenced by changes in another quantity (the independent variable).

graph: a pictorial representation of a set of data constructed on a set of coordinates that are drawn at right angles to each other. The graph illustrates one variable's effect on another.

independent variable: the quantity that the experimenter has control over.

ordinate: the vertical or y-axis of a graph. Normally the dependent variable is plotted along the ordinate.

scale: the value of each division along the *x*- or *y*- axis. In a linear scale, each division has equal weight. In a logarithmic scale, each division represents the same percentage change in the variable.

The following steps will guide you in preparing a graph:
1. Determine the type of scale that will be used. A linear scale is the most frequently used and will be discussed here. Choose a scale factor that enables all of the data to be plotted on the graph without being cramped. The most common scales are 1, 2, 5, or 10 units per division. Start both axes from 0 unless the data covers less than half of the length of the coordinate.
2. Number the *major* divisions along each axis. Do not number each small division as it will make the graph appear cluttered. Each division must have equal weight. *Note:* The experimental data is <u>not</u> used to number the divisions.
3. Label each axis to indicate the quantity being measured and the measurement units. Usually, the measurement units are given in parentheses.
4. Plot the data points with a small dot with a small circle around each point. If additional sets of data are plotted, use other distinctive symbols (such as triangles) to identify each set.
5. Draw a smooth line that represents the data trend. It is normal practice to consider data points but to ignore minor variations due to experimental errors. *(Exception:* calibration curves and other discontinuous data are connected "dot-to-dot".)
6. Title the graph, indicating with the title what the graph represents. The completed graph should be self-explanatory.

Safety in the Laboratory

The experiments in this lab book are designed for low voltages to minimize electric shock hazard; however, one should never assume that electric circuits are safe. A current of a few milliamps through the body can be lethal. In addition, electronic laboratories often contain other hazards such as chemicals and power tools. For your safety, you should review laboratory safety rules before beginning a course in electronics. In particular, you should:

1. A void contact with *any* voltage source. Turn off power before working on circuits.
2. Remove watches, jewelry, rings, and so forth before working on circuits – even those circuits with low voltages—as burns can occur.
3. Know *the* location of the emergency power-off switch.
4. Never work alone in *the* laboratory.
5. Keep a neat work area and handle tools properly. Wear safety goggles or gloves when required.
6. Ensure that line cords are in good condition and grounding pins are not missing or bent. Do not defeat *the* three-wire ground system in order *to* make "floating" measurements.
7. Check that transformers and instruments that are plugged into utility lines are properly fused and have no exposed wiring. If *you* are not certain about a procedure, check with your instructor before *you* begin.
8. Report any unsafe condition *to* your instructor.
9. Be aware of and follow laboratory rules.

Reference Guide to Laboratory Instruments

This section is provided to help familiarize you with basic laboratory instruments and may be used as a reference as the instruments are introduced in the experiments. It is impossible to cover all possible variations between instruments so only general features, common to a class of instruments, are described. Consult the operator's manual for detailed descriptions and safe operating practice of the particular instruments in your laboratory.

The Power Supply

Most electronic circuits require a source of regulated direct current (dc) to operate properly. A direct current regulated power supply is a circuit that provides the energy to allow electronic circuits to function. They do this by transforming a source of input electrical power (generally ac) into dc. Most regulated supplies are designed to maintain a fixed voltage that will stay within certain limits of voltage for normal operation. Voltage adjustment and current limits depend on the particular supply.

The power supply must provide the proper level of dc voltage for a given circuit. Some integrated circuits, for example, can function properly only if the voltage is within a very narrow range. You will normally have to set the voltage to the proper level before you connect a power supply to the test circuit. Most laboratory power supplies have more than one output and will have one or more built-in meters to help you set the voltage and monitor the current.

It is important that the user make good connections to the power supply output terminals with wire that is sufficient to carry the load current in case the output is accidentally shorted. Clip-leads are not recommended as they can produce measurement error due to high contact resistance. In situations where several circuits are operated from the same supply, the best policy is to operate each circuit with an independent set of leads.

The Multimeter

The digital multimeter (DMM) and analog volt-ohm-milliammeter (YOM) are multipurpose measuring instruments that combine the characteristics of a dc and ac voltmeter, dc and ac ammeter, and an ohmmeter in one instrument. The DMM indicates the measured quantity as a digital number, avoiding the necessity to interpret the scales as is required on analog instruments. Although in most labs the DMM has replaced the YOM as the instrument of choice, the YOM is still found in some labs.

Because the multimeter is a multipurpose instrument, it is necessary to determine which controls select the desired function. In addition, current measurements (and often high-range voltage measurements) usually require a separate set of lead connections to the meter. After you have selected the function, you need to select the appropriate range to make the measurement. It is important to select the function and range *before* connecting the meter to the circuit you are testing. DMMs can be autoranging, meaning that the instrument automatically selects the correct scale and sets the decimal place; or they can be manual ranging, meaning that the user must select the correct scale. For manual ranging instruments, when the approximate voltage or current is not known, always begin a measurement on the highest possible range to avoid instrument overload and possible damage. Change to a lower range as necessary to increase the precision. The life of range switches will be lengthened if you only change ranges with the probes disconnected from the circuit. On analog instruments the range selected should give a reading in the upper portion of the scale.

The voltmeter function of a DMM can measure either ac or dc volts. The dc voltage function is useful to measure the dc voltage *difference* between two points. If the meter's red lead is touching a more positive point than the meter's black lead, the reading on the meter will be positive; if the black lead is on the more positive point, the reading will be negative. Analog meters *must* be connected with the correct polarity, or the pointer will attempt to move backward, possibly damaging the movement.

The ac voltage function is designed to measure low-frequency sinusoidal waveforms. The meter is designed to indicate the rms (root-mean-square) value of a sinusoidal waveform. Frequency is the number of cycles per second, measured in Hz, for a waveform. All DMMs and VOMs are limited to some specified frequency range. The meter reading will be inaccurate if you attempt to measure waveforms outside the meter's specified frequency range. A typical DMM is not accurate on the ac scale below about 45 Hz or above about 1 kHz, although this range can be considerably better in some cases. It is important that you learn the limitations of your meter.

The ohms function (used for resistance measurements) is used only in circuits that are *not* powered. An ohmmeter works by inserting a small test voltage into a circuit and measuring the resulting current. Consequently, if any voltage is present, the reading will be in error. The meter will show the resistance of all possible paths between the probes. If you want to know the resistance of a single component, it is necessary to isolate that component from the remainder of the circuit by disconnecting one end. In addition, body resistance can affect the reading if you are holding the conducting portion of both probes in your fingers. This procedure should be avoided, particularly with high resistances.

The Function Generator

The basic function generator is used to produce sine, square, and triangle waveforms and may also have a pulse output for testing digital logic circuits. Function generators normally have controls that allow you to select the type of waveform and other controls to adjust the amplitude and dc level. The output voltage is adjusted by the AMPLITUDE control. The dc level is adjusted by the IX OFFSET control; this enables you to add or subtract a dc component to the waveform. These controls may not be calibrated, so amplitude and dc level settings should be verified with the oscilloscope.

The frequency is selected with a combination of a range switch and vernier control. A decade frequency switch or push buttons that enable you to select the frequency in decade increments (factors of ten) up to about 1 MHz select the range. The vernier control is usually a multiplier dial for adjusting the precise frequency needed.

The output voltage level of a function generator will drop from its open circuit voltage when it is connected to a circuit. Depending on the conditions, you generally will need to readjust the amplitude level of the generator after it is connected to the circuit. This is because of the generator's Thevenin resistance that will affect the circuit under test. Common values of Thevenin resistance are 50 _ and 600 _.

Better quality instruments will add features such as trigger or sync outputs to use in synchronizing an oscilloscope, modulation, increased frequency ranges, fixed attenuators on the output, and so forth. Fixed attenuators are handy if you want to reduce the output by an exact amount or you want to choose a very small, but known signal. Some function generators have a SYMMETRY or DUTY CYCLE control that allows you to control the pulse width of the rectangular pulse. Details of the particular features of your function generator and the controls can be found in the operator's manual.

The Oscilloscope

The oscilloscope is the most widely used general-purpose measuring instrument because it allows you see a graph of the voltage as a function of time in a circuit. Many circuits have specific timing requirements or phase relationships that can be readily measured with a two-channel oscilloscope. The voltage to be measured is converted into a visible display, which is presented on a screen.

There are two basic types of oscilloscope—analog and digital. In general, they each have specific characteristics. Analog scopes are the classic "real-time" instruments that show the waveform on a cathode-ray tube (CRT). Digital oscilloscopes are rapidly replacing analog scopes because of their ability to store waveforms and because of measurement automation and many other features such as connections for computers. The storage function is so important that it is usually incorporated in the name as a Digital Storage Oscilloscope (OSO). Some higher-end DSOs can emulate an analog scope in a manner that blurs the distinction between the two types. Tektronix, for example, has a line of scopes called DPOs (Digital Phosphor Oscilloscopes) that can characterize a waveform with intensity gradients like an analog scope and gives the benefits of a digital oscilloscope for measurement automation.

Analog and digital scopes have similar functions, and the basic controls are essentially the same for both types (certain enhanced features are not the same). In the descriptions that follow, the analog scope is introduced first to familiarize you with basic controls, then a specific digital storage oscilloscope is described (The Tektronix TDS220).

Analog Oscilloscopes
Block Diagram
The analog oscilloscope contains four functional blocks, as illustrated in Figure I-1. Shown within these blocks are the most important typical controls found on nearly all oscilloscopes.

Each of two input channels is connected to the vertical section, which can be set to attenuate or amplify the input signals to provide the proper voltage level to the vertical deflection plates of the CRT. In a dual-trace oscilloscope (the most common type), an electronic switch rapidly switches between channels to send one or the other to the display section.

The trigger section samples the input waveform and sends a synchronizing trigger signal at the proper time to the horizontal section. The trigger occurs at the same relative time, thus superimposing each succeeding trace on the previous trace. This action causes the signal to appear to stop, allowing you to examine it

The horizontal section contains the time-base (or sweep) generator, which produces a linear ramp, or "sweep," waveform that controls the rate the beam moves across the screen. The horizontal position of the beam is proportional to the time that elapsed from the start of the sweep, allowing the horizontal axis to be calibrated in units of time. The output of the horizontal section is applied to the horizontal deflection plates of the CRT.

Finally, the display section contains the CRT and beam controls. It enables the user to obtain a sharp presentation with the proper intensity. The display section usually contains other features such as a probe compensation jack and a beam finder.

Controls
Generally, controls for each section of the oscilloscope are grouped together according to function. Frequently, there are color clues to help you identify groups of controls. Details of these controls are explained in the operator's manual for the oscilloscope; however, a brief description of frequently used controls is given in the following paragraphs.

The important controls are shown on the block diagram of Figure I-1.

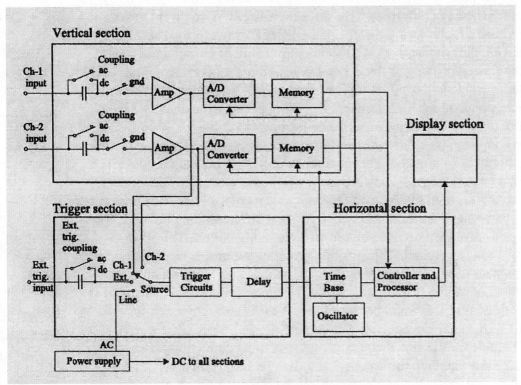

Figure I-1 Block diagram of a basic analog oscilloscope.

Display Controls   The display system contains controls for adjusting the electron beam, including FOCUS and INTENSITY controls. FOCUS and INTENSITY are adjusted for a comfortable viewing level with a sharp focus. The display section may also contain the BEAM FINDER, a control used in combination with the horizontal and vertical POSITION controls to bring the trace on the screen. Another control over the beam intensity is the z-axis input. A control voltage on the z-axis input can be used to turn the beam on or off or adjust its brightness. Some oscilloscopes also include the TRACE ROTATION control in the display section. TRACE ROTATION is used to align the sweep with a horizontal graticule line. This control is usually adjusted with a screwdriver to avoid accidental adjustment Usually a PROBE COMP connection point is included in the display group of controls. Its purpose is to allow a quick qualitative check on the frequency response of the probe-scope system.

Vertical Controls   The vertical controls include the VOLTS/DIV (vertical sensitivity) control and its vernier, the input COUPLING switch, and the vertical POSITION control. There is a duplicate set of these controls for each channel and various switches for selecting channels or other vertical operating modes. Each vertical input is connected through a selectable attenuator to a high input impedance dc amplifier. The VOLTS/DIV control on each channel selects a combination of attenuation/gain to determine the vertical sensitivity. For example, a low-level signal will need more gain and less attenuation than a higher level signal. The vertical sensitivity is adjusted in fixed VOLTS/DIV increments to allow the user to make calibrated voltage measurements. In addition, a concentric vernier control is usually provided to allow a continuous range of sensitivity. This knob must be in the detent (calibrated) position to make voltage measurements. The detent position can be felt by the user as the knob is turned because the knob tends to "lock" in the detent position. Some oscilloscopes have a warning light or message when the vernier is not in its detent position.

      The input coupling switch is a multiple-position switch than can be set for AC, GND, or DC and sometimes includes a 50 Ω position. The GND position of the switch internally disconnects the signal from the scope and grounds the input amplifier. This position is useful if you want to set a ground reference level on the screen for measuring the dc component of a waveform. The AC and DC positions are high-impedance inputs, typically 1 M Ω shunted by 15 pF of capacitance. High-impedance inputs are useful for general probing at frequencies below about 1 MHz. At higher frequencies, the shunt capacitance can load the signal source excessively, causing measurement error. Attenuating divider probes are good for high-frequency probing because they have very high impedance (typically 10 M Ω) with very low shunt capacitance (as low as 2.5 pF).

The AC position of the coupling switch inserts a series capacitor before the input attenuator, causing dc components of the signal to be blocked. This position is useful if you want to measure a small ac signal riding on top of a large dc signal—power supply ripple, for example. The DC position is used when you want to view both the AC and DC components of a signal. This position is best when viewing digital signals because the input *RC* circuit forms a differentiating network. The AC position can distort the digital waveform because of this differentiating circuit. The 50 Ω position places an accurate 50 12 load to ground. This position provides the proper termination for probing in 50 Ω systems and reduces the effect of a variable load, which can occur in high-impedance termination. The effect of source loading must be taken into account when using a 50 Ω input. It is important not to overload the 50 Ω input because the resistor is normally rated for only 2 W, implying a maximum of 10 V of signal can be applied to the input.

The vertical POSITION control varies the dc voltage on the vertical deflection plates, allowing you to position the trace anywhere on the screen. Each channel has its own vertical POSITION control, enabling you to separate the two channels on the screen. You can use vertical POSITION when the coupling switch is in the GND position to set an arbitrary level on the screen as ground reference.

There are two types of dual-channel oscilloscope—dual beam and dual trace. A dual-beam oscilloscope has two independent beams in the CRT and independent vertical deflection systems, allowing both signals to be viewed at the same time. A dual-trace oscilloscope has only one beam and one deflection system, it uses electronic switching to show the two signals. Dual-beam oscilloscopes are generally restricted to high-performance research instruments and are much more expensive than dual-trace oscilloscopes. The block diagram in Figure I-1 is for a typical dual-trace oscilloscope.

A dual-trace oscilloscope has user controls labeled CHOP or ALTERNATE to switch the beam between the channels so that the signals appear to occur simultaneously. The CHOP mode rapidly switches the beam between the two channels at a fixed high-speed rate, so the two channels appear to be displayed at the same time. The ALTERNATE mode first completes the sweep for one of the channels and then displays the other channel on the next (or alternate) sweep. When viewing slow signals, the CHOP mode is better because it reduces the flicker that would otherwise be observed. High-speed signals can usually be observed better in the ALTERNATE mode to avoid seeing the chop frequency.

Another feature on most dual-trace oscilloscopes is the ability to show the algebraic sum and difference of the two channels. For most measurements, you should have the vertical sensitivity (VOLTS/DIV) on the same setting for both channels. You can use the algebraic sum if you want to compare the balance on push-pull amplifiers, for example. Each amplifier should have identical out-of-phase signals. When the signals are added, the resulting display should be a straight line, indicating balance. You can use the algebraic difference when you want to measure the waveform across an ungrounded component. The probes are connected across the ungrounded component with probe ground connected to circuit ground. Again, the vertical sensitivity (VOLTS/DIV) setting should be the same for each channel. The display will show the algebraic difference of the two signals. The algebraic difference mode also allows you to cancel any unwanted signal that is equal in amplitude and phase and is common to both channels.

Dual-trace oscilloscopes also have an X-Y mode, which causes one of the channels to be graphed on the X-axis and the other channel to be graphed on the Y-axis. This is necessary if you want to change the oscilloscope base line to represent a quantity other than time. Applications include viewing a transfer characteristic (output voltage as a function of input voltage), swept frequency measurements, or showing Lissajous figures for phase measurements. Lissajous figures are patterns formed when sinusoidal waves drive both channels.

Horizontal Controls   The horizontal controls include the SEC/DIV control and its vernier, the horizontal magnifier, and the horizontal POSITION control. In addition, the horizontal section may include delayed sweep controls. The SEC/DIV control sets the sweep speed, which controls how fast the electron beam is moved across the screen. The control has a number of calibrated positions divided into steps of 1-2-5 multiples that allow you to set the exact time interval at which you view the input signal. For example, if the graticule has 10 horizontal divisions and the SEC/DIV control is set to 1.0 ms/div, then the screen will show a total time of 10 ms. The SEC/DIV control usually has a concentric vernier control that allows you to adjust the sweep speed continuously between the calibrated steps. This control must be in the detent position in order to make calibrated time measurements. Many scopes are also equipped with a horizontal magnifier that affects the time base. The magnifier increases the sweep time by the magnification factor, giving you increased resolution of signal details. Any portion of the original sweep can be viewed using the horizontal POSITION control in conjunction with the magnifier. This control actually speeds the sweep time by the magnification factor and therefore affects the calibration of the time base set on the SEC/DIV control. For example, if you are using a 10X magnifier, the SEC/DIV dial setting must be divided by 10.

Trigger Controls   The trigger section is the source of most difficulties when learning to operate an oscilloscope. These controls determine the proper time for the sweep to begin in order to produce a stable display. The trigger controls include the MODE switch, SOURCE switch, trigger LEVEL, SLOPE, COUPLING, and variable HOLDOFF controls. In addition, the trigger section includes a connector for applying an EXTERNAL trigger to start the sweep. Trigger controls may also include HIGH or LOW FREQUENCY REJECT switches and BANDWIDTH LIMITING.

The MODE switch is a multiple-position switch that selects either AUTO or NORMAL (sometimes called TRIGGERED) and may have other positions, such as TV or SINGLE sweep. In the AUTO position, the trigger generator selects an internal oscillator that will trigger the sweep generator as long as no other trigger is available. This mode ensures that a sweep will occur even in the absence of a signal because the trigger circuits will "free run" in this mode. This allows you to obtain a baseline for adjusting ground reference level or for adjusting the display controls. In the NORMAL or TRIGGERED mode, a trigger is generated from one of three sources selected by the SOURCE switch—the INTERNAL signal, an EXTERNAL trigger source, or the AC LINE. If you are using the internal signal to obtain a trigger, the normal mode will provide a trigger only if a signal is present and other trigger conditions (level, slope) are met. This mode is more versatile than AUTO as it can provide stable triggering for very low to very high frequency signals. The TV position is used for synchronizing either television fields or lines and SINGLE is used primarily for photographing the display.

The trigger LEVEL and SLOPE controls are used to select a specific point on either the rising or failing edge of the input signal for generating a trigger. The trigger SLOPE control determines which edge will generate a trigger, whereas the LEVEL control allows the user to determine the voltage level on the input signal that will start the sweep circuits.

The SOURCE switch selects the trigger source—either from the CH-1 signal, the CH-2 signal, an EXTERNAL trigger source, or the AC LINE. In the CH-1 position, a sample of the signal from channell is used to start the sweep. In the EXTERNAL position, a time-related external signal is used for triggering. The external trigger can be coupled with either AC or OC COUPLING. The trigger signal can be coupled with AC COUPLING if the trigger signal is riding on a dc voltage. DC COUPLING is used if the triggers occur at a frequency of less than about 20 Hz. The LINE position causes the trigger to be derived from the ac power source. This synchronizes the sweep with signals that are related to the power line frequency.

The variable HOLDOFF control allows you to exclude otherwise valid triggers until the holdoff time has elapsed. For some signals, particularly complex waveforms or digital pulse trains, obtaining a stable trigger can be a problem. This can occur when one or more valid trigger points occurs before the signal repetition time. If every event that the trigger circuits qualified as a trigger were allowed to start a sweep, the display could appear to be unsynchronized. By adjusting the variable HOLOOFF control, the trigger point can be made to coincide with the signal-repetition point.

Oscilloscope Probes

Signals should always be coupled into an oscilloscope through a probe. A probe is used to pick off a signal and couple it to the input with a minimum loading effect on the circuit under test. Various types of probes are provided by manufacturers but the most common type is a 10: 1 attenuating probe that is shipped with most general-purpose oscilloscopes. These probes have a short ground lead that should be connected to a nearby circuit ground point to avoid oscillation and power line interference. The ground lead makes a mechanical connection to the test circuit and passes the signal through a flexible, shielded cable to the oscilloscope. The shielding helps protect the signal from external noise pickup.

Begin any session with the oscilloscope by checking the probe compensation on each channel. Adjust the probe for a flat-topped square wave while observing the scope's calibrator output. This is a good signal to check the focus and intensity and verify trace alignment. Check the front-panel controls for the type of measurement you are going to make. Normally, the variable controls (VOLTSIDIV and SECIDIV) should be in the calibrated (detent) position. The vertical coupling switch is usually placed in the DC position unless the waveform you are interested in has a large dc offset. Trigger holdoff should be in the minimum position unless it is necessary to delay the trigger to obtain a stable sweep.

Digital Storage Oscilloscopes

Block Diagram

The digital storage oscilloscope (OSO) uses a fast analog-to-digital converter (ADC) on each channel (typically two or four channels) to convert the input voltage into numbers which can be stored in a memory. The digitizer samples the input at a uniform rate called the sample rate; the optimum sample rate depends on the speed of the signal. The process of digitizing the waveform has many advantages for accuracy, triggering, viewing hard to see events, and for waveform analysis. Although the method of acquiring and displaying the waveform is quite different than analog scopes, the basic controls on the instrument are similar.

A block diagram of the basic OSO is shown in Figure I-2. As you can see, functionally, the block diagram is like that of the analog scope. As in the analog oscilloscope, the vertical and horizontal controls include position and sensitivity, which are used to set up the display for the proper scaling.

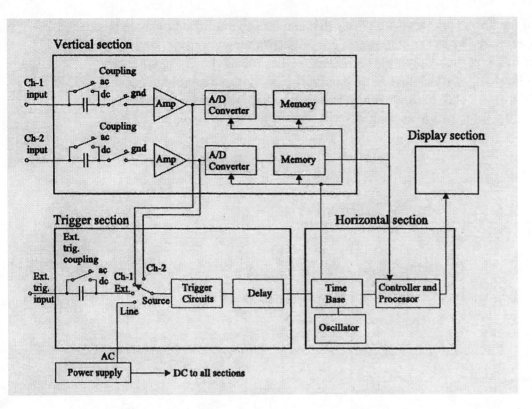

Figure I-2 Block diagram of a basic digital storage oscilloscope.

Specifications   Important parameters with DSOs include the resolution, maximum digitizing rate, and the size of the acquisition memory as well as the available analysis options. The resolution is determined by the number of bits digitized by the ADC. A low-resolution DSO may use only six bits (one part in 64). A typical DSO may use 8 bits, with each channel sampled simultaneously. High-end DSOs may use 12 bits. The maximum digitizing rate is important to capture rapidly changing signals; typically the maximum rate is 1 Gsample/s. The size of the memory determines the length of time the sample can be taken; it is also important in certain waveform measurement functions.

Triggering   One useful feature of digital storage oscilloscopes is their ability to capture waveforms either before or after the trigger event. Any segment of the waveform, either before or after the trigger event, can be captured for analysis. **Pretrigger capture** refers to acquisition of data that occurs *before* a trigger event. This is possible because the data are digitized continuously, and a trigger event can be selected to stop the data collection at some point in the sample window. With pretrigger capture, the scope can be triggered on the fault condition, and the signals that preceded the fault condition can be observed. For example, troubleshooting an occasional glitch in a system is one of the most difficult troubleshooting jobs; by employing pretrigger capture, trouble leading to the fault can be analyzed. A similar application of pretrigger capture is in material failure studies where the events leading to failure are most interesting but the failure itself causes the scope triggering.

Beside pretrigger capture, posttriggering can also be set to capture data that occur some time after a trigger event. The record that is acquired can begin after the trigger event by some amount of time or by a specific number of events as determined by a counter. A lowlevel response to a strong stimulus signal is an example of when posttriggering is useful.

A Specific DSO   Because of the large number of functions that can be accomplished by even basic DSOs, manufacturers have largely replaced the plethora of controls with menu options, similar to computer menus and detailed displays that show the controls as well as measurement parameters. CRTs have been replaced by liquid crystal displays, similar to those on laptop computers. As an example, the display for a Tektronix TDS220 digital storage oscilloscope is shown in Figure I-3. Although this is a basic scope, the information available to the user right on the display is impressive.

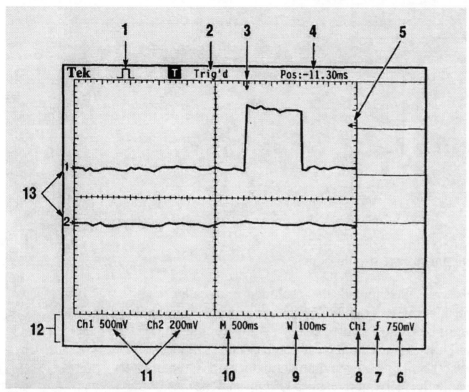

Figure I-3 The display area for a Tektronix TDS220 oscilloscope (Copyright 2001, Tektronix, Inc. Reprinted with permission. All rights reserved.).

The numbers on the display in Figure I-3 refer to the following parameters:
1. Icon display shows acquisition mode.

⎍	Sample Mode
⋀⋁	Peak detect mode
⎍	Average mode

2. Trigger status shows if there is an adequate trigger source or if the acquisition is stopped.
3. Marker shows horizontal trigger position. This also indicates the horizontal position since the Horizontal Position control actually moves the trigger position horizontally.
4. Trigger position display shows the difference (in time) between the center graticule and the trigger position. Center screen equals zero.
5. Marker shows trigger level.
6. Readout shows numeric value of the trigger level.
7. Icon shows selected trigger slope for edge triggering.
8. Readout shows trigger source used for triggering.
9. Readout shows window zone time-base setting.
10. Readout shows main time-base setting.

11. Readout shows channels 1 and 2 vertical scale factors.

12. Display area shows on-line messages momentarily.

13. On screen markers show the ground reference points of the displayed waveforms. No marker indicates the channel is not displayed.

Systematic Approach to Troubleshooting Digital and Microcomputing Systems

Troubleshooting digital circuitry is a complex process. Most digital functions have many inputs and usually several outputs. By comparison, most analog functions, such as amplifiers, have single inputs and single outputs. When troubleshooting digital circuits, you must observe these complex signals to determine whether they are correct. While a digital system may be extremely large and complex, it consists of only a few types of building blocks, and each one is quite simple. Thus, you can see the importance of having a solid foundation in digital *fundamentals*.

The purpose of this Appendix is to describe some of the types of problems that you will encounter in digital logic, along with proven approaches to solve these problems. To begin, you should make the following Preparations and Visual Inspections before starting the electrical testing of digital circuits.

PREPARATIONS

1. Define the problem accurately. Verify that all switches are in the desired positions. Have a clear understanding of how the circuit should function.
2. Be sure that the schematics and other documentation are available and correct for the circuit under test.
3. Be sure that your test equipment is functioning properly and the required tools are available.

VISUAL INSPECTION

1. Verify that all of the ICs are installed properly and are in the correct locations. Check for broken or bent IC leads.
2. Next, check for solder bridges, cold solder joints, and broken traces. Use a magnifying glass if necessary.
3. Look for components that have been discolored because of overheating. (Overheated components can also be detected by touch.)

GENERAL APPROACH TO ISOLATING FAULTS

Figure A-1 is a block diagram that could represent a single IC or a functional group of ICs. Testing may be started at one of three places:

1. at the inputs;
2. at the outputs, or
3. in the middle.

For a relatively simple circuit, begin by applying signals at the inputs, and check the outputs for proper response. Continue this process until you detect a defective node. A node is an electrical point in a circuit consisting of the electrical paths interconnecting IC outputs to IC inputs and other electrical components. Power and ground buses are also examples of nodes. The same voltage should be present at all connection points of a given node.

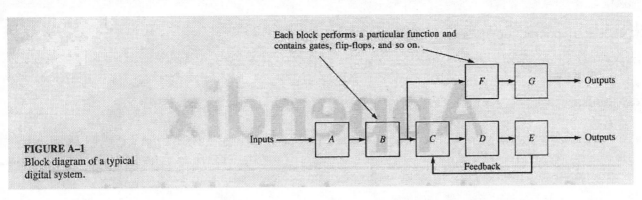

FIGURE A–1
Block diagram of a typical digital system.

Each block performs a particular function and contains gates, flip-flops, and so on.

For larger circuits, begin at the outputs and proceed back toward the inputs. You begin there because most digital circuits contain more inputs than outputs. When you detect a defective node, check the inputs of the IC driving that node. If any of these inputs are bad, then continue the process back toward the inputs. When all of the inputs of the IC driving the defective node are checked and found good, then the "source" defective node has been isolated. The experiments in this book describe some methods that help you determine the cause of this fault.

For very large systems, begin at a point such as the output of B in Figure A-1. If this output is bad, then test the output of A. However, if the output of B is good, then test the output of either G or E. The logic of this approach is to repeatedly divide the circuit into halves until the defective node is isolated. On average, this method requires fewer tests than starting at either end and working toward the other.

In many cases, you may use all three approaches to isolate a problem. In all cases, it is essential that you understand the functional relationships between the blocks of a system. For example, in Figure A-1, if output G is bad and E is good, then the problem is probably in F or G.

FEEDBACK LOOPS

Feedback loops are one of the most difficult situations to troubleshoot. A feedback loop is shown going from an output of E to an input of C in Figure A-1. A complete loop is formed, and therefore a defect in anyone of the blocks will cause the outputs of all the blocks to appear bad, because the "bad" signal is circulated through the entire loop. The usual method of isolating the fault is to disable the feedback path or to break the path and substitute an independent signal into C for it. Several experiments demonstrate this method.

FAILURE MODES

Most electrical failures can be classified as analog or digital. *Analog* failures cause the circuit to operate below performance requirements, although it may still be functional. Timing problems or low power drive are symptoms of analog failures. Other types of analog failures are incorrect voltage settings, ground loops, and insufficient decoupling of power buses.

The majority of the troubleshooting examples of this manual deal with *digital* failures. Digital failures are seen as opens or shorts or combinations of the two. They can occur either external or internal to the IC. Internal defects require that the IC be replaced.
Some of the causes of external shorts are

1. solder bridges,
2. leads of components of touch, and
3. defective insulation.

Some of the causes of external opens are

1. broken traces,
2. broken wires, and
3. cold solder joints.

Shorts can occur between nodes or between a node and a power or ground bus. Within an IC, internal shorts to a power or ground bus usually have a few ohms of resistance, while external shorts to a power or ground bus are direct. This difference can often be detected, as pointed out in the experiments.

Opens can occur in the signal paths or in a power or ground bus.

DIGITAL FAILURE MODES

Digital failure modes are classified by the voltage measured at the defective node. A node is said to be "stuck" when the device driving that node cannot cause it to change state. For example, if the input conditions of a driving device require that the output be HIGH but in fact it stays LOW, then this node is stuck.

The following list describes types of defective nodes:

1. A node that measures less than 0.8 V (TTL) is said to be stuck LOW or stuck at O.

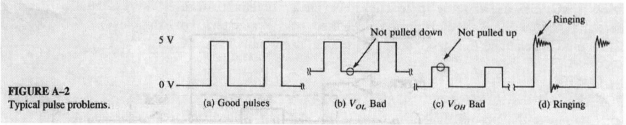

FIGURE A–2
Typical pulse problems.

2. A node that measures more than 2.0 V (TTL) is said to be stuck HIGH or stuck at 1.
3. An intermediate voltage, usually between 0.8 and 2.0 V, is called a *floating level*. This node is a high-impedance or floating node and is *not* considered stuck.

ISOLATION OF FAILURES

After you have verified that the failure is *not* because of a program or operator error, your job as a technician is to isolate this hardware failure by finding the *source bad (defective) node*. Keep in mind that this incorrect signal will propagate through the other circuits and cause a number of nodes to be in the wrong state. The source bad node is a node that is driven by a gate or flip-flop, for example, whose inputs are in the correct state but whose output is incorrect. The following is a summary of the steps for locating a source bad node.

First, measure the power supply voltages, checking both the levels and noise content. When checking the voltages on an IC, remember to read directly on the pins. It is also a good idea to measure the current drawn by the circuit board or system. If the current is excessively high or low, then there may be a short or open in the power system. Next, examine the clock pulses with an oscilloscope, checking the voltage levels, period, and for ringing or noise. Refer to Figure A-2, which illustrates three typical problems found with digital pulses. When making these measurements, make sure the oscilloscope is in the DC mode and also that the ground lead is connected to the ground pin of the IC being tested.

After you have verified that the clock is functioning properly, disable the clock so that you will be able to use the logic pulser and logic probe to analyze the circuit operation in a *static mode*. Because the circuit may not generate an error in all modes of operation, you must first step (using the logic pulser) or place (with switch controls) the circuit in a mode so that the error can be measured. In many cases, the most effective approach of locating the source bad node is to start at one of the outputs exhibiting an error and work back toward the inputs until the source bad node is found. Troubleshooting Example 1 in Figure A-3 demonstrates some of the techniques involved. Only three bits of an 8-bit buffer are shown in Figure A-3. The function of this circuit is to store the inputs (when the 7474 latches are clocked) and then to output this 8-bit word whenever the 3-state 74126s are enabled. When the 74126s are not enabled, the output bus is freed for transferring data between other circuits.

In this illustration, the D_1 output remained LOW when the data input was HIGH. The test results are summarized in Table A-1.

TYPES OF FAILURES

The 10 different types of failures that can occur in a digital system are listed in Table A-2. The failures consist of shorts or opens that can be either internal to the IC or external. After locating the source bad node, you will find one of four possible conditions. The node will be in

1. the wrong state,
2. floating,
3. stuck LOW, or
4. stuck HIGH.

Each of the failure types listed for the condition you have measured should be tested for in the order listed in Table A-2.

The "wrong state" condition occurs when an IC has an internal open input *(F_0 failure)*. This allows the output to change state (i.e., it is not "stuck"); however, it can produce incorrect outputs. In addition, there are nine *(F_1-F_9)* types of shorts or opens listed in Table A-2 that can cause a node to float, be stuck LOW, or be stuck HIGH. Any faults on the power and ground pins should have been detected during the initial tests and are not listed here.

These 10 failure types are illustrated in Figure A-4, along with the appropriate test for detecting the specific fault. You can use the figure like a flowchart. First, determine the type of fault, then test for the exact failure by using the tests in the sequence shown. For example, if the source bad node is stuck LOW, perform tests F_3 through F_6 in that order.

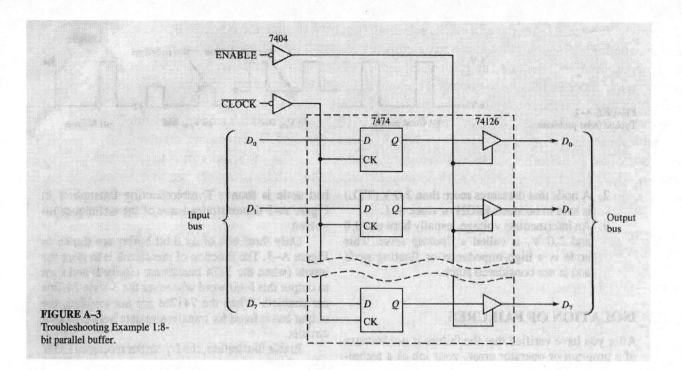

FIGURE A-3
Troubleshooting Example 1:8-bit parallel buffer.

TABLE A-1

Measurement	Remarks
Power supply	OK
Clock (See Note 1)	OK
74126 output of D_1	LOW
74126 enable input	This measures HIGH—OK
74126 data input (D_1)	This measures LOW—BAD
7474 data input (D_1)	HIGH—OK
7474 clock input	Place pulser directly on clock input and verify with logic probe

NOTE 1: At this point, disable the clock so that you can use the logic pulser, and tie the 7474 D_1 input HIGH. Make measurements with the logic probe. Although it was not essential to disable the clock in this illustration, it was done as an exercise.

CONCLUSION: Because the inputs of the 7474 check but the output of the 7474 is not correct, the source bad node is the output of the 7474. At this point, you do not know what the hardware failure is, but you have isolated it.

Wrong State

As shown in Figure A-4(a), the F_0 failure can be detected by applying a set of input conditions that generate an error on the output. In this type of failure, the output is not stuck but can change state. The input that is defective is the one that does not cause the output to change (when it should) when the input is changed from a HIGH to a LOW.

Floating Node

If the source bad node is floating, then the failure is either F_1 or F_2. As shown in Figure A-4(b), place the logic probe directly on the output pin of the IC that is driving the node. If you measure a good HIGH or LOW on the output pin, then the problem is an open in the signal path (an F_2 failure). A hairline crack in the printed circuit or a cold solder joint are typical causes of this failure. Use the logic probe to trace from the output pin to other points in the circuit. The exact point of the fault is where the measured signal goes from a good level to floating.

Node	Cause
Wrong state	F_0—open internal input in IC
Floating	F_1—open internal output in IC
	F_2—external open in signal path
Stuck LOW	F_3—external direct short to ground
	F_4—internal short to ground on an IC input
	F_5—short to another IC output that is LOW
	F_6—internal short to ground on an IC output
Stuck HIGH	F_7—external direct short to V_{CC}
	F_8—internal short to V_{CC} on an IC input
	F_9—internal short to V_{CC} on an IC output

If the output pin is floating, then there is an internal open in the IC *(F_1 failure)*, and the IC must be replaced. When possible, bench test the "defective" IC to verify your measurements.

Note Stuck LOW

If the logic probe indicates that the node is stuck LOW, then from Table A-2 the possible faults are F_3 through F_6. Figure A-4(c) indicates how the logic probe and pulser are used to determine which fault it is. As you will see, it is necessary to follow the tests in the order they are listed.

First, test for a direct short to ground *(F_3)*. At this time, you do not know if the node is being pulled down by an external direct short to ground or an internal short to ground in one of the ICs. Keep in

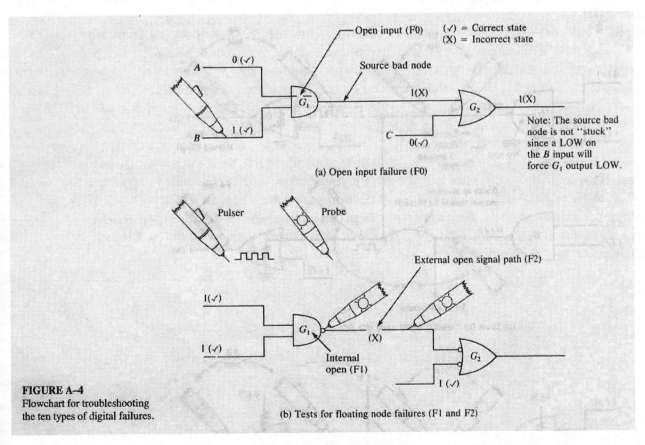

FIGURE A-4
Flowchart for troubleshooting
the ten types of digital failures.

(a) Open input failure (F0)

(b) Tests for floating node failures (F1 and F2)

mind that the logic pulser is unable to pull up a direct short to ground, but it is able to pull up an internal short to ground (because of the internal resistance within the IC). Therefore you will be able to tell the difference between an internal short and an external short. To do this, place the logic probe and pulser as shown for the F_3 test. If the logic probe does not indicate any pulses when the pulser is actuated, then there is a direct short to ground on this node. Solder bridges or bent pins are typical causes of this problem. If the fault cannot be detected visually, then a *current tracer* can be used. When the current tracer is passed over a short, the indicator light comes on. By moving the current tracer over the circuit path (with the logic pulser on), the short can be pinpointed.

If during the F_3 test the logic probe indicates pulse activity, then there is not a direct short *(F_3)*; therefore failures F_4, F_5, and F_6 remain as possibilities. The IC inputs can be tested for the F_4 failure as indicated in Figure A-4(c). If the input of the device is functional, then pulses applied to the input will be detected on the output of the device under test. Make sure all the other inputs of the device are enabled! For example, if the device under test is an OR gate, then all the other inputs must be LOW. If there are several other inputs connected to the stuck node, then they all must be tested in the same way. If the device fails the test for F_4, then it must be replaced. You should try to isolate the pin and retest before replacing the IC. The pin can usually be isolated by carefully removing the solder around it.

If no faulty inputs *(F_4)* are detected, then F_5 and F_6 failures remain. To detect a short to another node *(F_5)*, apply pulses with the pulser to the "stuck" node, and scan other nearby nodes with the logic probe. A solder bridge or bent pin could be the cause of this failure.

If a short between nodes *(F_5)* is not detected, then only the internal IC output short to ground failure *(F_6)* remains. There is no direct test for this failure, so you have to eliminate the other possible failures by using the sequence shown here. Again, the output pin under test should be isolated before replacing the IC.

Node Stuck HIGH

If the logic probe indicates that the node is stuck HIGH, then from Table A-2 the possible faults are F_7 through F_9. Figure A-4(d) indicates how the logic probe and pulser are used to determine which fault it is. As you will see, it is necessary to follow the tests in the order they are listed.

First, test for a direct short to V_{cc} *(F_7)*. At this time, you do not know if the node is being pulled up by an external direct short to V_{cc} or an internal short to V_{cc} in one of the ICs. Keep in mind that the logic pulser is unable to pull down a direct short to V_{cc}, but it is able to pull down an internal short to V_{cc} (because of the internal resistance within the IC). Therefore you will be able to tell the difference between an internal short and an external short. To do this, place the logic probe and pulser as shown for the F_7 test. If the logic probe does not indicate any pulses when the pulser is actuated, then there is a direct short to V_{cc} on this node. Solder bridges or bent pins are typical causes of this problem. If the fault cannot be detected visually, then a *current tracer* can be used. When the current tracer is passed over a short, the indicator light comes on. By moving the current tracer over the circuit path (with the logic pulser on), the short can be pinpointed.

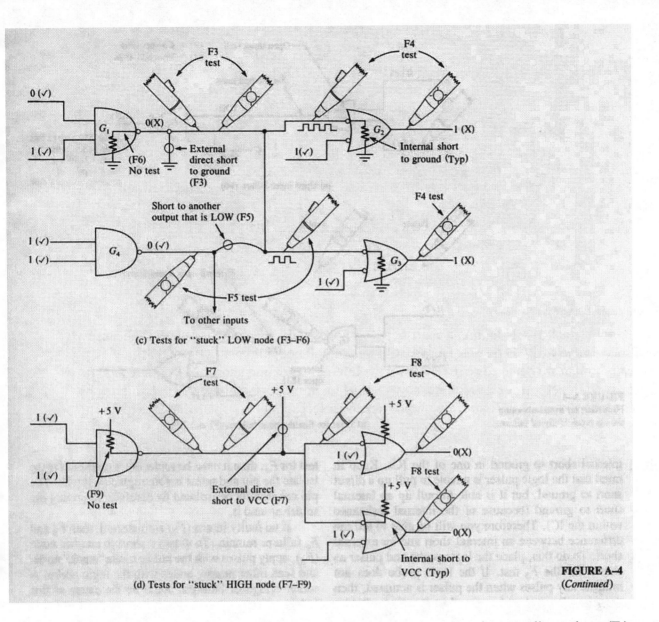

(c) Tests for "stuck" LOW node (F3–F6)

(d) Tests for "stuck" HIGH node (F7–F9)

FIGURE A–4
(*Continued*)

If during the F_7 test the logic probe indicates pulse activity, then there is not a direct short (F_7); therefore failures F_8 and F_9 remain as possibilities. The IC inputs can be tested for the F_8 failure as indicated in Figure A-4(d). If the input of the device is functional, then pulses applied to the input will be detected on the output of the device under test. Make sure all the other inputs of the device are enabled! For example, if the device under test is an AND gate, then all the other inputs must be HIGH. If there are several other inputs connected to the stuck node, then they all must be tested in the same way. If the device fails the test for F_8, then it must be replaced. You should try to isolate the pin and retest before replacing the IC. The pin can usually be isolated by carefully removing the solder around it.

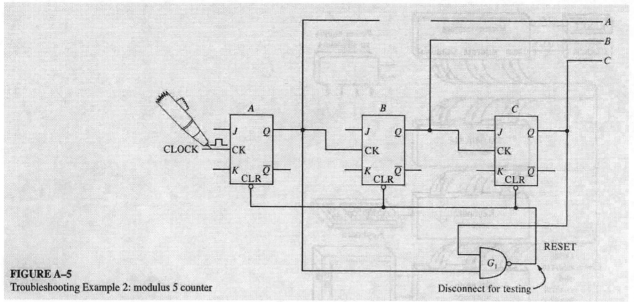

FIGURE A–5
Troubleshooting Example 2: modulus 5 counter   Disconnect for testing

Note that for a stuck HIGH failure, a short-between-nodes failure is not listed. This is because a LOW usually overrides a HIGH output (i.e., a HIGH output will not pull up a LOW output).

If no faulty inputs are detected (F_8), then only the internal IC output short to V_{cc} failure (F_9) remains. There is no direct test for this failure, so you have to eliminate the other possible failures by using the sequence shown here. Again, the output pin under test should be isolated before replacing the IC.

Troubleshooting Example 2

Figure A-5 shows a modulus 5 counter. Table A-3 shows both the correct counting sequence and the measured outputs. As you can see, it has only four states instead of five. One reason this example was chosen is that it has a RESET function. Notice that the reset line clears the flip-flop outputs after a certain count, making this a form of *feedback*. In addition, this reset pulse has a duration of less than 100 ns. In this example, the best technique is to disconnect the RESET line from the CLR inputs.

TABLE A–3
Counter outputs.

Correct C B A	Actual C B A
0 0 0	0 0 0
0 0 1	0 0 1
0 1 0	0 1 0
0 1 1	0 1 1
1 0 0	0 0 0
0 0 0	0 0 1
0 0 1	0 1 0
.	.
.	.
.	.

Using the logic pulser (disconnecting the CLOCK input if necessary), step the counter to the count at which the error occurs. This is when C B A = 100. Note that the counter will not reach this value before the RESET line is disconnected. Read the output of gate G1 with the logic probe. It should not go LOW until the next CLOCK pulse, but it is already LOW. Next, read the inputs of the gate. The input to the gate from flip-flop *A* is floating. This is the cause of the problem. A further examination might disclose a cold solder connection or a hairline crack in the printed circuit wiring.

The key point of this example is that by disabling the CLOCK and RESET lines, you were able to troubleshoot the circuit in a static mode using the logic probe and pulser instead of a dual-trace oscilloscope.

TROUBLESHOOTING MICROCOMPUTING SYSTEMS

The procedures and instruments used to troubleshoot microcomputers are similar to those used to troubleshoot other digital systems. Logic probes and pulsers are just as helpful when testing certain portions of microcomputer systems as they are in troubleshooting simpler systems. The basic approach is to isolate the problem to a small part of the circuit or system. Microcomputer systems differ from simple digital circuits in at least three ways:

1. Computer system signal paths are usually multiconductor buses instead of single-wire signal paths. The main components of a microcomputer system (Figure A-6) are interconnected by the data bus, the control bus, and the address bus. Symptom diagnosis may require that all the signals on a bus be analyzed simultaneously. An instrument designed for this purpose is the logic analyzer.

2. Microcomputer systems contain several complex IC devices, each containing many gates and flip-flops.

3. Many of these complex devices, including the MPU, are capable of several different functions. They operate in one mode with one set of inputs and in a completely different mode with another set of inputs. As a technician, you must know the functions of the *machine instructions* in detail before you can single-step through a program to detect a system problem.

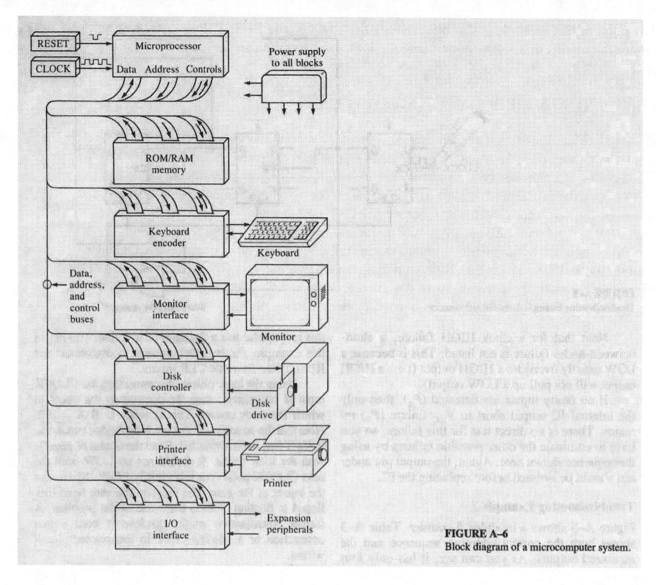

FIGURE A–6
Block diagram of a microcomputer system.

Logic Analyzer

A logic analyzer is a multitrace (eight to 16 traces) oscilloscope that allows all the signals on a bus to be displayed simultaneously. Another useful display mode converts the pulses to Is and Os, then lists the data in tabular form. For example, you can trigger the analyzer on a certain key word, and the data on the bus following the key word will be displayed as follows:

Trigger   0101 1001
                 1100 0111
                 0001 1011

Data in this form are much easier to analyze when you are looking for an error pattern in the data. However, the time-relationship display should be used to look for glitches or noise spikes.

TYPICAL MICROCOMPUTER SYSTEM FAULTS

A block diagram of a typical microcomputer system is shown in Figure A-6. As a technician, you should be familiar with how data are transferred between the processor and the peripherals.

Entire System Down

As the block diagram indicates, the power system is the only block that connects directly to all parts of the system. After all voltages have been checked, the next step is to disconnect the peripherals (when practical) one at a time. Unplugging the peripherals will eliminate the units as a problem or isolate the problem to one of them.

After the peripherals have been verified, the system clock should be checked. The entire microcomputer system depends on the clock for synchronization and timing; consult the schematics for exact voltages, frequencies, and phases.

If the RESET signal is not functioning (e.g., remains open), the computer will not begin operation at the startup sequence. If the RESET signal (usually an active-LOW momentary pulse) is stuck, then the entire system will remain in a locked-up condition.

Control Bus

The control bus is unidirectional. For example, the processor issues a MEMORY ENABLE signal to the memory whenever a valid memory address is on the address bus. Other control lines are used to control data into the processor. After the microcomputer system is reset, the control lines become active, indicating that the initialization process is beginning. The first step is to access the ROM to obtain the instructions to allow the microcomputer system to begin operations. Activity on the control bus can be tested with the logic probe or oscilloscope. If the control lines are not functioning properly, follow the procedure outlined earlier in the appendix to isolate the fault. If the fault cannot be found external to the processor IC, the best method is to substitute a known good microprocessor IC.

An example of a *tight endless loop* program that can be used to analyze control line signals and others is to put an instruction in a memory location containing an instruction that unconditionally jumps to that same location. When this program is run, an endless loop is entered, generating an endless cycle of read control signals. The logic analyzer or oscilloscope can be used to check signal levels and timing.

Address and Data Buses

The address bus is also unidirectional; addresses are sent from the processor to memory and, in some cases, to output devices. However, the data bus is bidirectional. More than one output is connected to a data line, although only one is enabled at a time. If the microcomputer system is still operating erratically or getting errors, then the problem may be in the address or data bus. At this point, put the microcomputer system in a simple program loop. Normally, with a program running, every line in one of these buses will be active. If any line is constantly HIGH, LOW, or floating, then a problem is indicated on that line. To isolate the problem, refer to the steps detailed earlier in the appendix.

Memory

When only a portion of the RAM is disabled, those programs not using that part of memory will be unaffected. In this case, the *memory diagnostic* (a software program to test all memory locations) should be run. This program will normally identify this faulty IC. If the problem is in the ROM, then many computer functions may be affected. The logic analyzer can be used to display the contents of each ROM location. The data from the analyzer are then compared against a listing of the ROM contents. Because the ROM probably contains several thousand locations, only a partial check is practical. Because the processor IC depends on the ROM for instructions, it is difficult to isolate a problem between these two components. If the processor and RAM are known to be good, then the ROM should be replaced.

Input/Output Devices

Input/output (I/O) devices consist of keyboards, disk drives, printers, monitors, and the like. Each of these devices requires a buffer (register) to hold data until the data bus or output device is ready for it. The keyboard requires an encoder to convert the electromechanical contacts to a binary code. Although there are more problems with I/O devices because of their mechanical nature, troubleshooting is straightforward as the problem can almost always be localized.

FINAL COMMENTS

The techniques described in this appendix apply equally well to any digital system, whether it is a printed circuit board or a computer system. The differences between a microcomputing simple digital system were described, and means to analyze these problems were discussed. However, the number of ways that a digital system can fail is virtually unlimited, and no single set of procedures will work in every case. If you have a specific plan and it does not succeed the first time, at least you will know what steps have already been taken. Before you abandon the plan, it is usually a sound idea to retest some of your earlier measurements.

You should resist the urge to change a component at the first suspicion. Changing parts always creates the possibility of introducing new errors. In particular, you should be aware of any recent changes made to the circuit you are testing.

Many of the techniques presented in this appendix are included in automatic testing systems. There is also a trend in larger systems to include error-detection and fault-diagnosis circuits and software. Such advanced equipment reduces some of the labor and time required to troubleshoot the systems for which they were designed. As new computer systems have become more complex, test-equipment designers have developed new test equipment, such as the logic analyzer and the signature analyzer, to assist the troubleshooter. As always, new and old products will continue to require technicians who are competent in the techniques of troubleshooting.

Name:_____

Date:_____

Course and Section:_____

Instructor:_____

Math Review
and Calculator
Fundamentals dc

MATH REVIEW
Fractions

Powers of Ten

Scientific Notation

Engineering Notation

Conversions Between Levels of Powers of Ten

Prefixes

Square and Cube Roots

Exponential Functions

Algebraic Manipulations

CALCULATOR FUNDAMENTALS
Initial Settings

Order of Operations

Powers of 10

Exponential Functions

From *Experiments in Circuit Analysis to Accompany Introductory Circuit Analysis*, Tenth Edition, Robert L. Boylestad and Gabriel Kousourou. Copyright © 2003 by Pearson Education, Inc. All rights reserved.

MATH REVIEW

The analysis of dc circuits requires that a number of fundamental mathematical operations be performed on an ongoing basis. Most of the operations are typically covered in a secondary-level education; a few others will be introduced in the early sessions of the lecture portion of this course.

The material to follow is a brief review of the important mathematical procedures along with a few examples and exercises. Derivations and detailed explanations are not included but are left as topics for the course syllabus or as research exercises for the student.

It is strongly suggested that the math review exercises be performed with and without a calculator. Although the modern-day calculator is a marvelous development, the student should understand how to perform the operations in the longhand fashion. Any student of a technical area should also develop a high level of expertise with the use of the calculator through frequent application with a variety of operations. The use of the calculator is covered later in this laboratory exercise.

Fractions

Addition and Subtraction:

Addition and subtraction of fractions require that each term have a common denominator. A direct method of determining the common denominator is simply to multiply the numerator and denominator of each fraction by the denominator of the other fractions. The method of "selecting the least common denominator" will be left for a class lecture or research exercise.

EXAMPLES

$$\frac{1}{2} + \frac{2}{3} = \left(\frac{3}{3}\right)\left(\frac{1}{2}\right) + \left(\frac{2}{2}\right)\left(\frac{2}{3}\right) = \frac{3}{6} + \frac{4}{6} = \frac{7}{6}$$

$$\frac{3}{4} - \frac{2}{5} = \left(\frac{5}{5}\right)\left(\frac{3}{4}\right) - \left(\frac{4}{4}\right)\left(\frac{2}{5}\right) = \frac{15}{20} - \frac{8}{20} = \frac{7}{20}$$

$$\frac{5}{6} + \frac{1}{2} - \frac{3}{4} = \left(\frac{2}{2}\right)\left(\frac{4}{4}\right)\left(\frac{5}{6}\right) + \left(\frac{6}{6}\right)\left(\frac{4}{4}\right)\left(\frac{1}{2}\right) - \left(\frac{6}{6}\right)\left(\frac{2}{2}\right)\left(\frac{3}{4}\right)$$

$$= \frac{40}{48} + \frac{24}{48} - \frac{36}{48} = \frac{28}{48} = \frac{7}{12}$$

(12 being the least common denominator for the three fractions)

Multiplication:

The multiplication of two fractions is straightforward, with the product of the numerator and denominator formed separately, as shown here.

EXAMPLES

$$\left(\frac{1}{3}\right)\left(\frac{4}{5}\right) = \frac{(1)(4)}{(3)(5)} = \frac{4}{15}$$

$$\left(\frac{3}{7}\right)\left(\frac{1}{2}\right)\left(-\frac{4}{5}\right) = \frac{(3)(1)(-4)}{(7)(2)(5)} = -\frac{12}{70} = -\frac{6}{35}$$

Division:

Division requires that the denominator be inverted and then multiplied by the numerator.

EXAMPLE

$$\frac{\frac{2}{3}}{\frac{4}{5}} = \frac{2}{3} \div \frac{4}{5} = \frac{2}{3} \times \frac{5}{4} = \frac{10}{12} = \frac{5}{6}$$

Simplest Form:

A fraction can be reduced to simplest form by finding the largest common divisor of both the numerator and denominator. As an illustration,

$$\frac{12}{60} = \frac{12/12}{60/12} = \frac{1}{5}$$

If the largest divisor is not obvious, start with a smaller common divisor, such as shown here:

$$\frac{12/6}{60/6} = \frac{2}{10} = \frac{2/2}{10/2} = \frac{1}{5}$$

Or, if you prefer, use repeated divisions of smaller common divisors, such as 2 or 3:

$$\frac{12/2}{60/2} = \frac{6}{30} = \frac{6/2}{30/2} = \frac{3}{15} = \frac{3/3}{15/3} = \frac{1}{5}$$

EXAMPLES

$$\frac{180}{300} = \frac{180/10}{300/10} = \frac{18}{30} = \frac{18/6}{30/6} = \frac{3}{5}$$

$$\frac{72}{256} = \frac{72/8}{256/8} = \frac{9}{32}$$

or

$$\frac{72}{256} = \frac{72/2}{256/2} = \frac{36}{128} = \frac{36/2}{128/2} = \frac{18}{64} = \frac{18/2}{64/2} = \frac{9}{32}$$

Mixed Numbers:

Numbers in mixed form (with whole and fractional parts) can be converted to fractional form by multiplying the whole number by the denominator of the fractional part and adding the numerator.

EXAMPLES

$$3\frac{4}{5} = \frac{(3 \times 5) + 4}{5} = \frac{19}{5}$$

$$60\frac{1}{3} = \frac{(60 \times 3) + 1}{3} = \frac{181}{3}$$

The reverse process is simply a division operation with the remainder left in fractional form.

Conversion to Decimal Form:

Fractions can be converted to decimal form by simply performing the indicated division.

EXAMPLES

$$\frac{1}{4} = 4\overline{)1.00}^{\,0.25} = \mathbf{0.25}$$

$$\frac{3}{7} = 7\overline{)3.0000}^{\,0.4285\ldots} = \mathbf{0.4285\ldots}$$

$$4\frac{1}{5} = 4 + 5\overline{)1.0}^{\,0.2} = \mathbf{4.2}$$

PROBLEMS

Perform each of the following operations without using a calculator. Be sure all solutions are in simplest form.

1. $\dfrac{3}{5} + \dfrac{1}{3} =$ _____

2. $\dfrac{5}{9} - \dfrac{2}{4} =$ _____

3. $\dfrac{2}{5} - \dfrac{1}{2} + \dfrac{1}{4} =$ _____

4. $\left(\dfrac{5}{6}\right)\left(\dfrac{9}{13}\right) =$ _____

5. $\left(-\dfrac{1}{7}\right)\left(+\dfrac{2}{9}\right)\left(-\dfrac{3}{5}\right) =$ _____

6. $\dfrac{5/6}{2/3} =$ _____

7. $\dfrac{9/10}{-6/7} =$ _____

8. Reduce to simplest form:

   (a) $\dfrac{72}{84} =$ _____

   (b) $\dfrac{144}{384} =$ _____

9. Convert to mixed form:

   (a) $\dfrac{16}{7} =$ _____

   (b) $\dfrac{320}{9} =$ _____

10. Convert to decimal form using a calculator:

(a) $\dfrac{3}{8}$ = _____

(b) $6\dfrac{5}{6}$ = _____

Powers of Ten

The need to work with very small and large numbers requires that the use of powers of 10 be appreciated and clearly understood.

The direction of the shift of the decimal point and the number of places moved will determine the resulting power of 10. For instance:

$$10{,}000. = 1 \times 10^{+4} = \mathbf{10^{+4}}$$
$$\underbrace{\phantom{10{,}000}}_{4}$$

$$5000. = \mathbf{5 \times 10^{+3}}$$
$$\underbrace{}_{3}$$

$$0.000001 = 1 \times 10^{-6} = \mathbf{10^{-6}}$$
$$\underbrace{}_{6}$$

$$0.00456 = \mathbf{4.56 \times 10^{-3}}$$
$$\underbrace{}_{3}$$

It is particularly important to remember that

$$\boxed{10^0 = 1} \tag{1}$$

EXAMPLES

$$50 \times 10^0 = 50(1) = \mathbf{50}$$
$$0.04 \times 10^0 = 0.04(1) = \mathbf{0.04}$$

Addition and Subtraction:

Addition or subtraction of numbers using scientific notation requires that the power of 10 of each term **be the same.**

EXAMPLES

$$45{,}000 + 3000 + 500 = 45 \times 10^3 + 3 \times 10^3 + 0.5 \times 10^3 = \mathbf{48.5 \times 10^3}$$
$$0.02 - 0.003 + 0.0004 = 200 \times 10^{-4} - 30 \times 10^{-4} + 4 \times 10^{-4}$$
$$= (200 - 30 + 4) \times 10^{-4} = \mathbf{174 \times 10^{-4}}$$

Multiplication:

Multiplication using powers of 10 employs the following equation, where a and b can be any positive or negative number:

$$\boxed{10^a \times 10^b = 10^{a+b}} \tag{2}$$

EXAMPLES

$$(100)(5000) = (10^2)(5 \times 10^3) = 5 \times 10^2 \times 10^3 = 5 \times 10^{2+3} = \mathbf{5 \times 10^5}$$

$$(200)(0.0004) = (2 \times 10^2)(4 \times 10^{-4}) = (2)(4)(10^2)(10^{-4}) = 8 \times 10^{2-4} = \mathbf{8 \times 10^{-2}}$$

Note in the preceding examples that the operations with powers of 10 can be separated from those with integer values.

Division:

Division employs the following equation, where a and b can again be any positive or negative number:

$$\boxed{\frac{10^a}{10^b} = 10^{a-b}} \tag{3}$$

EXAMPLES

$$\frac{320,000}{4000} = \frac{32 \times 10^4}{4 \times 10^3} = \frac{32}{4} \times 10^{4-3} = 8 \times 10^1 = \mathbf{80}$$

$$\frac{1600}{0.0008} = \frac{16 \times 10^2}{8 \times 10^{-4}} = 2 \times 10^{2-(-4)} = 2 \times 10^{2+4} = \mathbf{2 \times 10^6}$$

Note in the last example the importance of carrying the proper sign through Eq. (3).

Powers:

Powers of powers of 10 can be determined using the following equation, where a and b can be any positive or negative number:

$$\boxed{(10^a)^b = 10^{ab}} \tag{4}$$

EXAMPLES

$$(1000)^4 = (10^3)^4 = \mathbf{10^{12}}$$

$$(0.002)^3 = (2 \times 10^{-3})^3 = (2)^3 \times (10^{-3})^3 = \mathbf{8 \times 10^{-9}}$$

Scientific Notation

Scientific notation makes use of powers of 10 with restrictions on the mantissa (multiplier) or scale factor (power of the power of ten). It requires that the decimal point appear directly after the first digit greater than or equal to 1 but less than 10.

EXAMPLES

$$2400 = \mathbf{2.40 \times 10^3}$$

$$0.0006 = \mathbf{6.00 \times 10^{-4}}$$

$$5,100,000 = \mathbf{5.1 \times 10^6}$$

Engineering Notation

Engineering notation also makes use of powers of 10 with the restrictions that the power of 10 must be 0 or divisible by 3 and the mantissa must be greater than or equal to 1 but less than 1000.

EXAMPLES

$$22{,}000 = \mathbf{22.00 \times 10^3}$$
$$0.003 = \mathbf{3.00 \times 10^{-3}}$$
$$0.000065 = \mathbf{65.00 \times 10^{-6}}$$

Conversions Between Levels of Powers of Ten

It is often necessary to convert from one power of 10 to another. The process is rather straightforward if you simply keep in mind that an increase or decrease in the power of 10 must be associated with the opposite effect (same whole-number change) on the multiplying factor.

EXAMPLES

Increase by 3
$$160 \times 10^3 = \underline{\hspace{1.5cm}} \times 10^6$$
Decrease by 3

$$160 \times 10^3 = \mathbf{0.16 \times 10^6}$$

Decrease by 2
$$0.4 \times 10^{-3} = \underline{\hspace{1.5cm}} \times 10^{-5}$$
Increase by 2

$$0.4 \times 10^{-3} = \mathbf{40 \times 10^{-5}}$$

Increase by 4
$$5200 \times 10^{-6} = \underline{\hspace{1.5cm}} \times 10^{-2}$$
Decrease by 4

$$5200 \times 10^{-6} = \mathbf{0.52 \times 10^{-2}}$$

PROBLEMS

Perform the following operations by hand. Write your answer with the power of ten indicated.

11. $5{,}800{,}000 + 450{,}000 + 2000 = \underline{\hspace{2.5cm}} \times 10^3$

12. $0.04 + 0.008 - 0.3 = \underline{\hspace{2.5cm}} \times 10^{-3}$

13. $2400 + 0.05 \times 10^3 - 40{,}000 \times 10^{-3} = \underline{\hspace{2.5cm}} \times 10^3$

14. $(68{,}000)(40{,}000) = \underline{\hspace{2.5cm}} \times 10^9$

15. $(0.0009)(0.006) = \underline{\hspace{2.5cm}} \times 10^{-6}$

16. $(-5 \times 10^{-8})(8 \times 10^5)(-0.02 \times 10^4) = \underline{\hspace{2.5cm}} \times 10^0$

17. $\dfrac{0.00081}{0.009} = \underline{\hspace{2.5cm}} \times 10^{-2}$

18. $\dfrac{5000}{6 \times 10^6} = $ _____ $\times 10^{-4}$

19. $\dfrac{-8 \times 10^{-4}}{0.002} = $ _____ $\times 10^{-1}$

20. $(4 \times 10^5)^3 = $ _____ $\times 10^{16}$

21. $(0.0003)^4 = $ _____ $\times 10^{-15}$

22. $[(4000)(0.0003)]^3 = $ _____ $\times 10^0$

Prefixes

The frequent use of some powers of 10 has resulted in their being assigned abbreviations that can be applied as prefixes to a numerical value in order to quickly identify its relative magnitude.

The following is a list of the most frequently used prefixes in electrical and electronic engineering technology:

$$10^{12} = \text{tera (T)}$$
$$10^{9} = \text{giga (G)}$$
$$10^{6} = \text{mega (M)}$$
$$10^{3} = \text{kilo (k)}$$
$$10^{-3} = \text{milli (m)}$$
$$10^{-6} = \text{micro } (\mu)$$
$$10^{-9} = \text{nano (n)}$$
$$10^{-12} = \text{pico (p)}$$

EXAMPLES

$$6,000,000 \ \Omega = 6 \times 10^6 \ \Omega = \textbf{6 M}\boldsymbol{\Omega}$$
$$0.04 \ \text{A} = 40 \times 10^{-3} \ \text{A} = \textbf{40 mA}$$
$$0.00005 \ \text{V} = 50 \times 10^{-6} \ \text{V} = \textbf{50 } \boldsymbol{\mu}\textbf{V}$$

When converting from one form to another, be aware of the relative magnitude of the quantity before you start to provide a check once the conversion is complete. Starting out with a relatively small quantity and ending up with a result of large relative magnitude clearly indicates an error in the conversion process.

The most direct method of converting from one power of 10 to another is to write the number in the power-of-10 format and note the requested change in the power of 10. If the power of 10 is larger, the decimal point of the multiplier must be moved to the left a number of places equal to the increase in the power of 10. If the requested power of 10 is smaller, the decimal point is moved to the right a number of places equal to the decrease in the power of 10.

EXAMPLES

(a) Convert 0.008 MΩ to kilohms.

Decrease by 3

$$0.008 \times 10^{+6} \ \Omega \rightarrow 0.008. \times 10^{+3} \ \Omega = \textbf{8 k}\boldsymbol{\Omega}$$

Increase by 3

(b) Convert 5600 mA to ampere.

Increase by 3

$$5600 \times 10^{-3} \, A \rightarrow 5.600. \times 10^0 \, A = \textbf{5.6 A}$$

Decrease by 3

PROBLEMS

Apply the most appropriate prefix to each of the following quantities.

23. 0.00006 A = _____

24. 1,504,000 Ω = _____

25. 32,000 V = _____

26. 0.000000009 A = _____

Perform the following conversions.

27. 35 mA = _____ A

28. 0.005 kV = _____ V = _____ mV

29. 8,500,000 Ω = _____ MΩ = _____ kΩ

30. 4000 pF = _____ nF = _____ μF

Square and Cube Roots

When determining the square or cube root of a number by hand, the power of 10 must be divisible by 2 or 3, respectively, or the resulting power of 10 will not be a whole number.

EXAMPLES

$$\sqrt{200} = (200)^{1/2} = (2 \times 10^2)^{1/2} = (2)^{1/2} \times (10^2)^{1/2} \cong 1.414 \times 10^1 = \textbf{14.14}$$
$$\sqrt{0.004} = (0.004)^{1/2} = (40 \times 10^{-4})^{1/2} = (40)^{1/2} \times (10^{-4})^{1/2}$$
$$= 6.325 \times 10^{-2} = \textbf{0.06325}$$
$$\sqrt[3]{5000} = (5000)^{1/3} = (5 \times 10^3)^{1/3} = (5)^{1/3} \times 10^1 \cong 1.71 \times 10^1 = \textbf{17.1}$$

Some calculators provide the $\sqrt[3]{}$ function, whereas others require that you use the $\sqrt[x]{y}$ function. For some calculators, the y^x function is all that is available, requiring that the y value be entered first, followed by the y^x function and then the power ($x = 1/3 = 0.3333$).

The use of a calculator removes the need to worry about the power of 10 under the radical sign.

PROBLEMS

Use a calculator.

31. $\sqrt{6.4}$ = _____

32. $\sqrt[3]{3000}$ = _____

33. $\sqrt{0.00007}$ = _____

Exponential Functions

The exponential functions e^x and e^{-x} will appear frequently in the analysis of R-C and R-L networks with switched dc inputs (or square-wave inputs). On most calculators, only e^x is provided, requiring that the user insert the negative sign when necessary.

Keep in mind that e^x is equivalent to $(2.71828 . . .)^x$ or a number to a power x. For any positive values of x greater than 1, the result is a magnitude greater than 2.71828. . . . In other words, for increasing values of x, the magnitude of e^x will increase rapidly. For $x = 0$, $e^0 = 1$, and for increasing negative values of x, e^{-x} will become increasingly smaller.

When inserting the negative sign for e^{-x} functions, be sure to use the proper key to enter the negative sign.

EXAMPLES

$$e^{+2} \cong 7.3890$$
$$e^{+10} \cong 22{,}026.47$$
$$e^{-2} \cong 0.13534$$
$$e^{-10} \cong 0.0000454$$

Also keep in mind that

$$\boxed{e^{-x} = \frac{1}{e^x} \text{ and } e^{+x} = \frac{1}{e^{-x}}} \tag{5}$$

PROBLEMS

Use a calculator.

34. $e^{+4.2} = $ _____

35. $e^{+0.5} = $ _____

36. $e^{-0.02} = $ _____

37. $\dfrac{1}{e^{-3}} = $ _____

Algebraic Manipulations

The following is a brief review of some basic algebraic manipulations that must be performed in the analysis of dc circuits. It is assumed that a supporting math course will expand on the coverage provided here.

EXAMPLES

(a) Given $v = \dfrac{d}{t}$, solve for d and t.

Both sides of the equation must first be multiplied by t:

$$(t)(v) = \left(\frac{d}{\cancel{t}}\right)(\cancel{t})$$

resulting in $d = vt$.

Dividing both sides of $d = vt$ by v yields

$$\frac{d}{v} = \frac{\cancel{v}t}{\cancel{v}}$$

or

$$t = \frac{d}{v}$$

In other words, the proper choice of multiplying factors for both sides of the equation will result in an equation for the desired quantity.

(b) Given $R_1 + 4 = 3R_1$, solve for R_1.

In this case, $-R_1$ is added to both sides, resulting in

$$(R_1 + 4) - R_1 = 3R_1 - R_1$$

or

$$4 = 2R_1$$

so

$$R_1 = \frac{4}{2} = 2\ \Omega$$

(c) Given $\dfrac{1}{R_1} = \dfrac{1}{3R_1} + \dfrac{1}{6}$, solve for R_1.

Multiplying both sides of the equation by R_1 results in

$$\frac{\cancel{R_1}}{\cancel{R_1}} = \frac{\cancel{R_1}}{3\cancel{R_1}} + \frac{R_1}{6}$$

or

$$1 = \frac{1}{3} + \frac{R_1}{6}$$

Subtracting 1/3 from both sides gives

$$1 - \frac{1}{3} = \frac{1}{3} - \frac{1}{3} + \frac{R_1}{6}$$

or

$$\frac{2}{3} = \frac{R_1}{6}$$

so

$$R_1 = \frac{(6)(2)}{3} = \frac{12}{3} = 4\ \Omega$$

PROBLEMS

Show all work in an organized and neat manner.

38. Given $P = I^2R$, solve for R and I.

$R = $ _____ , $I = $ _____

39. Given $30I = 5I + 5$, solve for I.

$I = $ _____

40. Given $\dfrac{1}{R_T} = \dfrac{1}{R_1} + \dfrac{1}{4R_1}$, solve for R_T in terms of R_1.

$R_T = $ _____

41. Given $F = \dfrac{kQ_1Q_2}{r^2}$, solve for Q_1 and r.

$Q_1 = $ _____ , $r = $ _____

CALCULATOR FUNDAMENTALS

Calculators have become such a fundamental and important part of the technology program that every effort must be made to ensure the basic operations are correctly understood. Too often, the manual associated with a calculator is never read and the student assumes the operations he or she needs can easily be implemented by simply examining the keypad. The result, however, is that important facets of the calculator such as the hierarchy of operations, the proper input of data, etc., are learned only after disaster has occurred once or twice. The purpose of this introduction, therefore, is to discuss just the very important elements of calculator use to ensure the operations required in the dc section of this laboratory manual can be performed correctly.

Most of the content of this section applies to any handheld calculator. The authors refer to a Texas Instruments TI-86, because it is one of the most frequently used for electrical technology due to its friendly format and ease of use.

Initial Settings

Every scientific calculator has a mode setting whereby the two important choices of format and level of accuracy can be made. For the TI-86 the 2nd function followed by the MODE choice provides a list of options for the initial settings of the calculator. For calculators without a mode choice, consult your manual for the manner in which the format and level of accuracy are chosen.

Format:

The chosen format determines how the numbers will appear after any of the fundamental operations, such as addition, subtraction, multiplication, or square root, are performed. In other words, the numbers can be entered in *any* format, but the result will appear in the *chosen* format. For most scientific calculators the choices are **normal, scientific,** and **engineering.** Examples of each are shown for the basic operation of dividing 1 by 3.

$$\textbf{Normal:} \quad 1/3 = 0.33$$
$$\textbf{Scientific:} \quad 1/3 = 3.33\text{E-}1$$
$$\textbf{Engineering:} \quad 1/3 = 333.33\text{E-}3$$

Note that the normal format simply places the decimal point in the most logical location. The scientific ensures that the number preceding the decimal point is a single digit followed by the required power of 10. The engineering format will always ensure that the power of 10 is a multiple of 3 (whether it be positive, negative, or zero). Because specific names have been given to powers of 10 that are multiples or divisible by 3 in the engineering format, it will be the choice for the greater part of this manual. Once you have entered a number in the normal format, you can easily obtain the scientific or engineering format by first choosing the SCI or ENG format and then pressing the Enter key for some calculators or simply dividing or multiplying by 1 for others.

$$0.003 = \textbf{3.00E-3}$$
$$45,000 = \textbf{45.00E3}$$
$$0.000000000003 = \textbf{3.00E-12}$$

Accuracy:

In the preceding examples, the numbers are accurate to the hundredths place. Accuracy is set by returning to the MODE selection and choosing 2 to represent two-place accuracy, or hundredths place. Your instructor may prefer a different level of accuracy. However, whatever the choice, take the time now to learn how to set the level of accuracy so you don't end up with lengthy numbers whose level of accuracy makes no sense whatsoever for the operations to be performed.

PROBLEMS

Using a calculator convert the following from the normal to scientific format.

42. $0.000045 = $ _____

43. $3400000 = $ _____

44. $0.08 = $ _____

45. $220 = $ _____

46. $0.00000001 = $ _____

Convert to engineering format.

47. $0.000045 = $ _____

48. $3400000 = $ _____

49. $0.08 = $ _____

50. $220 = $ _____

51. $0.00000001 = $ _____

Order of Operations

If there is one element of using a calculator that is taken too lightly, it is the order in which the operations appearing in an equation are performed.

For instance, the equation

$$\frac{8}{3 + 1}$$

is often entered as

$$\boxed{8} \;\; \boxed{\div} \;\; \boxed{3} \;\; \boxed{+} \;\; \boxed{1} \Rightarrow \frac{8}{3} + 1 = 2.67 + 1 = 3.67$$

which is **totally incorrect** (2 is the correct answer).

You need to be aware that a calculator *will not* perform the addition first and then the division. In fact, addition and subtraction are the last operations to be performed in any equation. It is therefore very important that you carefully read and understand the next few paragraphs if you are to use your calculator properly.

1. The first operations to be performed by the calculator can be set using **parentheses ( )**. It does not matter which operations are within the parentheses. They dictate to the calculator that these operations are to be performed first. There is no limit on the number of parentheses used in each equation—they will all show operations to be performed first. For instance, for the preceding example, if parentheses are added as shown next, the addition will be performed first and the correct answer will be obtained.

$$\frac{8}{(3 + 1)} \Rightarrow \boxed{8} \;\; \boxed{\div} \;\; \boxed{(} \;\; \boxed{3} \;\; \boxed{+} \;\; \boxed{1} \;\; \boxed{)} \Rightarrow \frac{8}{4} = 2$$

2. Next, **powers and roots** (other than those appearing as a defined key, such as $\sqrt{}$) are performed such as x^3, $\sqrt[3]{2}$, etc.
3. **Negation** (applying a negative sign to a quantity) and **single-key operations,** such as $\sqrt{}$, sin, and $\tan^{-1}$ are performed.
4. **Multiplication** and **division** are then performed.
5. Lastly, **addition** and **subtraction** are performed.

A compressed visual review is provided below:

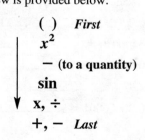

$$( ) \quad \textit{First}$$
$$x^2$$
$$- \text{ (to a quantity)}$$
$$\textbf{sin}$$
$$\text{x, } \div$$
$$+, - \quad \textit{Last}$$

It may take a few moments and some repetition to remember this order, but at least you are aware that there is some order to the operations and are aware that ignoring them can result in some disastrous conclusions.

EXAMPLES

(a) Determine

$$\sqrt{\frac{9}{3}}$$

The following calculator operations will result in an **incorrect** answer of 1 because the square root operation will be performed before the division.

$$\boxed{\sqrt{}}\quad\boxed{9}\quad\boxed{\div}\quad\boxed{3}\;\Rightarrow\;\frac{\sqrt{9}}{3}=\frac{3}{3}=1.00$$

However, recognizing that we must first divide 9 by 3, we can use parentheses as follows so this operation is the first to be performed and the correct answer is obtained.

$$\boxed{\sqrt{}}\quad\boxed{(}\quad\boxed{9}\quad\boxed{\div}\quad\boxed{3}\quad\boxed{)}\;\Rightarrow\;\sqrt{\left(\frac{9}{3}\right)}=\sqrt{3}=\mathbf{1.67}$$

(b) Determine

$$\frac{8+12}{2}$$

If you simply entered what is shown next, you will obtain an **incorrect** result, because the division is performed first.

$$\boxed{8}\quad\boxed{+}\quad\boxed{1}\quad\boxed{2}\quad\boxed{\div}\quad\boxed{2}\;\Rightarrow\;8+\frac{12}{2}=8+6=14.00$$

Using parentheses, however, results in the correct answer.

$$\boxed{(}\quad\boxed{8}\quad\boxed{+}\quad\boxed{1}\quad\boxed{2}\quad\boxed{)}\quad\boxed{\div}\quad\boxed{2}\;\Rightarrow\;\frac{(8+12)}{2}=\frac{20}{2}=\mathbf{10}$$

(c) Find

$$\sqrt{2^2+4^2}$$

In this case, you should square the numbers first, add, and then take the square root. If you enter the following, you will obtain an **incorrect** answer.

$$\boxed{\sqrt{}}\quad\boxed{2}\quad\boxed{x^2}\quad\boxed{+}\quad\boxed{4}\quad\boxed{x^2}\;\Rightarrow\;\sqrt{2^2}+4^2=2+16=18.00$$

However, if you enter the following sequence, you will get the correct answer.

$$\boxed{\sqrt{}}\quad\boxed{(}\quad\boxed{2}\quad\boxed{x^2}\quad\boxed{+}\quad\boxed{4}\quad\boxed{x^2}\quad\boxed{)}\;\Rightarrow\;\sqrt{(2^2+4^2)}=\sqrt{(4+16)}=\sqrt{20}=\mathbf{4.47}$$

(d) Calculate

$$\frac{6}{2+5}$$

If you enter this sequence, an incorrect answer of 8 will result

$$\boxed{6} \;\; \boxed{\div} \;\; \boxed{2} \;\; \boxed{+} \;\; \boxed{5} \;\Rightarrow \frac{6}{2} + 5 = 3 + 5 = 8$$

Using brackets to ensure the addition takes place before the division will result in the correct answer:

$$\boxed{6} \;\; \boxed{\div} \;\; \boxed{(} \;\; \boxed{2} \;\; \boxed{+} \;\; \boxed{5} \;\; \boxed{)} \;\Rightarrow \frac{6}{(2+5)} = \frac{6}{7} = \mathbf{0.86}$$

(e) Determine

$$\frac{2+3}{6^2}$$

The first operation to be performed is the squaring of the number six in the denominator, which is fine for the answer desired. However, since division is the next operation to be performed, 6^2 will be divided into 3, resulting in an **incorrect** answer of 2.08.

$$\boxed{2} \;\; \boxed{+} \;\; \boxed{3} \;\; \boxed{\div} \;\; \boxed{6} \;\; \boxed{\wedge} \;\; \boxed{2} \;\Rightarrow 2 + \frac{3}{6^2} = 2 + 0.08 = 2.08$$

Using parentheses will ensure that the addition takes place first and the correct answer is obtained:

$$\boxed{(} \;\; \boxed{2} \;\; \boxed{+} \;\; \boxed{3} \;\; \boxed{)} \;\; \boxed{\div} \;\; \boxed{6} \;\; \boxed{\wedge} \;\; \boxed{2} \;\Rightarrow \frac{(2+3)}{6^2} = \frac{5}{36} = \mathbf{0.14}$$

(f) Determine the sum

$$\frac{1}{4} + \frac{1}{6} + \frac{2}{3}$$

Because the division will occur first, the correct result will be obtained by simply performing the operations as indicated:

$$\boxed{1} \;\; \boxed{\div} \;\; \boxed{4} \;\; \boxed{+} \;\; \boxed{1} \;\; \boxed{\div} \;\; \boxed{6} \;\; \boxed{+} \;\; \boxed{2} \;\; \boxed{\div} \;\; \boxed{3} \;\Rightarrow \mathbf{1.08}$$

(g) Find the cube root of 3000:

$$\sqrt[3]{3000} = (3000)^{1/3}$$

Always keep in mind that the square root is the same as taking a quantity to the 1/2 power, the cube root is to the 1/3 power, the fourth root is to the 1/4 power, and so on. Remember, however, that the power is taken before the division, so a bracket must surround the division:

$$\boxed{3} \;\; \boxed{0} \;\; \boxed{.\,0} \;\; \boxed{0} \;\; \boxed{\wedge} \;\; \boxed{(} \;\; \boxed{1} \;\; \boxed{\div} \;\; \boxed{3} \;\; \boxed{)} \;\Rightarrow \mathbf{14.42}$$

PROBLEMS

Determine the following using a calculator.

52. $\dfrac{4+6}{2+8} = $ _____

53. $\dfrac{2 \times (8 + 6)}{10} = $ _____

54. $\dfrac{4 + 9}{6 \times 2} = $ _____

55. $\dfrac{4^3}{2(1 + 2)} = $ _____

56. $\dfrac{1}{6 + 3(2 + 3)} = $ _____

57. $\sqrt{(2 + 3)^2 + 4^2} = $ _____

58. $\dfrac{1}{(3 + 1)^2} = $ _____

59. $\dfrac{\sqrt[3]{5^2}}{3^2 - 2} = $ _____

Powers of 10

Powers of 10 are entered using the E, EE, or EXP key on your calculator. Always remember, however, to use the negative sign on the numeric keypad when entering a negative power. *Do not use the subtraction key.* In fact, for all operations, negative numbers are entered with the negative sign on the numeric keypad. The negative sign for subtraction is used only for that specific operation. The positive sign associated with positive powers is understood and does not appear on the display.

With the calculator set for the SCI and ENG mode, the proper power of 10 for any number can be found by simply entering the number in the decimal form and pressing the Enter key for some calculators or dividing or multiplying by 1 for others. For the ENG mode the following will result:

$$0.006 = \mathbf{6.00E{-}3}$$
$$80400 = \mathbf{80.40E3}$$

This sequence is also applicable to numbers in the power-of-10 format. Each number in the power-of-10 format is treated as a single digit in a defined sequence.

EXAMPLES

$0.04 + \dfrac{8}{3000} = 40\text{E}{-}3 + \left(\dfrac{8}{3\text{E}3}\right)$

$= \boxed{4}\,\boxed{0}\,\boxed{\text{E}}\,\boxed{-}\,\boxed{3}$

$\boxed{+}\,\boxed{(}\,\boxed{8}\,\boxed{\div}\,\boxed{3}\,\boxed{\text{E}}\,\boxed{3}\,\boxed{)} \Rightarrow \mathbf{42.67E{-}3}$

$(0.003)^2 \times 4000 = (3\text{E}{-}3)^2 \times 4\text{E}3$

$= \boxed{3}\,\boxed{\text{E}}\,\boxed{-}\,\boxed{3}\,\boxed{x^2}\,\boxed{\times}\,\boxed{4}\,\boxed{\text{E}}\,\boxed{3} \Rightarrow \mathbf{36.00E{-}3}$

PROBLEMS

Use a calculator.

60. 50E3 − 2.2E4 + 0.08E6 = _____

61. $\dfrac{(4 \times 10^{-6})^2}{8 \times 10^3}$ = _____

62. $0.008 \times (6 \times 10^3) + 5200 \times 10^{-3} - 200\text{E}{-}3 - 3 =$ _____

63. $80{,}000 \times \sqrt{(2000)^3}$ = _____

Exponential Functions

The exponential function appears on all scientific calculators because it is such a prominent element of many important equations. When e^x is chosen, the display will appear with a request for the power (x). As before, be sure to honor the sequence of operations if the power is the result of a mathematical operation. In addition, be sure to use the negative sign from the numeric keyboard for negative powers.

EXAMPLES

(a) Determine $e^{6/2} = e^{(6/2)}$.

$\boxed{\text{2nd}}\ \boxed{e^x}\ \boxed{(}\ \boxed{6}\ \boxed{\div}\ \boxed{2}\ \boxed{)}$ = 20.09E0 = **20.09**

(b) Find $\dfrac{3}{e^{1+4/3}} + e^{-2} = \dfrac{3}{e^{(1+4/3)}} + e^{-2}$.

$\boxed{3}\ \boxed{\div}\ \boxed{\text{2nd}}\ \boxed{e^x}\ \boxed{(}\ \boxed{1}\ \boxed{+}\ \boxed{4}\ \boxed{\div}\ \boxed{3}\ \boxed{)}$

$\boxed{+}\ \boxed{\text{2nd}}\ \boxed{e^x}\ \boxed{-}\ \boxed{2}$ = **426.25E−3**

PROBLEMS

Use a calculator.

64. $e^{\sqrt{10/3}}$ = _____

65. e^{e^2} = _____

66. $\dfrac{68\text{E}3 \times e^{-1}}{4\text{E}3 + e^8}$ = _____

The primary purpose of this entire section of the laboratory manual is to ensure your understanding of the importance of being aware of which calculations are performed first when using a calculator. Too often there is no awareness of the order of operations and ridiculous results are accepted as correct because the entry is carefully checked and everything looks fine. The same priority of operations discussed here applies to most computers, so the carryover is almost universal.

Measurement of Resistance

Name _____

Date _____

Class _____

OBJECTIVES

After performing this experiment, you will be able to:
1. Determine the listed value of a resistor using the resistor color code.
2. Use the DMM (or VOM) to measure the value of a resistor.
3. Determine the percent difference between the measured and listed values of a resistor.
4. Measure the resistance of a potentiometer and explain its operation.

MATERIALS NEEDED

Resistors: Ten assorted values
One potentiometer (any value)

SUMMARY OF THEORY

Resistance is the opposition a substance offers to current. The unit for resistance is the *ohm,* symbolized with the Greek letter capital omega (Ω). A resistor is a component designed to have a specific resistance and wattage rating. Resistors limit current but, in doing so, produce heat. The physical size of a resistor is related to its ability to dissipate heat, *not* to its resistance. A physically large resistor can dissipate more heat than a small resistor, hence the larger one would have a higher wattage rating than the smaller one.

Resistors are either fixed (constant resistance) or variable. Fixed resistors are usually color coded with a four-band code that indicates the specific resistance and tolerance. Each color stands for a number, as described in Floyd's text and reprinted in Table 1 for convenience. Figure 1 shows how to read the resistance and tolerance of a four-band resistor.

The resistance of resistors is measured using a DMM or VOM, as described in the experiment on Laboratory Meters and Power Supply. If you are using a VOM, the zero reading should be checked

Table 1

	Digit	Color
	0	Black
	1	Brown
	2	Red
	3	Orange
Resistance value,	4	Yellow
first three bands	5	Green
	6	Blue
	7	Violet
	8	Gray
	9	White
Tolerance, fourth band	5%	Gold
	10%	Silver
	20%	No band

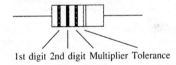

1st digit 2nd digit Multiplier Tolerance

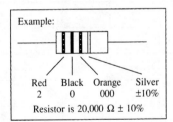

Example:

Red	Black	Orange	Silver
2	0	000	±10%

Resistor is 20,000 Ω ± 10%

Note: In the multiplier band, Gold = X 0.1
Silver = X 0.01

Figure 1

whenever you change ranges on the meter by touching the test leads together. If you are using a nonautoranging DMM, a suitable range needs to be selected. Resistance normally should not be measured in a circuit as other resistors in the circuit will affect the reading. The resistor to be measured is removed from the circuit, and the test leads are connected across the resistance. The resistor under test should not be held between the fingers as body resistance can affect the reading, particularly with high-value resistors. (It is okay to hold one end of the resistor under test.)

The most common form of variable resistor is the potentiometer. The potentiometer is a three-terminal device with the outer terminals having a fixed resistance between them and the center terminal connected to a moving wiper. The moving wiper is connected to a shaft that is used to vary the resistance between it and the outer terminals. Potentiometers are commonly found in applications such as volume controls.

Another type of variable resistor is the rheostat. A rheostat consists of two terminals. The control varies the resistance between the two terminals. A potentiometer can be connected as a rheostat by connecting the moving wiper and one of the outer terminals.

PROCEDURE

1. Obtain 10 four-band fixed resistors. Record the colors of each resistor in Table 2. Use the resistor color code to determine the color-code resistance of each resistor. Then measure the resistance of each resistor and record the measured value in Table 2. The first line has been completed as an example.

2. Compute the percent difference between the measured and color-coded values using the equation:

$$\% \text{ difference} = \frac{|R_{measured} - R_{color\ code}|}{R_{color\ code}} \times 100$$

The percent difference is shown as an absolute (positive) value for all resistors. Complete Table 2.

Table 2

Resistor	Color of Band				Color-Code Value	Measured Value	% Difference
	1st	2nd	3rd	4th			
0	brown	green	red	silver	1.5 kΩ ± 10%	1.46 kΩ	2.7%
1							
2							
3							
4							
5							
6							
7							
8							
9							
10							

3.   Obtain a potentiometer. Number the terminals 1, 2, and 3 as illustrated in Figure 2.

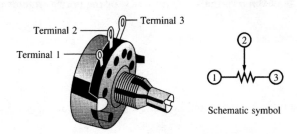

Figure 2

Measure and record the resistance between terminals 1 and 3 of the potentiometer (the outside terminals). $R_{1,3}$ = _____

Vary the potentiometer's shaft and monitor the resistance between terminals 1 and 3. Does the resistance change? _____ Explain. _____

4.   Turn the potentiometer completely counterclockwise (CCW). Measure the resistance between terminals 1 and 2. Then measure the resistance between terminals 2 and 3. Record the measured resistance in Table 3. Compute the sum of the two readings and enter it into Table 3.

5.   Turn the shaft 1/3 turn clockwise (CW) and repeat the measurements in step 4.

6.   Turn the shaft 2/3 turn CW and repeat the measurements in step 4. What did you find about the sum of the resistance in steps 4, 5, and 6?

Table 3

Step	Shaft Position	Resistance Measured Between		Sum of Resistance Readings
		Terminals 1–2	Terminals 2–3	
4	CCW			
5	⅓ CW			
6	⅔ CW			

CONCLUSION

EVALUATION AND REVIEW QUESTIONS

1.   Predict the resistance between terminals 1–2 and 2–3 for the potentiometer if the shaft is rotated fully CW.

2.   (a)   Are any of the resistors measured in Table 2 out of tolerance? _____

        (b)   You suspect that the percent difference between color-code and measured values could be due to error in the meter. How could you find out if you are correct?

3.   Determine the resistor color code for the following resistors. The tolerance is 10%.
        (a)   12 Ω _____
        (b)   6.8 kΩ _____
        (c)   910 Ω _____
        (d)   4.7 MΩ _____
        (e)   1.0 Ω _____

4.   Determine the expected value and tolerance for resistors with the following color codes:
        (a)   red-red-black-gold _____
        (b)   violet-green-brown-silver _____
        (c)   green-brown-brown-gold _____
        (d)   white-brown-gold-gold _____
        (e)   gray-red-yellow-silver _____

5.   A resistor is color coded: red-violet-orange-gold.
        (a)   What is the largest value the resistor can be and still be in tolerance? _____

        (b)   What is the smallest value? _____

6.   What is the difference between a potentiometer and a rheostat?

FOR FURTHER INVESTIGATION

Obtain 20 resistors marked with the same color code on each resistor. Carefully measure each resistor. Determine the average value of resistance. Then find the deviation of each resistor from the average by computing the amount each value differs from the average. The average deviation can then be found by computing the average of the deviations. Summarize your findings. Are any resistors outside the marked tolerance? Is there any evidence that all resistors are either higher or lower than their marked values? What do differing values of resistors tell you about actual measurements as opposed to calculated or color-code values?

Voltage Measurement and Circuit Ground

Name _____

Date _____

Class _____

OBJECTIVES
After performing this experiment, you will be able to:
1. Connect a circuit from a schematic diagram.
2. Use voltages measured with respect to ground to compute the voltage drop across a resistor.
3. Explain the meaning of circuit ground and subscripts used in voltage definitions.

MATERIALS NEEDED
Resistors:

One 330 Ω, one 680 Ω, and 1.0 kΩ

SUMMARY OF THEORY
Energy is required to move a charge from a point of lower potential to one of higher potential. Voltage is a measure of this energy per charge. Energy is given up when a charge moves from a point of higher potential to one of lower potential.

Voltage is always measured with respect to some point in the circuit. For this reason, only potential *differences* have meaning. We can refer to the voltage *across* a component, in which case the reference is one side of the component. Alternatively, we can refer to the voltage at some point in the circuit. In this case the reference point is assumed to be "ground." Circuit ground is usually called *reference ground* to differentiate it from the potential of the earth, which is called *earth ground.*

An analogy can clarify the meaning of reference ground. Assume a building has two floors below ground level. The floors in the building could be numbered from the ground floor, by numbering the lower floors with negative numbers. Alternatively, the reference for numbering the floors could be made the lowest floor in the basement. Then all floors would have a positive floor number. The choice of the numbering system does not change the height of the building, but it does change each floor number. Likewise, the ground reference is used in circuits as a point of reference for voltage measurements. The circuit is not changed by the ground reference chosen.

Figure 1 illustrates the same circuit with two different ground reference points. The circuit in Figure 1(a) has as its reference point **B.** Positive and negative voltages are shown. If the reference point is moved to point **C,** the circuit voltages are all positive, as shown in Figure 1(b). Voltage is always measured between two points. To define the two points, subscripts are used. The voltage difference (or simply voltage) between points **A** and **B** is written as V_{AB} where the second letter in the subscript identifies the reference point. If a single subscripted letter is shown, the voltage is defined between the lettered point and the circuit's reference ground.

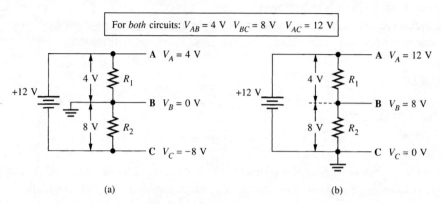

For *both* circuits: $V_{AB} = 4$ V $V_{BC} = 8$ V $V_{AC} = 12$ V

(a)   (b)

Figure 1

PROCEDURE

1.   Measure three resistors with the listed values given in Table 1. Record the measured values in Table 1. You should always use the measured value in experimental work.

2.   Construct the circuit shown in Figure 2. An example of how a series circuit like this can be built on a protoboard (solderless breadboard) is shown in the Introduction to the Student section, Figure 2. (Consult your instructor if you need this section.) Set the power supply to +10 V. Measure the voltage across each resistor in the circuit. Enter the measured values in Table 2.

Table 1

Component	Listed Value	Measured Value
R_1	330 Ω	
R_2	680 Ω	
R_3	1.0 kΩ	

Table 2

	Measured Value
V_S	
V_{AB}	
V_{BC}	
V_{CD}	

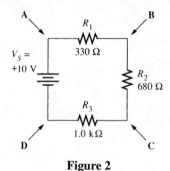

Figure 2

3. Assign point **D** as the reference ground. Measure the voltage at points **A, B,** and **C** with respect to point **D.** The voltage readings are made with the reference probe connected to point **D.** Enter the measured values in Table 3. Then use the measured voltages to compute the voltage differences V_{AB}, V_{BC}, and V_{CD}.

Table 3

	Measured Voltage	Voltage Difference Calculation
V_A		
		$V_{AB} = V_A - V_B =$
V_B		
		$V_{BC} = V_B - V_C =$
V_C		
		$V_{CD} = V_C - V_D =$
V_D	0.0 V (ref)	

4. Now measure the voltages in the circuit with respect to point **C.** The circuit is *not changed.* Only the reference point changes. Move the reference probe of the voltmeter to point **C.** This point will now represent ground. The voltage at point **D** now has a negative value. Enter the measured voltages in Table 4. Compute the voltage differences as before and enter them in Table 4.

Table 4

	Measured Voltage	Voltage Difference Calculation
V_A		
		$V_{AB} = V_A - V_B =$
V_B		
		$V_{BC} = V_B - V_C =$
V_C	0.0 V (ref)	
		$V_{CD} = V_C - V_D =$
V_D		

5. Move the circuit reference point to point **B.** Again, there is no change to the circuit other than the reference ground. Repeat the measurements of the voltages with respect to circuit ground. Compute the voltage differences and enter the data in Table 5.

Table 5

	Measured Voltage	Voltage Difference Calculation
V_A		
		$V_{AB} = V_A - V_B =$
V_B	0.0 V (ref)	
		$V_{BC} = V_B - V_C =$
V_C		
		$V_{CD} = V_C - V_D =$
V_D		

6. Now make point **A** the reference point and repeat the measurements. Enter the data in Table 6.

Table 6

	Measured Voltage	Voltage Difference Calculation
V_A	0.0 V (ref)	
V_B		$V_{AB} = V_A - V_B =$
V_C		$V_{BC} = V_B - V_C =$
V_D		$V_{CD} = V_C - V_D =$

CONCLUSION

EVALUATION AND REVIEW QUESTIONS

1. Compare the *voltage difference calculation* in Table 3 through Table 6. Does the circuit's reference point have any effect on the voltage differences across any of the resistors? Explain your answer.

2. Define the term *reference ground*.

3. If you measured V_{AB} as 12.0 V, what is the V_{BA}? _____

4. Assume $V_M = -220$ V and $V_N = -150$ V. What is V_{MN}? _____

5. If a test point in a circuit is marked +5.0 V and a second test point is marked −3.3 V, what voltage reading would you expect on a voltmeter connected between the two test points? Assume the reference lead on the meter is at the lowest potential. _____

FOR FURTHER INVESTIGATION

Warning: The power supplies used in this procedure must have floating output terminals. If you are not sure, check with your instructor before proceeding with this investigation.

Replace the +10 V supply used in this experiment with two +5 V supplies in series. Attach the +5 V output of one supply to the common of the second supply. Call this point the reference ground for the circuit. Measure the voltages throughout the circuit. Summarize your results.

Ohm's Law

Name _____
Date _____
Class _____

OBJECTIVES
After performing this experiment, you will be able to:
1. Measure the current-voltage curve for a resistor.
2. Construct a graph of the data from objective 1.
3. Given a graph of current-voltage for a resistor, determine the resistance.

MATERIALS NEEDED
Resistors:
　　　　One 1.0 kΩ, one 1.5 kΩ, one 2.2 kΩ
One dc ammeter, 0–10 mA
For Further Investigation:
　　One Cds photocell (Jameco 120299 or equivalent)

SUMMARY OF THEORY
The flow of electrical charge in a circuit is called *current*. Current is measured in units of *amperes,* or amps for short. The ampere is defined as one coulomb of charge moving past a point in one second. Current is symbolized by the letter *I* (for *Intensity*) and is frequently shown with an arrow to indicate the direction of flow. Conventional current is defined as the direction a positive charge would move under the influence of an electric field. When electrons move, the direction is opposite to the direction defined for conventional current. To clarify the difference, the term *electron flow* is frequently applied to current in the opposite direction of conventional current. The experiments in this lab book work equally well with either definition.

　　　　The relationship between current and voltage is an important characteristic that defines various electronic devices. The relationship is frequently shown with a graph. Usually, the voltage is controlled (the independent variable), and the current is observed (the dependent variable). This is the basic method for this experiment, for which a series of resistors will be tested. As discussed in the Introduction to the Student, the independent variable is plotted along the *x*-axis and the dependent variable is plotted along the *y*-axis.

　　　　Fixed resistors have a straight-line or *linear* current-voltage curve. This linear relationship illustrates the basic relationship of Ohm's law—namely, that the current is proportional to the voltage for constant resistance. Ohm's law is the most important law of electronics. It is written in equation form as:

$$I = \frac{V}{R}$$

where *I* represents current, *V* represents voltage, and *R* represents resistance.

PROCEDURE

1. Measure three resistors with listed values of 1.0 kΩ, 1.5 kΩ, and 2.2 kΩ. Record the measured values in Table 1.

Table 1

Component	Listed Value	Measured Value
R_1	1.0 kΩ	
R_2	1.5 kΩ	
R_3	2.2 kΩ	

2. Connect the circuit shown in Figure 1(a). Notice that the ammeter is in series with the resistor and forms a single "loop" as shown in the protoboard wiring diagram in Figure 1(b). The voltmeter is then connected directly across the resistor.

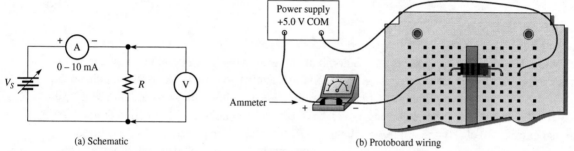

(a) Schematic   (b) Protoboard wiring

Figure 1

Caution! Ammeters can be easily damaged if they are incorrectly connected. Have your instructor check your connections before applying power.

3. Adjust the power supply for a voltage of 2.0 V. Read the current that is through the resistor and record it in Table 2.

4. Adjust the power supply for 4.0 V and measure the current. Record the current in Table 2. Continue taking current readings for each of the voltages listed in Table 2.

Table 2 (R_1)

$V_S =$	2.0 V	4.0 V	6.0 V	8.0 V	10.0 V
$I =$					

5.   Replace R_1 with R_2 and repeat steps 3 and 4. Record the data in Table 3.

Table 3 (R_2)

$V_S =$	2.0 V	4.0 V	6.0 V	8.0 V	10.0 V
$I =$					

6.   Replace R_2 with R_3 and repeat steps 3 and 4. Record the data in Table 4.

Table 4 (R_3)

$V_S =$	2.0 V	4.0 V	6.0 V	8.0 V	10.0 V
$I =$					

7.   On Plot 1, graph all three I-V curves using the data from Tables 2, 3, and 4. Plot the dependent variable (current) on the y-axis and the independent variable (voltage) on the x-axis. Choose a scale for the graph that spreads the data over the entire grid.

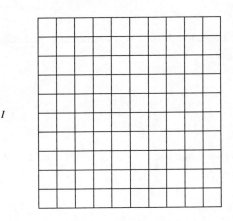

I

V

Plot 1

CONCLUSION

EVALUATION AND REVIEW QUESTIONS

1. The slope of a line is the change in the *y* direction divided by the change in the *x* direction. The definition for slope is illustrated in Figure 2. Find the slope for each resistor on Plot 1. Notice that the slope has units. If the change in *y* is measured in mA and the change in *x* is measured in V, the slope is mA/V = mS.

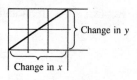

$$\text{Slope} = \frac{\text{Change in } y}{\text{Change in } x}$$

$$= \frac{2}{3}$$

Figure 2

2. What happens to the slope of the *I-V* curve for larger resistors?

3. (a) If the resistance is halved and the voltage is not changed, what will happen to the current in a resistive circuit?

   (b) If the voltage is doubled and the resistance is not changed, what will happen to the current in a resistive circuit?

4. If the current in a resistive circuit is 24 mA and the applied voltage is 48 V, what is the resistance?

5. What current is through a 10 Ω resistor with a 5.0 V applied?

FOR FURTHER INVESTIGATION

One interesting type of resistor is called a CdS cell (for Cadmium Sulfide). CdS cells are widely used as light-sensing elements in electronics. The resistance of the CdS cell decreases as the incident light increases.

In this investigation, find out if a CdS cell has an *I-V* curve like other resistors (a straight line) if the light is constant. Set up the experiment as in Figure 1, but use a CdS cell instead of a normal resistor. You will need to have a constant amount of light on the CdS cell as much as possible. Try adjusting the CdS cell to look at a light source such as a room light. You will notice that pointing it in different ways will change the current. A good starting point is to adjust it so that you have about 2 mA when the source voltage is 2.0 V. Then increase the voltage by increments of 2.0 V and record the current in Table 5 for each voltage setting. Plot the data in Plot 2 and summarize your findings.

Table 5 (CdS cell)

$V_S =$	2.0 V	4.0 V	6.0 V	8.0 V	10.0 V
$I =$					

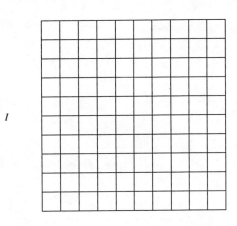

I

V

Plot 2

Power in DC Circuits

Name _____

Date _____

Class _____

OBJECTIVES

After performing this experiment, you will be able to:

1. Determine the power in a variable resistor at various settings of resistance.
2. Plot data for power as a function of resistance. From the plot, determine when maximum power is delivered to the variable resistor.

MATERIALS NEEDED

One 2.7 kΩ resistor

One 10 kΩ potentiometer

SUMMARY OF THEORY

When there is current through a resistor, electrical energy is converted into heat. Heat is then radiated from the resistor. The *rate* that heat is dissipated is called *power*. Power is measured in units of joules per second (J/s), which defines the unit called the watt (W). The power dissipated by a resistor is given by the power law equation:

$$P = IV$$

By applying Ohm's law to the power law equation, two more useful equations for power can be found. These are:

$$P = I^2 R$$

and

$$P = \frac{V^2}{R}$$

The three power equations given above are also known as Watt's law. In this experiment, you will determine power using the last equation. Notice that if you measure the voltage in volts (V) and the resistance in kilohms (kΩ), the power will have units of milliwatts (mW).

The physical size of a resistor is related to the amount of heat it can dissipate. Therefore, larger resistors are rated for more power than smaller ones. Carbon composition resistors are available with standard power ratings ranging from 1/8 W to 2 W. For most typical low voltage applications (15 V or less and at least 1 kΩ of resistance), a 1/4 W resistor is satisfactory.

PROCEDURE

1.   Measure the resistance of R_1. The color-code value is 2.7 kΩ. R_1 = _____

2.   Construct the circuit shown in Figure 1(a). Figure 1(b) shows an example of the circuit constructed on a protoboard. R_2 is a 10 kΩ potentiometer. Connect the center (variable) terminal to one of the outside terminals. Use this and the remaining terminal as a variable resistor. Adjust the potentiometer for 0.5 kΩ. (Always remove power when measuring resistance and make certain you are measuring only the potentiometer's resistance.)

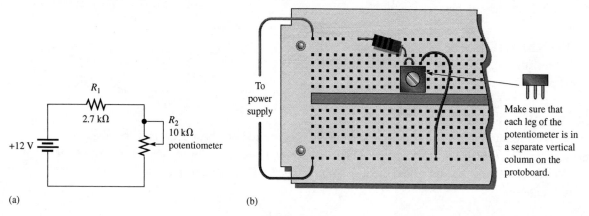

(a)   (b)

Figure 1

3.   Use Ohm's law to compute the total current in the circuit. The total voltage is +12.0 V. The total resistance is $R_1 + R_2$. Enter the total current in Table 1. The first entry has been completed as an example.

Table 1

Variable Resistance Setting (R_2)	$I_T = \dfrac{V_T}{R_T}$	V_1 (measured)	V_2 (measured)	Power in R_2: P_2
0.5 kΩ	3.75 mA			
1.0 kΩ				
2.0 kΩ				
3.0 kΩ				
4.0 kΩ				
5.0 kΩ				
7.5 kΩ				
10.0 kΩ				

4.   Measure the voltage across R_1 and the voltage across R_2. Enter the measured voltages in Table 1. As a check, make sure that the sum of V_1 and V_2 is equal to 12.0 V. Then compute the power in R_2 using either of the following equations:

$$P_2 = I_T R_2 \quad \text{or} \quad P_2 = \frac{V_2^2}{R_2}$$

Enter the computed power, in milliwatts, in Table 1.

5.   Disconnect the power supply and set R_2 to the next value shown in Table 1. Reconnect the power supply and repeat the measurements made in steps 3 and 4. Continue in this manner for each of the resistance settings shown in Table 1.

6.   Using the data in Table 1, graph the relationship of the power, P_2, as a function of resistance R_2 on Plot 1. Since resistance is the independent variable, plot it along the x-axis and plot power along the y-axis. An *implied* data point can be plotted at the origin because there can be no power dissipated in R_2 without resistance. A smooth curve can then be drawn to the origin.

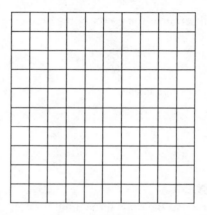

Plot 1

CONCLUSION

EVALUATION AND REVIEW QUESTIONS

1.   Observe the graph of resistance versus power for your experiment. Compare the resistance of R_1 and R_2 when power in R_2 is a maximum.

2.   What was happening to the total current in the circuit as R_2 was increasing?

3.　　What was happening to the power in R_1 as the resistance of R_2 was increasing? Explain your answer.

4.　　A 1.5 kΩ resistor is found to have 22.5 V across it.

　　(a)　　What is the current in the resistor? _____

　　(b)　　What is the power dissipated in the resistor? _____

　　(c)　　Could a 1/4 W resistor be used in this application? Explain your answer.

5.　　What physical characteristic determines the power rating of a resistor?

6.　　What happens to electrical energy in a resistor?

FOR FURTHER INVESTIGATION

Because it is a series circuit, the current was the same throughout for each setting of R_2. Find the current for each row in Table 1 by dividing the measured value of V_1 by the measured value of R_1. Plot this current as a function of R_2. On the same graph, plot V_2 as a function of R_2. What is the shape of the product of these two lines?

Series Circuits

Name _____
Date _____
Class _____

OBJECTIVES

After performing this experiment, you will be able to:
1.   Use Ohm's law to find the current and voltages in a series circuit.
2.   Apply Kirchhoff's voltage law to a series circuit.

MATERIALS NEEDED

Resistors:
         One 330 Ω, one 1.0 kΩ, one 1.5 kΩ, one 2.2 kΩ
One dc ammeter, 0–10 mA

SUMMARY OF THEORY

Consider the simple circuit illustrated in Figure 1. The source voltage is the total current multiplied by the total resistance as given by Ohm's law. This can be stated in equation form as

$$V_S = I_T R_T$$

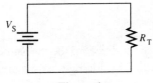

Figure 1

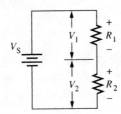

Figure 2

In a series circuit, the circuit elements are connected with only one path for current. For this reason, *the current is the same throughout a series circuit.*

Whenever we connect resistors in series, the total resistance increases. The total resistance of a series circuit is the sum of the individual resistors. Figure 2 illustrates a series circuit with two resistors. The total resistance is

$$R_T = R_1 + R_2$$

Substituting this equation into Ohm's law for the total circuit gives:

$$V_S = I_T(R_1 + R_2)$$

Multiplying both terms by I_T results in:

$$V_S = I_T R_1 + I_T R_2$$

Since the identical current, I_T, must be through each resistor, the voltage drops across the resistors can be found:

$$V_S = V_1 + V_2$$

This result illustrates that the source voltage is equal to the sum of the voltage drops across the resistors. This relationship is called Kirchhoff's voltage law, which is more precisely stated:

The algebraic sum of all voltage rises and drops around any single closed loop in a circuit is equal to zero.

It is important to pay attention to the polarity of the voltages. Current from the source creates a voltage drop across the resistors. The voltage drop across the resistors will have an opposite polarity to the source voltage as illustrated in Figure 2. We may apply Kirchhoff's voltage law by using the following rules:

1. Choose an arbitrary starting point. Go either clockwise or counterclockwise from the starting point.
2. For each voltage source or load, write down the first sign you see and the magnitude of the voltage.
3. When you arrive at the starting point, equate the algebraic sum of the voltages to zero.

PROCEDURE

1. Obtain the resistors listed in Table 1. Measure each resistor and record the measured value in Table 1. Compute the total resistance for a series connection by adding the measured values. Enter the computed total resistance in Table 1 in the column for the listed value.

2. Connect the resistors in series as illustrated in Figure 3. Test various combinations of series resistors. Can you conclude that the total resistance of series resistors is the sum of the individual resistors? Then measure the total resistance of the series connection and verify that it agrees with your computed value. Enter your measured value in Table 1.

Table 1

Component	Listed Value	Measured Value
R_1	1.0 kΩ	
R_2	1.5 kΩ	
R_3	2.2 kΩ	
R_4	330 Ω	
$R_T =$		

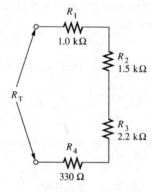

Figure 3

3.   Complete the circuit shown in Figure 4. Be certain the ammeter is connected in *series,* otherwise damage to the meter may result. Before applying power, have your instructor check your circuit. Compute the current in the circuit by substituting the source voltage and the total resistance into Ohm's law. That is:

$$I_T = \frac{V_S}{R_T}$$

Record the computed current in Table 2. Apply power, and confirm that your computed current is within experimental uncertainty of the measured current.

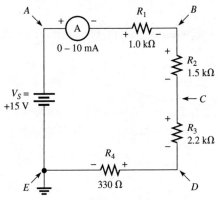

Figure 4

Table 2

	Computed Value	Measured Value
I_T		
V_{AB}		
V_{BC}		
V_{CD}		
V_{DE}		

4.   In a series circuit, the same current is through all components. (Can you think of a simple proof of this?) You can use the total current measured in step 3 and Ohm's law to compute the voltage drop across each resistor. Compute V_{AB} by multiplying the total current in the circuit by the resistance between **A** and **B.** Record the results as the computed voltage in Table 2.

5.   Repeat step 4 for the other voltages listed in Table 2.

6.   Measure and record each of the voltages listed in Table 2.

7.   Using the source voltage (+15 V) and the *measured voltage drops* listed in Table 2, prove that the algebraic sum of the voltages is zero. Do this by applying the rules listed in the Summary of Theory. The polarities of voltages are shown in Figure 4.

_____

8.   Repeat step 7 by starting at a different point in the circuit and traversing the circuit in the opposite direction.

_____

9.   Open the circuit at point **B.** Measure the voltage across the open circuit. Call this voltage V_{open}. Prove that Kirchhoff's voltage law is still valid for the open circuit.

_____

CONCLUSION

EVALUATION AND REVIEW QUESTIONS

1. Why doesn't the starting point for summing the voltages around a closed loop make any difference?

2. Kirchhoff's voltage law applies to any closed path, even one without current. How did the result of step 9 show that this is true?

3. Based on the result you observed in step 9, what voltage would you expect in a 110 V circuit across an open (blown) fuse?

4. Use Kirchhoff's voltage law to find V_X in Figure 5:

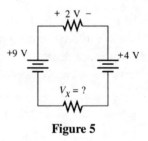

Figure 5

5. A 10 Ω resistor is in series with a bulb and a 12 V source.
   (a) If 8.0 V is across the bulb, what voltage is across the resistor? _____

   (b) What is the current in the circuit? _____

   (c) What is the resistance of the bulb? _____

FOR FURTHER INVESTIGATION

Resistors R_1, R_2, and R_3 used in this experiment have the same listed values as R_1, R_2, and R_3 from the experiment on Ohm's Law. Refer to your results of the current-voltage curve on Plot 1 of the experiment on Ohm's Law. Using the measured voltage in Table 2, find the current in the resistor based on Plot 1 of the experiment on Ohm's Law.

$I_1 = \underline{\hspace{2cm}}$

$I_2 = \underline{\hspace{2cm}}$

$I_3 = \underline{\hspace{2cm}}$

What observation did you make from this about the current in a series circuit?

MULTISIM TROUBLESHOOTING

This experiment has four Multisim files on the CD. Three of the four files contain a simulated "fault"; one has "no fault." The file with no fault is named EXP7-4-nf.msm. You may want to open this file to compare your results with the computer simulation. Then open each of the files with faults. Use the simulated instruments to investigate the circuit and determine the problem. The following are the filenames for circuits with troubleshooting problems for this experiment.

EXP7-4-f1.msm

      Fault: $\underline{\hspace{10cm}}$

EXP7-4-f2.msm

      Fault: $\underline{\hspace{10cm}}$

EXP7-4-f3.msm

      Fault: $\underline{\hspace{10cm}}$

The Voltage Divider

Name _____

Date _____

Class _____

OBJECTIVES

After performing this experiment, you will be able to:

1. Apply the voltage divider rule to series resistive circuits.
2. Design a voltage divider to meet a specific voltage output.
3. Confirm experimentally the circuit designed in step 2.
4. Determine the range of voltages available when a variable resistor is used in a voltage divider.

MATERIALS NEEDED

Resistors:

One 330 Ω, one 470 Ω, one 680 Ω, one 1.0 kΩ

One 1.0 kΩ potentiometer

SUMMARY OF THEORY

A voltage divider consists of two or more resistors connected in series with a voltage source. Voltage dividers are used to obtain a smaller voltage from a larger source voltage. As you may have seen in the experiment on Series Circuits, the voltage drops in a series circuit equal the source voltage. If you have two equal resistors in series, the voltage across each will be one-half of the source voltage. The voltage has thus been divided between the two resistors. The idea can be extended to circuits with more than two resistors and with different values.

Consider the series circuit illustrated in Figure 1. If the resistors are equal, the voltage across R_2 will be one-half the source voltage. But what happens if one of the resistors is larger than the other? Since both resistors must have the *same* current, Ohm's law tells us that the larger resistor must drop a larger voltage. In fact, the voltage across any resistor in a series circuit can be found by finding the *fraction* of the total resistance represented by the resistor in question. For example, if a series resistor represents one-third of the total resistance, the voltage across it will be one-third of the source voltage.

To find the voltage across R_2, the ratio of R_2 to R_T is multiplied by the source voltage. That is:

$$V_2 = V_S \left(\frac{R_2}{R_T} \right)$$

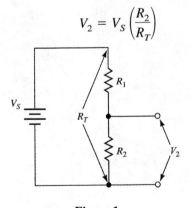

Figure 1

The voltage divider formula can be extended to find the voltage in a series circuit between any number of resistors. Call the resistance that is between the output terminals R_X. Then the voltage across this resistance can be written:

$$V_X = V_S\left(\frac{R_X}{R_T}\right)$$

where R_X represents the resistance between the output terminals.

This equation is a general form of the voltage divider equation. It can be stated as: "The output voltage from a voltage divider is equal to the input voltage multiplied by the ratio of the resistance between the output terminals to the total resistance." When several resistors are used, the output is generally taken with respect to the ground reference for the divider, as shown in Figure 2. In this case the output voltage can be found by substituting the value of R_2 and R_3 for R_X as shown.

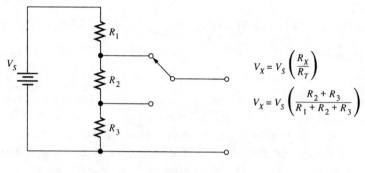

$$V_X = V_S\left(\frac{R_X}{R_T}\right)$$

$$V_X = V_S\left(\frac{R_2 + R_3}{R_1 + R_2 + R_3}\right)$$

Figure 2

Voltage dividers can be made to obtain variable voltages by using a potentiometer. The full range of the input voltage is available at the output, as illustrated in Figure 3(a). If one desires to limit the output voltage, this can be done by using fixed resistors in series as illustrated in the example shown in Figure 3(b).

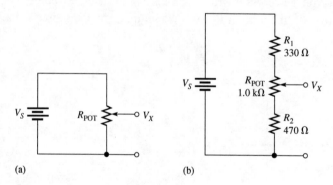

(a)

(b)

Figure 3

PROCEDURE

1. Obtain the resistors listed in Table 1. Measure each resistor and record the measured value in Table 1, column 3. Compute the total resistance for a series connection by adding the measured values. Enter the computed total resistance in Table 1.

Table 1

Resistor	Listed Value	Measured Value	$V_X = V_S\left(\dfrac{R_X}{R_T}\right)$	V_X (measured)
R_1	330 Ω			
R_2	470 Ω			
R_3	680 Ω			
R_4	1000 Ω			
Total			10.0 V	

2. Connect the resistors in the series circuit illustrated in Figure 4. With the source disconnected, measure the total resistance of the series connection and verify that it agrees with your computed value.

3. Apply the voltage divider rule to each resistor, one at a time, to compute the expected voltage across that resistor. Use the measured values of resistance and a source voltage of $+10$ V. Record the computed voltages (V_X) in Table 1, column 4.

4. Turn on the power and measure the voltage across each resistor. Record the measured voltage drops in Table 1, column 5. Your measured voltages should agree with your computed values.

5. Observe the voltages measured in step 4. In the space provided, draw the voltage divider, showing how you could obtain an output of $+6.8$ V.

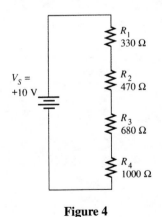

Figure 4

Circuit for step 5

6. Using the 330 Ω, 680 Ω, and 1.0 kΩ resistors, design a voltage divider with a +5.0 V output from a source voltage of +10 V. Draw your design in the space provided below.

7. Construct the circuit you designed and measure the actual output voltage. Indicate the measured value on your drawing.

8. Use two of the resistors from this experiment to design a divider with a +10 V input and a +7.5 V output. Draw your design in the space provided.

Circuit for step 6	Circuit for step 8

9. The circuit shown in Figure 3(b) uses a 1.0 kΩ potentiometer and R_1 and R_2 to limit the range of voltages. Assume V_S is +10 V. Use the voltage divider formula to compute the minimum and maximum voltages available from this circuit:

V_{MIN} = _____ V_{MAX} = _____

10. Construct the circuit computed in step 9. Measure the minimum and maximum output voltages:

V_{MIN} = _____ V_{MAX} = _____

CONCLUSION

EVALUATION AND REVIEW QUESTIONS

1.   (a)   If all the resistors in Figure 4 were 10 times larger than the specified values, what would happen to the output voltage?

      (b)   What would happen to the power dissipated in the voltage divider?

2.   Refer to Figure 3(b). Assume V_S is 10.0 V.
      (a)   If R_1 is open, what is the output voltage? _____

      (b)   If R_2 is open, what is the output voltage? _____

3.   If a student used a potentiometer in the circuit of Figure 3(b) that was 10 kΩ instead of 1.0 kΩ, what would happen to the range of output voltages?

4.   For the circuit in Figure 5, compute the output voltage for each position of the switch:
      V_A _____
      V_B _____
      V_C _____
      V_D _____

5.   Compute the minimum and maximum voltage available from the circuit shown in Figure 6:

$V_{MIN} =$ _____ $V_{MAX} =$ _____

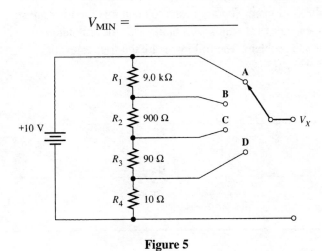

Figure 5

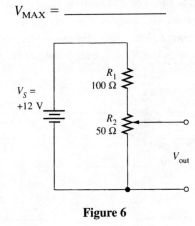

Figure 6

91

FOR FURTHER INVESTIGATION

The voltage dividers in this experiment were *unloaded*—that is, they were not required to furnish current to a load. If a load is put on the output, then current is supplied to the load and the output voltage of the divider changes. Investigate this effect by placing some load resistors on the voltage divider from this experiment (Figure 4). What size load resistor causes a 10% or less effect? Does the size of the resistors in the divider string affect your results? Why would you choose one set of resistors over another? Summarize your findings in a short laboratory report.

MULTISIM TROUBLESHOOTING

This experiment has four Multisim files on the CD. Three of the four files contain a simulated "fault"; one has "no fault". The file with no fault is named EXP8-3-nf.msm. You may want to open this file to compare your results with the computer simulation. Then open each of the files with faults. Use the simulated instruments to investigate the circuit and determine the problem. The following are the filenames for circuits with troubleshooting problems for this experiment.

EXP8-3-f1.msm

    Fault: _____

EXP8-3-f2.msm

    Fault: _____

EXP8-3-f3.msm

    Fault: _____

Parallel Circuits

Name _____

Date _____

Class _____

OBJECTIVES

After performing this experiment, you will be able to:

1.   Demonstrate that the total resistance in a parallel circuit decreases as resistors are added.
2.   Compute and measure resistance and currents in parallel circuits.
3.   Explain how to troubleshoot parallel circuits.

MATERIALS NEEDED

Resistors:

        One 3.3 kΩ, one 4.7 kΩ, one 6.8 kΩ, one 10 kΩ

One dc ammeter, 0–10 mA

SUMMARY OF THEORY

A *parallel* circuit is one in which there is more than one path for current. Parallel circuits can be thought of as two parallel lines, representing conductors, with a voltage source and components connected between the lines. This idea is illustrated in Figure 1. The source voltage appears across each component. Each path for current is called a *branch*. The current in any branch is dependent only on the resistance of that branch and the source voltage.

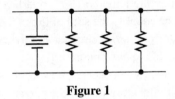

Figure 1

        As more branches are added to a parallel circuit, the total resistance decreases. This is easy to see if you consider each added path in terms of conductance. Recall that conductance is the reciprocal of resistance. As parallel branches are added, new paths are provided for current, increasing the conductance. There is more total current in the circuit. If the total current in a circuit increases, with no change in source voltage, the total resistance must decrease according to Ohm's law. The total conductance of a parallel circuit is the sum of the individual conductances. This can be written:

$$G_T = G_1 + G_2 + G_3 + \ldots + G_n$$

By substituting the definition for resistance into the formula for conductance, the reciprocal formula for resistance in parallel circuits is obtained. It is:

$$\frac{1}{R_T} = \frac{1}{R_1} + \frac{1}{R_2} + \frac{1}{R_3} + \dots + \frac{1}{R_n}$$

In parallel circuits, there are junctions where two or more components are connected. Figure 2 shows a circuit junction labeled A. Since electrical charge cannot accumulate at a point, the current into the junction must be equal to the current from the junction. In this case, $I_1 + I_2$ is equal to $I_3 + I_4$. This idea is expressed in Kirchhoff's current law, which is stated:

> The sum of the currents entering a circuit junction is equal to the sum of the currents leaving the junction.

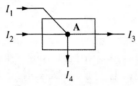

Figure 2

One important idea can be seen by applying Kirchhoff's current law to a point next to the source voltage. The current leaving the source must be equal to the sum of the individual branch currents. While Kirchhoff's voltage law is developed in the study of series circuits, and the current law is developed in the study of parallel circuits, both laws are applicable to any circuit.

In the experiment on The Voltage Divider, you observed how a series circuit causes voltage to be divided between the various resistances. In parallel circuits, it is the *current* that is divided between the resistances. Keep in mind that the larger the resistance, the smaller the current. The general current divider rule can be written:

$$I_X = \left(\frac{R_T}{R_X}\right) I_T$$

Notice that the fraction R_T/R_X is always less than 1.0 and represents the fraction of the total current in R_X. This equation can be simplified for the special case of exactly two resistors. The special two-resistor current divider is written:

$$I_1 = \left(\frac{R_2}{R_1 + R_2}\right) I_T \qquad I_2 = \left(\frac{R_1}{R_1 + R_2}\right) I_T$$

PROCEDURE

1.   Obtain the resistors listed in Table 1. Measure and record the value of each resistor.

Table 1

Component	Listed Value	Measured Value
R_1	3.3 kΩ	
R_2	4.7 kΩ	
R_3	6.8 kΩ	
R_4	10.0 kΩ	

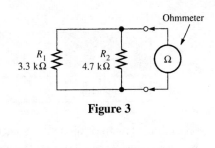

Figure 3

2.   In Table 2 you will tabulate the total resistance as resistors are added in parallel. (Parallel connections are indicated with two parallel lines shown between the resistors.) Enter the measured value of R_1 in the table. Then connect R_2 in parallel with R_1 and measure the total resistance as shown in Figure 3. Enter the measured resistance of R_1 in parallel with R_2 in Table 2.

Table 2

	R_1	$R_1\|R_2$	$R_1\|R_2\|R_3$	$R_1\|R_2\|R_3\|R_4$
R_T (measured)				
I_T (measured)				

3.   Add R_3 in parallel with R_1 and R_2. Measure the parallel resistance of all three resistors. Then add R_4 in parallel with the other three resistors and repeat the measurement. Record your results in Table 2.

4.   Complete the parallel circuit by adding the voltage source and the ammeter as shown in Figure 4. Be certain that the ammeter is connected in series with the voltage source as shown. If you are not sure, have your instructor check your circuit. Measure the total current in the circuit and record it in Table 2.

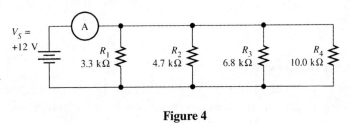

Figure 4

5.   Measure the voltage across each resistor. How does the voltage across each resistor compare to the source voltage?

Table 3

	$I_1 = \dfrac{V_S}{R_1}$	$I_2 = \dfrac{V_S}{R_2}$	$I_3 = \dfrac{V_S}{R_3}$	$I_4 = \dfrac{V_S}{R_4}$
I (computed)				

6. Use Ohm's law to compute the branch current in each resistor. Use the source voltage and the measured resistances. Tabulate the computed currents in Table 3.

7. Use the general current divider rule to compute the current in each branch. Use the total current and total resistance that you recorded in Table 2. Compare the calculation using the current divider rule with the results using Ohm's law. Show your results in Table 4.

Table 4

	$I_1 = \left(\dfrac{R_T}{R_1}\right) I_T$	$I_2 = \left(\dfrac{R_T}{R_2}\right) I_T$	$I_3 = \left(\dfrac{R_T}{R_3}\right) I_T$	$I_4 = \left(\dfrac{R_T}{R_4}\right) I_T$
I (computed)				

8. Prove Kirchhoff's current law for the circuit by showing that the total current is equal to the sum of the branch currents:

_____

9. Simulate a burned-out resistor by removing R_4 from the circuit. What is the new total current?

$I_T = $ _____

CONCLUSION

EVALUATION AND REVIEW QUESTIONS

1. In step 9, you simulated an open resistor by removing it from the circuit, and you observed that the total current dropped. Explain how the open resistor could be found in this experiment from the observed change in current and the source voltage.

2. If one of the resistors in this experiment were shorted, what would you expect to see happen? (Do not simulate this!)

3. Three resistors are connected in parallel across a 40 V source. The values of the resistors are 620 Ω, 750 Ω, and 820 Ω.

   (a) What should the total source current be?

   (b) If the measured current was 118 mA, what fault could account for this?

4. The known currents for a circuit junction are shown in Figure 5. What is the value and direction of the unknown current, I_4?

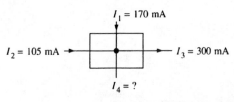

$$I_1 = 170 \text{ mA}$$

$I_2 = 105 \text{ mA}$ $I_3 = 300 \text{ mA}$

$I_4 = ?$

Figure 5

5. Could a shorted component in a parallel circuit cause an open to occur elsewhere? Explain.

FOR FURTHER INVESTIGATION

Kirchhoff's current law can be applied to any junction in a circuit. The currents in this circuit were I_1, I_2, I_3, I_4, and I_T. Apply Kirchhoff's current law to these currents by writing the numeric value of the current entering and leaving junction X, Y, and Z in Figure 6. Then verify that you computed the correct currents by measuring them with the ammeter. For each current measurement, the circuit must be broken, and the ammeter must be inserted in series with the path you are measuring. Summarize your results in a laboratory report.

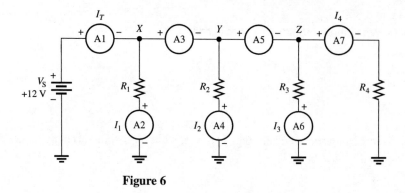

Figure 6

Series-Parallel Combination Circuits

Name _____
Date _____
Class _____

OBJECTIVES
After performing this experiment, you will be able to:
1.   Use the concept of equivalent circuits to simplify series-parallel circuit analysis.
2.   Compute the currents and voltages in a series-parallel combination circuit and verify your computation with circuit measurements.

MATERIALS NEEDED
Resistors:
        One 2.2 kΩ, one 4.7 kΩ, one 5.6 kΩ, one 10 kΩ

SUMMARY OF THEORY
Most electronic circuits are not just series or just parallel circuits. Instead they may contain combinations of components. Many circuits can be analyzed by applying the ideas developed for series and parallel circuits to them. Remember that in a *series* circuit the same current is through all components, and that the total resistance of series resistors is the sum of the individual resistors. By contrast, in *parallel* circuits, the applied voltage is the same across all branches and the total resistance is given by the reciprocals formula.

     In this experiment, the circuit elements are connected in composite circuits containing both series and parallel combinations. The key to solving these circuits is to form equivalent circuits from the series or parallel elements. You need to recognize when circuit elements are connected in series or parallel in order to form the equivalent circuit. For example, in Figure 1(a) we see that the identical current must go through both R_2 and R_3. We conclude that these resistors are in series and could be replaced by an equivalent resistor equal to their sum. Figure 1(b) illustrates this idea. The circuit has been simplified to an equivalent parallel circuit. After finding the currents in the equivalent circuit, the results can be applied to the original circuit to complete the solution.

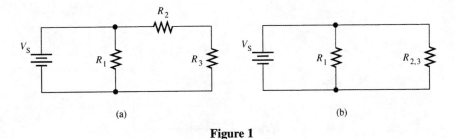

(a)   (b)

Figure 1

The answer to two questions will help you identify a series or parallel connection: (1) Will the *identical* current go through both components? If the answer is yes, the components are in series. (2) Are *both ends* of one component connected directly to *both ends* of another component? If yes, the components are in parallel. The components that are in series or parallel may be replaced with an equivalent component. This process continues until the circuit is reduced to a simple series or parallel circuit. After solving the equivalent circuit, the process is reversed in order to apply the solution to the original circuit. This idea is studied in this experiment.

PROCEDURE

1. Measure and record the actual values of the four resistors listed in Table 1.

Table 1

Component	Listed Value	Measured Value
R_1	2.2 kΩ	
R_2	4.7 kΩ	
R_3	5.6 kΩ	
R_4	10.0 kΩ	

2. Connect the circuit shown in Figure 2. Then answer the following questions:

    (a) Are there any resistors for which the identical current will go through the resistors? Answer yes or no for each resistor:

    R_1 _____ R_2 _____ R_3 _____ R_4 _____

    (b) Does any resistor have both ends connected directly to both ends of another resistor? Answer yes or no for each resistor:

    R_1 _____ R_2 _____ R_3 _____ R_4 _____

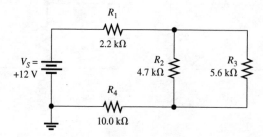

Figure 2

3.	The answer to these questions should clarify in your mind which resistors are in series and which resistors are in parallel. You can begin solving for the currents and voltages in the circuit by replacing resistors that are either in series or in parallel with an equivalent resistor. In this case, begin by replacing R_2 and R_3 with an equivalent resistor labeled $R_{2,3}$. Draw the equivalent circuit in the space provided. Show the value of all components including $R_{2,3}$.

4.	The equivalent circuit you drew in step 3 is a simple series circuit. Compute the total resistance of this equivalent circuit and enter it in the first two columns of Table 2. Then disconnect the power supply and measure the total resistance to confirm your calculation.

Table 2

	Computed		Measured
	Voltage Divider	Ohm's Law	
R_T			
I_T			
V_1			
$V_{2,3}$			
V_4			
I_2			
I_3			
V_T	12.0 V	12.0 V	

5.	The voltage divider rule can be applied directly to the series equivalent circuit to find the voltages across R_1, $R_{2,3}$, and R_4. Find V_1, $V_{2,3}$, and V_4 using the voltage divider rule. Tabulate the results in Table 2 in the Voltage Divider column.

6.	Find the total current, I_T, in the circuit by substituting the total voltage and the total resistance into Ohm's law. Enter the computed total current in Table 2 in the Ohm's Law column.

7.	In the equivalent series circuit, the total current is through R_1, $R_{2,3}$, and R_4. The voltage drop across each of these resistors can be found by applying Ohm's law to each resistor. Compute V_1, $V_{2,3}$, and V_4 using this method. Enter the voltages in Table 2 in the Ohm's Law column.

8. Use $V_{2,3}$ and Ohm's law to compute the current in R_2 and R_3 of the original circuit. Enter the computed current in Table 2. As a check, verify that the computed sum of I_2 and I_3 is equal to the computed total current.

9. Measure the voltages V_1, $V_{2,3}$, and V_4. Enter the measured values in Table 2.

10. Change the original circuit to the new circuit shown in Figure 3. In the space provided below, draw an equivalent circuit by combining the resistors that are in series. Enter the values of the equivalent resistors on your schematic and in Table 3.

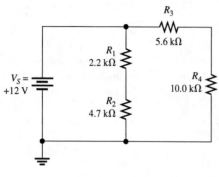

Figure 3

Table 3

	Computed	Measured
$R_{1,2}$		
$R_{3,4}$		
R_T		
I_T		
$I_{1,2}$		
$I_{3,4}$		
V_1		
V_2		
V_3		
V_4		

11. Compute the resistance of each branch ($R_{1,2}$ and $R_{3,4}$) for the equivalent circuit drawn in step 10. Then compute the total resistance, R_T, of the equivalent circuit. Apply Ohm's law to find the total current I_T. Enter the computed resistance for each branch and the total resistance, R_T, in Table 3.

12. Complete the computed values for the circuit by solving for the remaining currents and voltages listed in Table 3. Then measure the voltages across each resistor to confirm your computation.

CONCLUSION

EVALUATION AND REVIEW QUESTIONS

1. The voltage divider rule was developed for a series circuit, yet it was applied to the circuit in Figure 2.

    (a) Explain.

    (b) Could the voltage divider rule be applied to the circuit in Figure 3? Explain your answer.

2. As a check on your solution of the circuit in Figure 3, apply Kirchhoff's voltage law to each of two separate paths around the circuit. Show the application of the law.

3. Show the application of Kirchhoff's current law to the junction of R_2 and R_4 of the circuit in Figure 3.

4. In the circuit of Figure 3, assume you found that I_T was the same as the current in R_3 and R_4.

    (a) What are the possible problems?

    (b) How would you isolate the specific problem using only a voltmeter?

5. The circuit in Figure 4 has three equal resistors. If the voltmeter reads $+8.0$ V, find V_S.

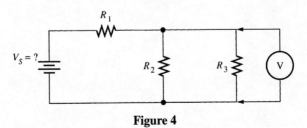

Figure 4

FOR FURTHER INVESTIGATION

Figure 5 illustrates another series-parallel circuit using the same resistors. Develop a procedure for solving the currents and voltages throughout the circuit. Summarize your procedure in a laboratory report. Confirm your method by computing and measuring the voltages in the circuit.

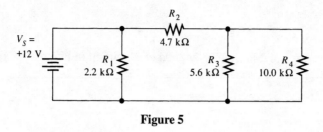

Figure 5

MULTISIM TROUBLESHOOTING

This experiment has four Multisim files on the CD. Three of the four files contain a simulated "fault"; one has "no fault". The file with no fault is named EXP10-2-nf.msm. You may want to open this file to compare your results with the computer simulation. Then open each of the files with faults. Use the simulated instruments to investigate the circuit and determine the problem. The following are the filenames for circuits with troubleshooting problems for this experiment.

EXP10-2-f1.msm
     Fault: _____

EXP10-2-f2.msm
     Fault: _____

EXP10-2-f3.msm
     Fault: _____

The Oscilloscope

Name _____
Date _____
Class _____

OBJECTIVES

After performing this experiment, you will be able to:
1. Explain the four functional blocks on an oscilloscope and describe the major controls within each block.
2. Use an oscilloscope to measure ac and dc voltages.

MATERIALS NEEDED

None

SUMMARY OF THEORY

The oscilloscope is an extremely versatile instrument that lets you see a picture of the voltage in a circuit as a function of time. There are two basic types of oscilloscopes—analog oscilloscopes and digital storage oscilloscopes (DSOs). DSOs are rapidly replacing older analog scopes because they offer significant advantages in measurement capabilities including waveform processing, automated measurements, waveform storage, and printing, as well as many other features. Operation of either type is similar; however, most digital scopes tend to have menus and typically provide the user with information on the display and may have automatic setup provisions.

There is not room in this Summary of Theory to describe all of the controls and features of oscilloscopes, so this is by necessity a limited description. You are encouraged to read the Oscilloscope Guide, which can be obtained from your instructor, and which describes the controls in some detail and highlights some of the key differences between analog scopes and DSOs. You can obtain further information from the User Manual packaged with your scope and from manufacturers' websites.

Both analog and digital oscilloscopes have a basic set of four functional groups of controls that you need to be completely familiar with, even if you are using a scope with automated measurements. In this experiment, a generic analog scope is described. Keep in mind, that if you are using a DSO, the controls referred to operate in much the same way but you may see some small operating differences.

Although the process for waveform display is very different between an analog oscilloscope and a DSO, the four main functional blocks and primary controls are equivalent. Figure 1 shows a basic analog oscilloscope block diagram which illustrates these four main functional blocks. These blocks are broken down further in the Oscilloscope Guide for both types of scope.

Controls for each of the functional blocks are usually grouped together. Frequently, there are color clues to help you identify groups of controls. Look for the controls for each functional group on your oscilloscope. The display controls include INTENSITY, FOCUS, and BEAM FINDER. The vertical controls include input COUPLING, VOLTS/DIV, vertical POSITION, and channel selection (CH1, CH2, DUAL, ALT, CHOP). The triggering controls include MODE, SOURCE, trigger COUPLING, trigger LEVEL, and others. The horizontal controls include the SEC/DIV, MAGNIFIER, and horizontal POSITION controls. Details of these controls are explained in the referenced reading and in the operator's manual for the oscilloscope.

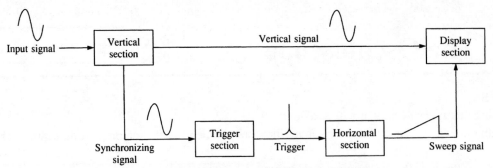

Figure 1 Block diagram of an analog oscilloscope

With all the controls to learn, you may experience difficulty obtaining a trace on an analog oscilloscope. If you do not see a trace, start by setting the SEC/DIV control to 0.1 ms/div, select AUTO triggering, select CH1, and press the BEAM FINDER. Keep the BEAM FINDER button depressed and use the vertical and horizontal POSITION controls to center the trace. If you still have trouble, check the INTENSITY control. Note that it's hard to lose the trace on a digital scope, so there is no BEAM FINDER.

Because the oscilloscope can show a voltage-versus-time presentation, it is easy to make ac voltage measurements with a scope. However, care must be taken to equate these measurements with meter readings. Typical digital multimeters show the *rms* (root-mean-square) value of a sinusoidal waveform. This value represents the effective value of an ac waveform when compared to a dc voltage when both produce the same heat (power) in a given load. Usually the *peak-to-peak* value is easiest to read on an oscilloscope. The relationship between the ac waveform as viewed on the oscilloscope and the equivalent rms reading that a DMM will give is illustrated in Figure 2.

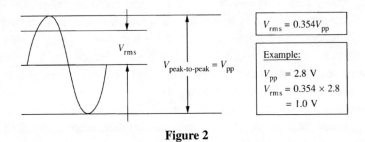

Figure 2

Many automated oscilloscopes can measure peak-to-peak or even rms readings of waveforms directly on the screen. They may include horizontal and vertical cursors. Be careful using an automated rms measurement of a sine wave. It may include any dc offset present. If you want to avoid including the dc component, ac couple the signal.

Waveforms that are not sinusoidal cannot be directly compared with an oscilloscope and DMM except for the dc component. The dc level of any waveform can be represented by a horizontal line which splits the waveform into equal areas above and below the line. For a sinusoidal wave, the dc level is always halfway between the maximum and minimum excursions. The dc component can be correctly read by a DMM no matter what the shape of the wave when it is in the DC volts mode.

The amplitude of any periodic waveform can be expressed in one of four ways: the peak-to-peak, the peak, the rms, or the average value. The peak-to-peak value of any waveform is the total magnitude of the change and is *independent* of the zero position. The peak value is the maximum excursion of the wave and is usually referenced to the dc level of the wave. To indicate that a reported value includes a dc offset, you need to state both the maximum and minimum excursions of the waveform.

An important part of any oscilloscope measurement is the oscilloscope probe. The type of probe that is generally furnished with an oscilloscope by the manufacturer is called an *attenuator probe* because it attenuates the input by a known factor. The most common attenuator probe is the 10× probe, because it reduces the input signal by a factor of 10. It is a good idea, before making any measurement, to check that the probe is properly compensated, meaning that the frequency response of the probe/scope system is flat. Probes have a small variable capacitor either in the probe tip or a small box that is part of the input connector. This capacitor is adjusted while observing a square wave to ensure that the displayed waveform has vertical sides and square corners. Most oscilloscopes have the square-wave generator built in for the purpose of compensating the probe.

PROCEDURE

1. Review the front panel controls in each of the major groups. Then turn on the oscilloscope, select CH1, set the SEC/DIV to 0.1 ms/div, select AUTO triggering, and obtain a line across the face of the CRT. Although many of the measurements described in this experiment are automated in newer scopes, it is useful to learn to make these measurements manually.

2. Turn on your power supply and use the DMM to set the output for 1.0 V. Now we will use the oscilloscope to measure this dc voltage from the power supply. The following steps will guide you:

   (a) Place the vertical COUPLING (AC-GND-DC) in the GND position. This disconnects the input to the oscilloscope. Use the vertical POSITION control to set the ground reference level on a convenient graticule line near the bottom of the screen.

   (b) Set the CH1 VOLTS/DIV control to 0.2 V/div. Check that the vernier control is in the CAL position or your measurement will not be accurate. Note that digital scopes do not have a vernier control. For fine adjustments, the VOLTS/DIV control can be changed to a more sensitive setting that remains calibrated.

   (c) Place the oscilloscope probe on the positive side of the power supply. Place the oscilloscope ground on the power supply common. Move the vertical coupling to the DC position. The line should jump up on the screen by 5 divisions. *Note that 5 divisions times 0.2 V per division is equal to 1.0 V (the supply voltage)*. Multiplication of the number of divisions of deflection times volts per division is equal to the voltage measurement.

3. Set the power supply to each voltage listed in Table 1. Measure each voltage using the above steps as a guide. The first line of the table has been completed as an example. To obtain accurate readings with the oscilloscope, it is necessary to select the VOLTS/DIV that gives several divisions of change between the ground reference and the voltage to be measured. The readings on the oscilloscope and meter should agree with each other within approximately 3%.

Table 1

Power Supply Setting	VOLTS/DIV Setting	Number of Divisions of Deflection	Oscilloscope (measured voltage)	DMM (measured voltage)
1.0 V	0.2 V/DIV	5.0 DIV	1.0 V	1.0 V
2.5 V				
4.5 V				
8.3 V				

4. Before viewing ac signals, it is a good idea to check the probe compensation for your oscilloscope. To check the probe compensation, set the VOLT/DIV control to 0.1 V/div, the AC-GND-DC coupling control to DC, and the SEC/DIV control to 2 ms/div. Touch the probe tip to the PROBE COMP connector. You should observe a square wave with a flat top and square corners. If necessary, adjust the compensation to achieve a good square wave.

5. Set the function generator for an ac waveform with a frequency of 1.0 kHz. Adjust the amplitude of the function generator for 1.0 V_{rms} as read on your DMM. Set the SEC/DIV control to 0.2 ms/div and the VOLTS/DIV to 0.5 V/div. Connect the scope probe and its ground to the function generator. Adjust the vertical POSITION control and the trigger LEVEL control for a stable display near the center of the screen. You should observe approximately two cycles of an ac waveform with a peak-to-peak amplitude of 2.8 V. This represents 1.0 V_{rms}, as shown in Figure 3.

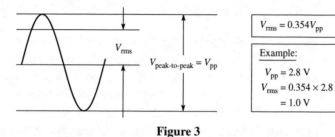

$$V_{rms} = 0.354V_{pp}$$

Example:
$$V_{pp} = 2.8 \text{ V}$$
$$V_{rms} = 0.354 \times 2.8$$
$$= 1.0 \text{ V}$$

Figure 3

6. Use the DMM to set the function generator amplitude to each value listed in Table 2. Repeat the ac voltage measurement as outlined in step 5. The first line of the table has been completed as an example. Remember, to obtain accurate readings with the oscilloscope, you should select a VOLTS/DIV setting that gives several divisions of deflection on the screen.

Table 2

Signal Generator Amplitude	VOLTS/DIV Setting	Number of Divisions (peak-to-peak)	Oscilloscope Measured (peak-to-peak)	Oscilloscope Measured (rms)
1.0 V_{rms}	0.5 V/DIV	5.6 DIV	2.8 V_{pp}	1.0 V_{rms}
2.2 V_{rms}				
3.7 V_{rms}				
4.8 V_{rms}				

7. Do this step only if you are using an analog oscilloscope. You can observe both the power supply and the function generator at the same time. Select both channels (marked DUAL on some scopes). Each channel can be displayed with its own ground reference point. You will need to leave the trigger SOURCE on channel 2 because the ac waveform is connected to that channel. You can select either ALTernate or CHOP mode to view the waveforms. To really see the effects of this control, slow the function generator to 10 Hz and change the horizontal SEC/DIV control to 20 ms/div. Compare the display using ALTernate and CHOP. At this slow frequency, it is easier to see the waveforms using the CHOP mode; at high frequencies the ALTernate mode is generally preferred.

CONCLUSION

EVALUATION AND REVIEW QUESTIONS

1.   (a)   Compute the percent difference between the DMM measurement and the oscilloscope
           measurement for each dc voltage measurement summarized in Table 1.

      (b)   Which do you think is most accurate? Why?

2.   Describe the four major groups of controls on the oscilloscope and the purpose of each group.

3.   If you are having difficulty obtaining a stable display, which group of controls should you adjust?

4.   (a)   If an ac waveform has 3.4 divisions from peak to peak and the VOLTS/DIV control is set
           to 5.0 V/div, what is the peak-to-peak voltage?

      (b)   What is the rms voltage?

5.   If you wanted to view an ac waveform that was 20.0 V$_{rms}$, what setting of the VOLTS/DIV control would be best?

6.   Most analog oscilloscopes have a single beam, which is shared with two signals. If you are using an analog oscilloscope, when should you select ALTernate and when should you choose CHOP?

FOR FURTHER INVESTIGATION

Most function generators have a control that allows you to add or subtract a dc offset voltage to the signal. Set up the function generator for a 1.0 kHz sine wave signal, as shown in Figure 4. To do this, the AC-GND-DC coupling switch on the oscilloscope should be in the DC position and the offset control should be adjusted on the function generator. When you have the signal displayed on the oscilloscope face, switch the AC-GND-DC coupling switch into the AC position. Explain what this control does. Then measure the signal with your DMM. First measure it in the AC VOLTAGE position; then measure in the DC VOLTAGE position. How does this control differ from the AC-GND-DC coupling switch on the oscilloscope? Summarize your findings.

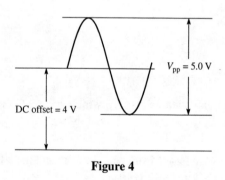

Figure 4

Capacitors

Name _____

Date _____

Class _____

OBJECTIVES

After performing this experiment, you will be able to:

1. Compare total capacitance, charge, and voltage drop for capacitors connected in series and in parallel.
2. Test capacitors with an ohmmeter and a voltmeter.
3. Determine the value of small capacitors from coded markings.

MATERIALS NEEDED:

Two LEDs

Resistors:

      Two 1.0 kΩ

Capacitors:

      One of each : 100 μF, 47 μF, 1.0 μF, 0.1 μF, 0.01 μF (35 WV or greater)

SUMMARY OF THEORY

A capacitor is formed whenever two conductors are separated by an insulating material. When a voltage exists between the conductors, there will be an electric charge between the conductors. The ability to store an electric charge is a fundamental property of capacitors and affects both dc and ac circuits. Capacitors are made with large flat conductors called *plates*. The plates are separated with an insulating material called a *dielectric*. The ability to store charge increases with larger plate size and closer separation.

When a voltage is connected across a capacitor, charge will flow in the external circuit until the voltage across the capacitor is equal to the applied voltage. The charge that flows is proportional to the size of the capacitor and the applied voltage. This is a fundamental concept for capacitors and is given by the equation

$$Q = CV$$

where Q is the charge in coulombs, C is the capacitance in farads, and V is the applied voltage. An analogous situation is that of putting compressed air into a bottle. The quantity of air is directly proportional to the capacity of the bottle and the applied pressure. (In this analogy, pressure is like voltage, the capacity of the bottle is like capacitance, and the amount of air is like charge.)

Recall that current is defined as charge per time. That is,

$$I = \frac{Q}{t}$$

where I is the current in amperes, Q is the charge in coulombs, and t is the time in seconds. This equation can be rearranged as

$$Q = It$$

If we connect two capacitors in series with a voltage source, the same charging current is through both capacitors. Since this current is for the same amount of time, the total charge, Q_T, must be the same as the charge on each capacitor. That is,

$$Q_T = Q_1 = Q_2$$

Charging capacitors in series causes the same charge to be across each capacitor; however, as shown in Floyd's text, the total capacitance *decreases*. In a series circuit, the total capacitance is given by the formula:

$$\frac{1}{C_T} = \frac{1}{C_1} + \frac{1}{C_2} + \ldots + \frac{1}{C_n}$$

Now consider capacitors in parallel. In a parallel circuit, the total current is equal to the sum of the currents in each branch as stated by Kirchhoff's current law. If this current is for the same amount of time, the total charge leaving the voltage source will equal the sum of the charges which flow in each branch. That is,

$$Q_T = Q_1 + Q_2 + \ldots + Q_n$$

Capacitors connected in parallel will raise the total capacitance because more charge is stored at the same voltage. The equation for the total capacitance of parallel capacitors is:

$$C_T = C_1 + C_2 + \ldots + C_n$$

There are two quick tests you can make to check capacitors. The first is an ohmmeter test, useful for capacitors larger than 0.01 μF. This test is best done with an analog ohmmeter rather than a digital meter. The test will sometimes indicate a faulty capacitor is good; however, you can be sure that if a capacitor fails the test, it is bad. The test is done as follows:

(a)   Remove one end of the capacitor from the circuit and discharge it by placing a short across its terminals.

(b)   Set the ohmmeter on a high-resistance scale and place the negative lead from an ohmmeter on the negative terminal of the capacitor. You must connect the ohmmeter with the proper polarity. *Do not assume the common lead from the ohmmeter is the negative side!*

(c)   Touch the other lead of the ohmmeter onto the remaining terminal of the capacitor. The meter should indicate very low resistance and then gradually increase resistance. If you put the meter in a higher range, the ohmmeter charges the capacitor slower and the capacitance "kick" will be emphasized. For small capacitors (under 0.01 μF), this charge may not be seen. Large electrolytic capacitors require more time to charge, so use a lower range on your ohmmeter. Capacitors should never remain near zero resistance, as this indicates a short. An immediate high resistance reading indicates an open for larger capacitors.

A capacitor that passes the ohmmeter test may still fail when voltage is applied. A voltmeter can be used to check a capacitor with voltage applied. The voltmeter is connected in *series* with the capacitor.

When voltage is first applied, the capacitor charges. As it charges, voltage will appear across it, and the voltmeter indication should be a very small voltage. Large electrolytic capacitors may have leakage current that makes them appear bad, especially with a very high impedance voltmeter. As in the case of the ohmmeter test, small capacitors may charge so quickly they appear bad. In these cases, use the test as a relative test, comparing the reading with a similar capacitor that you know is good. Ohmmeter and voltmeter tests are never considered comprehensive tests but are indicative that a capacitor is capable of being charged.

Capacitor Identification

There are many types of capacitors available with a wide variety of specifications for size, voltage rating, frequency range, temperature stability, leakage current, and so forth. For general-purpose applications, small capacitors are constructed with paper, ceramic, or other insulation material and are not polarized. Three common methods for showing the value of a small capacitor are shown in Figure 1. In Figure 1(a), a coded number is stamped on the capacitor that is read in pF. The first two digits represent the first two digits, the third number is a multiplier. For example, the number 473 is a 47000 pF capacitor. Figure 1(b) shows the actual value stamped on the capacitor in μF. In the example shown, .047 μF is the same as 47000 pF. In Figure 1(c), a ceramic color-coded capacitor is shown that is read in pF. Generally, when 5 colors are shown, the first is a temperature coefficient (in ppm/°C with special meanings to each color). The second, third, and fourth colors are read as digit 1, digit 2, and a multiplier. The last color is the tolerance. Thus a 47000 pF capacitor will have a color representing the temperature coefficient followed by yellow, violet, and orange bands representing the value. Unlike resistors, the tolerance band is generally green for 5% and white for 10%. More information on capacitor color codes is given in the text in the appendix.

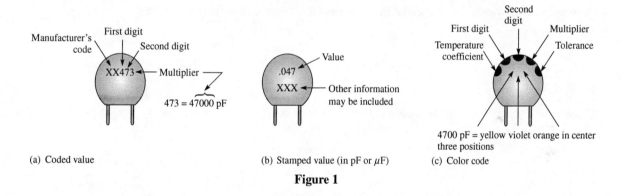

(a) Coded value (b) Stamped value (in pF or μF) (c) Color code

Figure 1

Larger electrolytic capacitors will generally have their value printed in uncoded form on the capacitor and a mark indicating either the positive or negative lead. They also have a maximum working voltage printed on them which must not be exceeded. Electrolytic capacitors are always polarized, and it is very important to place them into a circuit in the correct direction based on the polarity shown on the capacitor. They can overheat and explode if placed in the circuit backwards.

PROCEDURE

1. Obtain five capacitors as listed in Table 1. Check each capacitor using the ohmmeter test described in the Summary of Theory. Record the results of the test in Table 1.

2. Test each capacitor using the voltmeter test as illustrated in Figure 2. Large electrolytic capacitors or very small capacitors may appear to fail this test, as mentioned in the Summary of Theory. Check the voltage rating on the capacitor to be sure it is not exceeded. The working voltage is the maximum voltage that can safely be applied to the capacitor. Record your results in Table 1.

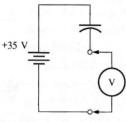

Figure 2

Table 1

Capacitor	Listed Value	Ohmmeter Test Pass/Fail	Voltmeter Test Pass/Fail
C_1	100 μF		
C_2	47 μF		
C_3	1.0 μF		
C_4	0.1 μF		
C_5	0.01 μF		

3. Connect the circuit shown in Figure 3. The switches can be made from jumper wires. Leave both switches open. The light-emitting diodes (LEDs) and the capacitor are both polarized components—they must be connected in the correct direction in order to work properly.

4. Close S_1 and observe the LEDs. Describe your observation.

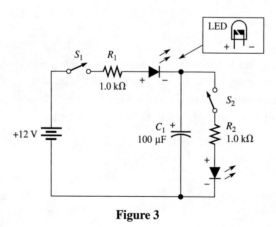

Figure 3

5.   Open S_1 and close S_2. What happens?

6.   Now connect C_2 in series with C_1. Open S_2. Make certain the capacitors are fully discharged by shorting them with a piece of wire; then close S_1. Measure the voltage across each capacitor. Do this quickly to prevent the meter from causing the capacitors to discharge. Record the voltages and describe your observations.

$V_1 = $ _____ $V_2 = $ _____

Observations:

7.   Using the measured voltage, compute the charge on each capacitor.

$Q_1 = $ _____ $Q_2 = $ _____

Then open S_1 and close S_2. Observe the result.

8.   Change the capacitors from series to parallel. Ensure that the capacitors are fully discharged. Open S_2 and close S_1. Measure the voltage (quickly) across the capacitors. Record the voltages and describe your observations.

$V_1 = $ _____ $V_2 = $ _____

Observations:

9.   Using the measured voltage, calculate the charge across each capacitor.

$Q_1 = $ _____ $Q_2 = $ _____

10. Replace the 12 V dc source with a signal generator. Close both S_1 and S_2. Set the signal generator to a square wave and set the amplitude to 12 V_{pp}. Set the frequency to 10 Hz. Notice the difference in the LED pulses. This demonstrates one of the principal applications of large capacitors—that of filtering. Explain your observations.

CONCLUSION

EVALUATION AND REVIEW QUESTIONS

1. Why did the LEDs flash for a shorter time in step 6 than in steps 4 and 5?

2. What would happen if you added more series capacitance in step 6?

3. (a) What is the total capacitance when a 1.0 μF capacitor is connected in parallel with a 2.0 μF capacitor?

   (b) If the capacitors are connected in series, what is the total capacitance?

   (c) In the series connection, which capacitor has the greater voltage across it?

4.   Determine the value in pF and μF for each small capacitor with the coded numbers as shown:

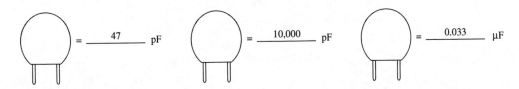

683 = _____ pF   102 = _____ pF   224 = _____ pF

     = _____ μF   = _____ μF   = _____ μF

5.   Write the coded number that should appear on each capacitor for the values shown:

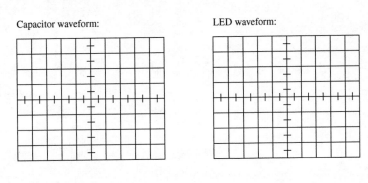

= ___47___ pF   = __10,000__ pF   = __0.033__ μF

FOR FURTHER INVESTIGATION

Use the oscilloscope to measure the waveforms across the capacitors and the LEDs in step 10. Try speeding up the signal generator and observe the waveforms. Use the two-channel difference measurement explained in the experiment on Sine Wave Measurements to see the waveform across the ungrounded LED. Draw and label the waveforms.

Capacitor waveform: LED waveform:

Plot 1   **Plot 2**

Capacitive Reactance

Name _____
Date _____
Class _____

OBJECTIVES

After performing this experiment, you will be able to:
1. Measure the capacitive reactance of a capacitor at a specified frequency.
2. Compare the reactance of capacitors connected in series and parallel.

MATERIALS NEEDED

One 1.0 kΩ resistor
Two 0.1 μF capacitors
For Further Investigation:
   Two 100 μF capacitors, two LEDs, one 100 kΩ resistor

SUMMARY OF THEORY

If a resistor is connected across a sine wave generator, the current is *in phase* with the applied voltage. If, instead of a resistor, we connect a capacitor across the generator, the current is not in phase with the voltage. This is illustrated in Figure 1. Note that the current and voltage have exactly the same frequency, but the current is *leading* the voltage by 1/4 cycle.

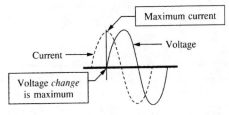

Figure 1

Current in the capacitor is directly proportional to the capacitance and the rate of change of voltage. The largest current is when the voltage *change* is a maximum. If the capacitance is increased or the frequency is increased, there is more current. This is why a capacitor is sometimes thought of as a high-frequency short.

Reactance is the opposition to ac current and is measured in ohms, like resistance. Capacitive reactance is written with the symbol X_C. It can be defined as:

$$X_C = \frac{1}{2\pi f C}$$

where f is the generator frequency in hertz and C is the capacitance in farads.

Ohm's law can be generalized to ac circuits. For a capacitor, we can find the voltage across the capacitor using the current and the capacitive reactance. Ohm's law for the voltage across a capacitor is

$$V_C = IX_C$$

PROCEDURE

1.   Obtain two capacitors with the values shown in Table 1. If you have a capacitance bridge available, measure their capacitance and record in Table 1; otherwise, record the listed value of the capacitors. Measure and record the value of resistor R_1.

2.   Set up the circuit shown in Figure 2. Set the generator for a 1.0 kHz sine wave with a 1.0 V rms output. Measure the rms voltage with your DMM while it is connected to the circuit.[1] Check the frequency and voltage with the oscilloscope. Note: $1.0 \text{ V}_{rms} = 2.828 \text{ V}_{pp}$.

Table 1

Component	Listed Value	Measured Value
C_1	0.1 µF	
C_2	0.1 µF	
R_1	1.0 kΩ	

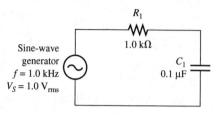

Figure 2

3.   The circuit is a series circuit, so the current in the resistor is the identical current seen by the capacitor. You can find this current easily by applying Ohm's law to the resistor. Measure the voltage across the resistor, V_R, using the DMM. Record the measured voltage in Table 2 in the column labeled Capacitor C_1. Compute the current in the circuit by dividing the measured voltage by the resistance of R_1 and enter in Table 12.

Table 2

	Capacitor C_1	Capacitor C_2
Voltage across R_1, V_R		
Total current, I		
Voltage across C, V_C		
Capacitive reactance, X_C		
Computed capacitance, C		

---

[1]DMMs have a relatively low bandwidth, although most can measure 1.0 kHz. Verify that the DMM you are using has at least a 1.0 kHz bandwidth; if it does not, use the oscilloscope for all voltage measurements.

4.   Measure the rms voltage across the capacitor, V_C. Record this voltage in Table 2. Then use this voltage to compute the capacitive reactance using Ohm's law:

$$X_C = \frac{V_C}{I}$$

Enter this value as the capacitive reactance in Table 2.

5.   Using the capacitive reactance found in step 4, compute the capacitance using the equation

$$C = \frac{1}{2\pi f X_C}$$

Enter the computed capacitance in Table 2. This value should agree with the value marked on the capacitor and measured in step 1 within experimental tolerances.

6.   Repeat steps 3, 4, and 5 using capacitor C_2. Enter the data in Table 2 in the column labeled Capacitor C_2.

7.   Now connect C_1 in series with C_2. The equivalent capacitive reactance and capacitance can be found for the series connection by measuring across both capacitors as if they were one capacitor. Enter the data in Table 3 in the column labeled Series Capacitors. The following steps will guide you:
   (a)   Check that the generator is set to 1.0 V rms. Find the current in the circuit by measuring the voltage across the resistor as before and dividing by the resistance. Enter the measured voltage and the current you found in Table 3.
   (b)   Measure the voltage across *both* capacitors. Enter this voltage in Table 3.
   (c)   Use Ohm's law to find the capacitive reactance of both capacitors. Use the voltage measured in step (b) and the current measured in step (a).
   (d)   Compute the total capacitance by using the equation

$$C_T = \frac{1}{2\pi f X_{CT}}$$

8.   Connect the capacitors in parallel and repeat step 7. Assume the parallel capacitors are one equivalent capacitor for the measurements. Enter the data in Table 3 in the column labeled Parallel Capacitors.

Table 3

Step		Series Capacitors	Parallel Capacitors
(a)	Voltage across R_1, V_R		
	Total current, I		
(b)	Voltage across capacitors, V_C		
(c)	Capacitive reactance, X_{CT}		
(d)	Computed capacitance, C_T		

CONCLUSION

EVALUATION AND REVIEW QUESTIONS

1. Compare the capacitive reactance of the series capacitors with the capacitive reactance of the parallel capacitors. Use your data in Table 3.

2. Compare the total capacitance of the series capacitors with the total capacitance of the parallel capacitors.

3. If someone had mistakenly used too small a capacitor in a circuit, what would happen to the capacitive reactance?

4. How could you apply the method used in this experiment to find the value of the unknown capacitor?

5. Compute the capacitive reactance for an 800 pF capacitor at a frequency of 250 kHz.

FOR FURTHER INVESTIGATION

A voltage multiplier is a circuit that uses diodes and capacitors to increase the peak value of a sine wave. Voltage multipliers can produce high voltages without requiring a high-voltage transformer. The circuit illustrated in Figure 3 is a full-wave voltage doubler. The circuit is drawn as a bridge with diodes in two arms and capacitors in two arms. The diodes allow current in only one direction, charging the capacitors to near the peak voltage of the sine wave. Generally, voltage doublers are used with 60 Hz power line frequencies and with ordinary diodes, but in order to clarify the operation of this circuit, you can use the LEDs that were used in this experiment. (Note that this causes the output voltage to be reduced slightly.) Connect the circuit, setting the function generator to 20 V_{pp} sine wave at a frequency of 1.0 Hz. (If you cannot obtain a 20 V_{pp} signal, use the largest signal you can obtain from your generator.) Observe the operation of the circuit, then try speeding up the generator. Look at the waveform across the load resistor with your oscilloscope using the two-channel difference method. What is the dc voltage across the load resistor? What happens to the output as the generator is speeded up? Try a smaller load resistor. Can you explain your observations?

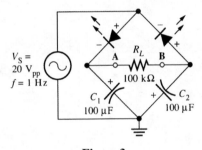

Figure 3

MULTISIM TROUBLESHOOTING

This experiment has four Multisim files on the CD. To simulate the winding resistance of the inductor, a 100 Ω resistor has been added in series in the computer simulations. The resistance of coils varies widely with the size of the coil and the wiring used to make the coil, so you may have found a much different resistance in the experiment. The frequency response has been plotted on the Bode plotter, a fictitious instrument but with characteristics similar to a spectrum analyzer.

Three of the four files contain a simulated "fault"; one has "no fault". The file with no fault is named EXP19-2-nf.msm. You may want to open this file to compare your results with the computer simulation. Then open each of the files with faults. Use the simulated instruments to investigate the circuit and determine the problem. The following are the filenames for circuits with troubleshooting problems for this experiment.

EXP19-2-f1.msm

    Fault: _____

EXP19-2-f2.msm

    Fault: _____

EXP19-2-f3.msm

    Fault: _____

Series *RC* Circuits

Name _____

Date _____

Class _____

OBJECTIVES

After performing this experiment, you will be able to:

1. Compute the capacitive reactance of a capacitor from voltage measurements in a series *RC* circuit.
2. Draw the impedance and voltage phasor diagrams for a series *RC* circuit.
3. Explain how frequency affects the impedance and voltage phasors in a series *RC* circuit.

MATERIALS NEEDED

One 6.8 kΩ resistor
One 0.01 µF capacitor

SUMMARY OF THEORY

When a sine wave at some frequency drives a circuit that contains only linear elements (resistors, capacitors, and inductors), the waveforms throughout the circuit are also sine waves at that same frequency. To understand the relationship between the sinusoidal voltages and currents, we can represent ac waveforms as phasor quantities. A *phasor* is a complex number used to represent a sine wave's amplitude and phase. A graphical representation of the phasors in a circuit is a useful tool for visualizing the amplitude and phase relationship of the various waveforms. The algebra of complex numbers can then be used to perform arithmetic operations on sine waves.

Figure 1(a) shows an *RC* circuit with its impedance phasor diagram plotted in Figure 1(b). The total impedance is 5 kΩ, producing a current in this example of 1.0 mA. In any series circuit, the same current is throughout the circuit. By multiplying each of the phasors in the impedance diagram by the current in the circuit, we arrive at the voltage phasor diagram illustrated in Figure 1(c). It is convenient to use current as the reference for comparing voltage phasors because the current is the same throughout. Notice the direction of current. The voltage and the current are in the same direction across the resistor because they are in phase, but the voltage across the capacitor lags the current by 90°. The generator voltage is the phasor sum of the voltage across the resistor and the voltage across the capacitor.

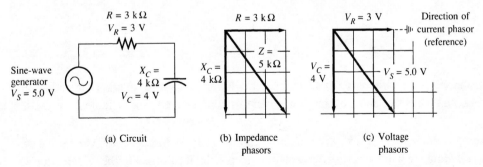

(a) Circuit

(b) Impedance phasors

(c) Voltage phasors

Figure 1

The phasor diagram illustrated by Figure 1 is correct only at one frequency. This is because the reactance of a capacitor is frequency dependent as given by the equation:

$$X_C = \frac{1}{2\pi f C}$$

As the frequency is raised, the reactance (X_C) of the capacitor decreases. This changes the phase angle and voltages across the components. These changes are investigated in this experiment.

PROCEDURE

1. Measure the actual capacitance of a 0.01 µF capacitor and a 6.8 kΩ resistor. Enter the measured values in Table 1. If you cannot measure the capacitor, use the listed value.

2. Connect the series RC circuit shown in Figure 2. Set the signal generator for a 500 Hz sine wave at 3.0 V_{pp}. The voltage should be measured with the circuit connected. Set the voltage with a voltmeter, and check both voltage and frequency with the oscilloscope. Record all voltages and currents throughout this experiment as peak-to-peak values.

Table 1

Component	Listed Value	Measured Value
C_1	0.01 µF	
R_1	6.8 kΩ	

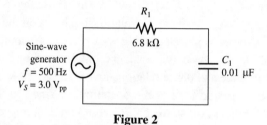

Figure 2

3. Using the two-channel-difference technique described in the experiment on Sine Wave Measurements, measure the peak-to-peak voltage across the resistor (V_R). Then measure the peak-to-peak voltage across the capacitor (V_C). Record the voltage readings on the first line of Table 2.

4. Compute the peak-to-peak current in the circuit by applying Ohm's law to the measured value of the resistor:

$$I = \frac{V_R}{R}$$

Since the current is the same throughout a series circuit, this is a simple method for finding the current in both the resistor and the capacitor. Enter this computed current in Table 2.

5. Compute the capacitive reactance, X_C, by applying Ohm's law to the capacitor. The reactance is found by dividing the voltage across the capacitor (step 3) by the current in the circuit (step 4). Enter the capacitive reactance in Table 2.

Table 2

Frequency	V_R	V_C	I	X_C	Z
500 Hz					
1000 Hz					
1500 Hz					
2000 Hz					
4000 Hz					
8000 Hz					

6. Compute the total impedance of the circuit by applying Ohm's law to the entire circuit. Use the generator voltage set in step 2 and the current determined in step 4. Enter the computed impedance in Table 2.

7. Change the frequency of the generator to 1000 Hz. Check the generator voltage and reset it to 3.0 V_{pp} if necessary. Repeat steps 3 through 6, entering the data in Table 2. Continue in this manner for each frequency listed in Table 2.

8. From the data in Table 2 and the measured value of R_1, draw the impedance phasors for the circuit at a frequency of 1000 Hz on Plot 1(a) and the voltage phasors on Plot 1(b).

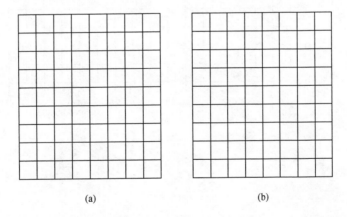

(a)   (b)

Plot 1

9. Repeat step 8 for a frequency of 4000 Hz. Draw the impedance phasors on Plot 2(a) and the voltage phasors on Plot 2(b).

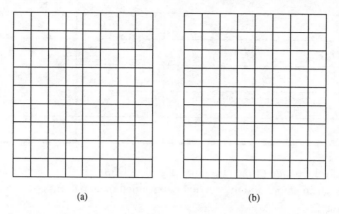

(a)   (b)

Plot 2

10. The phasor drawings reveal how the impedance and voltage phasors change with frequency. Investigate the frequency effect further by graphing both the voltage across the capacitor and the voltage across the resistor as a function of frequency. Label each curve. Use Plot 3.

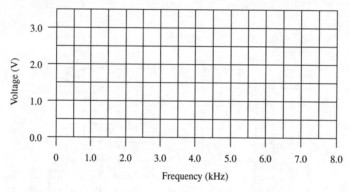

Plot 3

CONCLUSION

EVALUATION AND REVIEW QUESTIONS

1. The Pythagorean theorem can be applied to the phasors drawn in Plots 1 and 2. Show that the data in both plots satisfy the following equations

$$Z = \sqrt{R^2 + X_C^2}$$

$$V_S = \sqrt{V_R^2 + V_C^2}$$

2.   Assume you needed to pass high frequencies through an *RC* filter but block low frequencies. From the data in Plot 3, should you connect the output across the capacitor or across the resistor? Explain your answer.

3.   (a)   What happens to the total impedance of a series *RC* circuit as the frequency is increased?

      (b)   Explain why the phase angle between the generator voltage and the resistor voltage decreases as the frequency is increased.

4.   A student accidentally used a capacitor that was ten times larger than required in the experiment. Predict what happens to the frequency response shown in Plot 3 with the larger capacitor.

5.   Assume there was no current in the series *RC* circuit because of an open circuit. How could you quickly determine if the resistor or the capacitor were open?

FOR FURTHER INVESTIGATION

This experiment showed that the voltage phasor diagram can be obtained by multiplying each quantity on the impedance phasor diagram by the current in the circuit. In turn, if each of the voltage phasors is multiplied by the current, the resulting diagram is the power phasor diagram. Using the data from Table 2, convert the current and source voltage to an rms value. Then determine the true power, the reactive power, and the apparent power in the *RC* circuit at a frequency of 1000 Hz and a frequency of 4000 Hz. On Plot 4, draw the power phasor diagrams. (See Section 10–7 of Floyd's text for further discussion of the power phasors.)

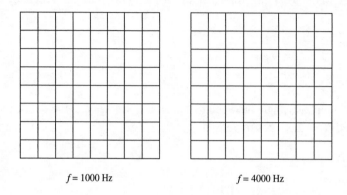

f = 1000 Hz　　　　　f = 4000 Hz

Plot 4

MULTISIM TROUBLESHOOTING

This experiment has four Multisim files on the CD. Three of the four files contain a simulated "fault"; one has "no fault". The file with no fault is named EXP20-2-nf.msm. You may want to open this file to compare your results with the computer simulation. Then open each of the files with faults. Use the simulated instruments to investigate the circuit and determine the problem. The following are the filenames for circuits with troubleshooting problems for this experiment.

EXP20-2-f1.msm
　　　Fault: _____

EXP20-2-f2.msm
　　　Fault: _____

EXP20-2-f3.msm
　　　Fault: _____

Inductors

Name _____

Date _____

Class _____

OBJECTIVES

After performing this experiment, you will be able to:

1. Describe the effect of Lenz's law in a circuit.
2. Measure the time constant of an *LR* circuit and test the effects of series and parallel inductances on the time constant.

MATERIALS NEEDED

Two 7 H inductors (approximate value) (The secondary of a low-voltage transformer will work.
   The second inductor may be shared from another experiment.)
One neon bulb (NE-2 or equivalent)
One 33 kΩ resistor
For Further Investigation:
   One unknown inductor

SUMMARY OF THEORY

When there is a current through a coil of wire, a magnetic field is created around the wire. This electromagnetic field accompanies any moving electric charge and is proportional to the magnitude of the current. If the current changes, the electromagnetic field causes a voltage to be induced across the coil, which opposes the change. This property, which causes a voltage to oppose a change in current, is called *inductance*.

Inductance is the electrical equivalent of inertia in a mechanical system. It opposes a change in *current* in a manner similar to the way capacitance opposed a change in *voltage*. This property of inductance is described by Lenz's law. According to Lenz's law, an inductor develops a voltage across it that counters the effect of a *change* in current in the circuit. The induced voltage is equal to the inductance times the rate of change of current. Inductance is measured in *henries*. *One henry is defined as the quantity of inductance present when one volt is generated as a result of a current changing at the rate of one ampere per second.* Coils that are made to provide a specific amount of inductance are called *inductors*.

When inductors are connected in series, the total inductance is the sum of the individual inductors. This is similar to resistors connected in series. Likewise, the formula for parallel inductors is similar to the formula for parallel resistors. Unlike resistors, an additional effect can appear in inductive circuits. This effect is called *mutual inductance* and is caused by the interaction of the magnetic fields. The total inductance can be either increased or decreased due to mutual inductance.

Inductive circuits have a time constant associated with them, just as capacitive circuits do, except the rising exponential curve is a picture of the *current* in the circuit rather than the *voltage* as in the case of the capacitive circuit. Unlike the capacitive circuit, if the resistance is greater, the time constant is shorter. The time constant is found from the equation

$$\tau = \frac{L}{R}$$

where τ represents the time constant in seconds when L is in henries and R is in ohms.

PROCEDURE

1.   In this step, you can observe the effect of Lenz's law. Connect the circuit shown in Figure 1 with a neon bulb in parallel with a large inductor. As noted in the materials list, the secondary of a low-voltage transformer can be used. Power should NOT be applied to the primary. Neon bulbs contain two insulated electrodes in a glass envelope containing neon gas. The gas will not conduct unless the voltage reaches approximately 70 V. When the gas conducts, the bulb will glow. When the switch is closed, dc current in the inductor is determined by the inductor's winding resistance. Close and open S_1 several times and observe the results.

Observations:

2.   Find out if the neon bulb will fire if the voltage is lowered. How low can you reduce the voltage source and still observe the bulb to glow? _____

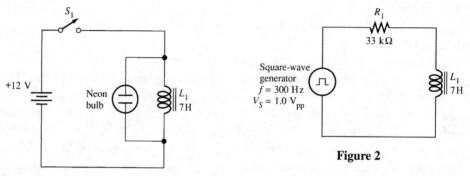

Figure 1

Figure 2

3.   Connect the circuit shown in Figure 2. This circuit will be used to view the waveforms from a square wave generator. Set the generator, V_S, for a 1.0 V_{pp} square wave at a frequency of 300 Hz. This frequency is chosen to allow sufficient time to see the effects of the time constant. View the generator voltage on CH1 of a two-channel oscilloscope and the inductor waveform on CH2. If both channels are calibrated and have the VOLTS/DIV controls set to the same setting, you will be able to see the voltage across the resistor using the difference channel. Set the oscilloscope SEC/DIV control to 0.5 ms/div. Sketch the waveforms you see on Plot 1.

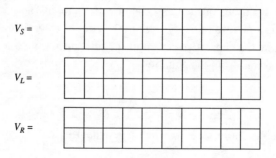

Plot 1

4. Compute the time constant for the circuit. Enter the computed value in Table 1. Now measure the time constant by viewing the waveform across the resistor. The resistor voltage has the same shape as the current in the circuit, so you can measure the time constant by finding the time required for the resistor voltage to change from 0 to 63% of its final value. Stretch the waveform across the oscilloscope screen to make an accurate time measurement. Enter the measured time constant in Table 1.

Table 1

	Computed	Measured
Time constant, τ		

5. When inductors are connected in series, the total inductance increases. When they are connected in parallel, the total inductance decreases. You can see the effect of decreasing the inductance by connecting a second 7 H inductor in parallel with the first. Note what happens to the voltage waveforms across the resistor and the inductor. Then connect the inductors in series and compare the effect on the waveforms. Describe your observations.

CONCLUSION

EVALUATION AND REVIEW QUESTIONS

1. The ionizing voltage for a neon bulb is approximately 70 V. Explain how a 12 V source was able to cause the neon bulb to conduct.

2. When a circuit containing an inductor is opened suddenly, an arc may occur across the switch. How does Lenz's law explain this?

3. What is the total inductance when two 100 mH inductors are connected
    in series? _____   in parallel? _____

4.   What would happen to the time constant in Figure 2 if a 3.3 kΩ resistor were used instead of the 33 kΩ resistor?

5.   What effect does an increase in the frequency of the square wave generator have on the waveforms observed in Figure 2?

FOR FURTHER INVESTIGATION

Suggest a method in which you could use a square wave generator and a known resistor to determine the inductance of an unknown inductor. Then obtain an unknown inductor from your instructor and measure its inductance. Report on your method, results, and how your result compares to the accepted value for the inductor.

Inductive
Reactance

Name _____
Date _____
Class _____

OBJECTIVES

After performing this experiment, you will be able to:
1.   Measure the inductive reactance of an inductor at a specified frequency.
2.   Compare the reactance of inductors connected in series and parallel.

MATERIALS NEEDED

Two 100 mH inductors
One 1.0 kΩ resistor
For Further Investigation:
    One 12.6 V center-tapped transformer

SUMMARY OF THEORY

When a sine wave is applied to an inductor, a voltage is induced across the inductor as given by Lenz's law. When the *change* in current is a maximum, the largest induced voltage appears across the inductor. This is illustrated in Figure 1. Notice that when the current is not changing (at the peaks), the induced voltage is zero. For this reason, the voltage that appears across an inductor leads the current in the inductor by 1/4 cycle.

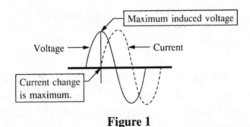

Figure 1

If we *raise* the frequency of the sine wave, the rate of change of current is increased and the value of the opposing voltage is increased. This results in a net *decrease* in the amount of current. Thus, the inductive reactance is increased by an increase in frequency. The inductive reactance is given by the equation

$$X_L = 2\pi fL$$

This equation reveals that a linear relationship exists between the inductance and the reactance at a constant frequency. Recall that in series, the total inductance is the sum of individual inductors (ignoring mutual inductance). The reactance of series inductors is, therefore, also the sum of the individual reactances. Likewise, in parallel, the reciprocal formula which applies to parallel resistors can be applied to both the inductance and the inductive reactance.

Ohm's law can be applied to inductive circuits. The reactance of an inductor can be found by dividing the voltage across the inductor by the current in it. That is,

$$X_L = \frac{V_L}{I_L}$$

PROCEDURE

1.   Measure the inductance of each of two 100 mH inductors and record their measured values in Table 1. Measure and record the value of a 1.0 kΩ resistor. Use the listed values if you cannot measure the inductors.

2.   Connect the circuit shown in Figure 2. Set the generator for a 1.0 kHz sine wave with a 1.0 V_{rms}. Measure the generator voltage with your DMM while it is connected to the circuit.[1] Check the frequency and voltage with the oscilloscope. Remember to convert the oscilloscope voltage reading to rms voltage to compare it to the DMM.

Table 1

Component	Listed Value	Measured Value
L_1	100 mH	
L_2	100 mH	
R_1	1.0 kΩ	

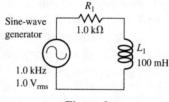

Figure 2

3.   The circuit is a series circuit, so the current in the resistor is the identical current that is through the inductor. First, find the voltage across the resistor with the DMM. Then apply Ohm's law to the resistor to find the current in the circuit. Record the measured voltage and the computed current in Table 2 in the column labeled Inductor L_1.

4.   Measure the voltage across the inductor with the DMM. Then find the inductive reactance by Ohm's law. Enter the values in Table 2.

5.   Now compute the inductance based on the equation

$$L = \frac{X_L}{2\pi f}$$

Enter the computed inductance in Table 2.

---

[1]DMMs have a relatively low bandwidth, although most can measure 1.0 kHz. Verify that the DMM you are using has at least a 1.0 kHz bandwidth; if it does not, use the oscilloscope for all voltage measurements.

Table 2

	Inductor L_1	Inductor L_2
Voltage across R_1, V_R		
Total current, I		
Voltage across L, V_L		
Inductive reactance, X_L		
Computed inductance, L		

6.   Replace L_1 with L_2 and repeat steps 3, 4, and 5. Enter the data in Table 2 in the column labeled Inductor L_2.

7.   Place L_2 in series with L_1. Then find the inductive reactance for the series combination of the inductors as if they were one inductor. Enter the data in Table 3 in the column labeled Series Inductors. The following steps will guide you:

     (a)   Check that the generator is set to 1.0 V rms. Find the current in the circuit by measuring the voltage across the resistor as before and dividing by the resistance.

     (b)   Measure the voltage across *both* inductors.

     (c)   Use Ohm's law to find the inductive reactance of both inductors. Use the voltage measured in step (b) and the current found in step (a).

     (d)   Compute the total inductance by using the equation

$$L = \frac{X_L}{2\pi f}$$

8.   Connect the inductors in parallel and repeat step 7. Assume the parallel inductors are one equivalent inductor for the measurements. Enter the data in Table 3 in the column labeled Parallel Inductors.

Table 3

Step		Series Inductors	Parallel Inductors
(a)	Voltage across R_1, V_R		
	Total current, I		
(b)	Voltage across inductors, V_L		
(c)	Inductive reactance, X_L		
(d)	Computed inductance, L		

CONCLUSION

EVALUATION AND REVIEW QUESTIONS

1. (a) Using the data in Table 2, compute the sum of the inductive reactances of the two inductors:

$$X_{L1} + X_{L2} =$$

   (b) Using the data in Table 2, compute the product-over-sum of the inductive reactances of the two inductors:

$$\frac{(X_{L1})(X_{L2})}{X_{L1} + X_{L2}} =$$

   (c) Compare the results from (a) and (b) with the reactances for the series and parallel connections listed in Table 3. What conclusion can you draw from these data?

2. Repeat Question 1 using the data for the inductance, L. Compare the inductance of series and parallel inductors.

3. What effect would an error in the frequency of the generator have on the data for this experiment?

4. How could you apply the method used in this experiment to find the value of an unknown inductor?

5.   Compute the inductive reactance of a 50 μH inductor at a frequency of 50 MHz.

FOR FURTHER INVESTIGATION

A transformer consists of two or more coils wound on a common iron core. Frequently, one or more windings has a *center tap,* which splits a winding into two equal inductors. Because the windings are on the same core, mutual inductance exists between the windings. Obtain a small power transformer that has a low-voltage center-tapped secondary winding. Determine the inductance of each half of the winding using the method in this experiment. Then investigate what happens if the windings are connected in series. Keep the output of the signal generator constant for the measurements. Summarize your results.

MULTISIM TROUBLESHOOTING

This experiment has four Multisim files on the CD. Three of the four files contain a simulated "fault"; one has "no fault". The file with no fault is named EXP23-2-nf.msm. You may want to open this file to compare your results with the computer simulation. Then open each of the files with faults. Use the simulated instruments to investigate the circuit and determine the problem. The following are the filenames for circuits with troubleshooting problems for this experiment.

EXP23-2-f1.msm
    Fault: _____

EXP23-2-f2.msm
    Fault: _____

EXP23-2-f3.msm
    Fault: _____

Series *RL* Circuits

Name _____
Date _____
Class _____

OBJECTIVES
After performing this experiment, you will be able to:
1. Compute the inductive reactance of an inductor from voltage measurements in a series *RL* circuit.
2. Draw the impedance and voltage phasor diagram for the series *RL* circuit.
3. Measure the phase angle in a series circuit using either of two methods.

MATERIALS NEEDED
One 10 kΩ resistor
One 100 mH inductor

SUMMARY OF THEORY
When a sine wave drives a linear series circuit, the phase relationships between the current and the voltage are determined by the components in the circuit. The current and voltage are always in phase across resistors. With capacitors, the current is always leading the voltage by 90°, but for inductors, the voltage always leads the current by 90°. (A simple memory aid for this is *ELI the ICE man,* where *E* stands for voltage, *I* for current, and *L* and *C* for inductance and capacitance.)

Figure 1(a) illustrates a series *RL* circuit. The graphical representation of the phasors for this circuit is shown in Figure 1(b) and (c). As in the series *RC* circuit, the total impedance is obtained by adding the resistance and inductive reactance using the algebra for complex numbers. In this example, the current is 1.0 mA, and the total impedance is 5 kΩ. The current is the same in all components of a series circuit, so the current is drawn as a reference in the direction of the *x*-axis. If the current is multiplied by the impedance phasors, the voltage phasors are obtained as shown in Figure 1(c).

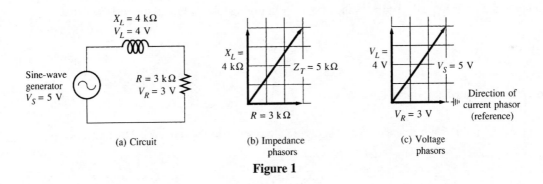

(a) Circuit   (b) Impedance phasors   (c) Voltage phasors

Figure 1

In this experiment, you learn how to make measurements of the phase angle. Actual inductors may have enough resistance to affect the phase angle in the circuit. You will use a series resistor that is large compared to the inductor's resistance to avoid this error.

PROCEDURE

1.   Measure the actual resistance of a 10 kΩ resistor and the inductance of a 100 mH inductor. If the inductor cannot be measured, record the listed value. Record the measured values in Table 1.

2.   Connect the circuit shown in Figure 2. Set the generator voltage with the circuit connected to 3.0 V_{pp} at a frequency of 25 kHz. The generator should have no dc offset. Measure the generator voltage and frequency with the oscilloscope as many meters cannot respond to the 25 kHz frequency. Use peak-to-peak readings for all voltage and current measurements in this experiment.

Table 1

Component	Listed Value	Measured Value
L_1	100 mH	
R_1	10 kΩ	

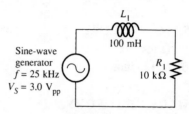

Figure 2

3.   Using a two-channel oscilloscope, measure the peak-to-peak voltage across the resistor (V_R) and the peak-to-peak voltage across the inductor (V_L). (See Figure 3 for the setup.) Measure the voltage across the inductor using the difference technique described in Experiment 16. Record the voltage readings in Table 2.

Table 2   (f = 25 kHz)

V_R	V_L	I	X_L	Z_T

4.   Compute the peak-to-peak current in the circuit by applying Ohm's law to the resistor. That is,

$$I = \frac{V_R}{R}$$

Enter the computed current in Table 2.

5.   Compute the inductive reactance, X_L, by applying Ohm's law to the inductor. The reactance is

$$X_L = \frac{V_L}{I}$$

Enter the computed reactance in Table 2.

6.   Calculate the total impedance (Z_T) by applying Ohm's law to the entire circuit. Use the generator voltage set in step 2 (V_S), and the current determined in step 4. Enter the computed impedance in Table 2.

7. Using the values listed in Tables 1 and 2, draw the impedance phasors on Plot 1(a) and the voltage phasors on Plot 1(b) for the circuit at a frequency of 25 kHz.

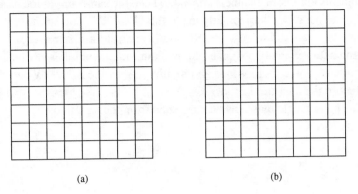

(a)   (b)

Plot 1

8. Compute the phase angle between V_R and V_S using the trigonometric relation

$$\theta = \tan^{-1}\left(\frac{V_L}{V_R}\right)$$

Enter the computed phase angle in Table 3.

9. Two methods for measuring phase angle will be explained. The first method can be used with any oscilloscope. The second can only be used with oscilloscopes that have a "fine" or variable SEC/DIV control. Measure the phase angle between V_R and V_S using one or both methods. The measured phase angle will be recorded in Table 3.

Phase Angle Measurement—Method 1
(a) Connect the oscilloscope so that channel 1 is across the generator and channel 2 is across the resistor. (See Figure 3.) Obtain a stable display showing between one and two cycles while viewing channel 1 (V_S). The scope should be triggered from channel 1.
(b) Measure the period, T, of the generator. Record it in Table 3. You will use this time in step (e).

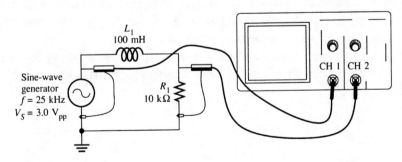

Figure 3

(c) Set the oscilloscope to view both channels. (Do not have channel 2 inverted.) Adjust the amplitudes of the signals using the VOLTS/DIV, VERT POSITION, and the vernier controls until both channels *appear* to have the same amplitude as seen on the scope face.

(d) Spread the signal horizontally using the SEC/DIV control until both signals are just visible across the screen. The SEC/DIV control must remain calibrated. Measure the time between the two signals, Δt, by counting the number of divisions along a horizontal graticule of the oscilloscope and multiplying by the SEC/DIV setting. (See Figure 4.) Record the measured Δt in Table 3.

(e) The phase angle may now be computed from the equation

$$\theta = \left(\frac{\Delta t}{T}\right) \times 360°$$

Enter the measured phase angle in Table 3 under Phase Angle—Method 1.

Table 3

Computed Phase Angle θ	Measured Period T	Time Difference Δt	Phase Angle	
			Method 1 θ	Method 2 θ

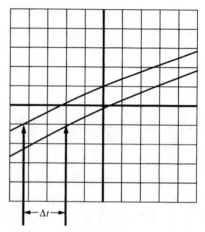

Figure 4

Phase Angle Measurement—Method 2

(a) In this method the oscilloscope face will represent degrees, and the phase angle can be measured directly. The probes are connected as before. View channel 1 and obtain a stable display. Then adjust the SEC/DIV control and its vernier until you have exactly one cycle across the scope face. This is equivalent to 360° in 10 divisions, so each division is worth 36°.[1]

(b) Now switch the scope to view both channels. As before, adjust the amplitudes of the signals using the VOLTS/DIV, VERT POSITION, and the vernier controls until both channels *appear* to have the same amplitude.

(c) Measure the number of divisions between the signals and multiply by 36° per division. Record the measured phase angle in Table 3 under Phase Angle—Method 2.

---

[1]For even better resolution, you can set one-half cycle across the screen, making each division worth 18°. Care must be taken to center the waveform.

CONCLUSION

EVALUATION AND REVIEW QUESTIONS
1.   (a)   What will happen to the impedance in this experiment if the frequency increases?

      (b)   What would happen to the impedance if the inductance were larger?

2.   (a)   What will happen to the phase angle in this experiment if the frequency increases?

      (b)   What would happen to the phase angle if the inductance were larger?

3.   Compute the percent difference between the computed phase angle and the method 1 phase angle measurement.

4.   The critical frequency for an *RL* circuit occurs at the frequency at which the resistance is equal to the inductive reactance. That is, $R = X_L$. Since $X_L = 2\pi f L$ for an inductor, it can easily be shown that the circuit frequency for an *RL* circuit is

$$f_{crit} = \frac{R}{2\pi L}$$

Compute the critical frequency for this experiment. What is the phase angle between V_R and V_S at the critical frequency?

$f_{crit} = $ _____ $\theta = $ _____

5.   A series *RL* circuit contains a 100 Ω resistor and a 1.0 H inductor and is operating at a frequency of 60 Hz. If 3.0 V are across the resistor, compute:

(a)   the current in the inductor _____

(b)   the inductive reactance, X_L _____

(c)   the voltage across the inductor, V_L _____

(d)   the source voltage, V_S _____

(e)   the phase angle between V_R and V_S _____

FOR FURTHER INVESTIGATION

An older method for measuring phase angles involved interpreting Lissajous figures. A Lissajous figure is the pattern formed by the application of a sinusoidal waveform to both the *x*- and *y*-axes of an oscilloscope. Two signals of equal amplitude and exactly in phase will produce a 45° line on the scope face. If the signals are the same amplitude and exactly 90° apart, the waveform will appear as a circle. Other phase angles can be determined by applying the formula

$$\theta = \arcsin\frac{OA}{OB}$$

Figure 5 illustrates a Lissajous figure phase measurement. The measurements of *OA* and *OB* are along the *y*-axis. Try measuring the phase angle in this experiment using a Lissajous figure. You will have to have the signals the same amplitude and centered on the oscilloscope face. Then switch the time base of the oscilloscope to the XY mode.

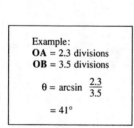

Example:
OA = 2.3 divisions
OB = 3.5 divisions

$$\theta = \arcsin\ \frac{2.3}{3.5}$$

$$= 41°$$

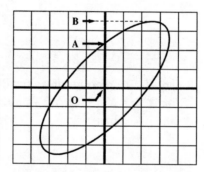

Figure 5

Series Resonance

OBJECTIVES
After performing this experiment, you will be able to:
1.   Compute the resonant frequency, Q, and bandwidth of a series resonant circuit.
2.   Measure the parameters listed in objective 1.
3.   Explain the factors affecting the selectivity of a series resonant circuit.

MATERIALS NEEDED
Resistors:
        One 100 Ω, one 47 Ω
One 0.01 μF capacitor
One 100 mH inductor

SUMMARY OF THEORY
The reactance of inductors increases with frequency according to the equation

$$X_L = 2\pi fL$$

On the other hand, the reactance of capacitors decreases with frequency according to the equation

$$X_C = \frac{1}{2\pi fC}$$

Consider the series LC circuit shown in Figure 1(a). In any LC circuit, there is a frequency at which the inductive reactance is equal to the capacitive reactance. The point at which there is equal and opposite reactance is called *resonance*. By setting $X_L = X_C$, substituting the relations given above, and solving for f, it is easy to show that the resonant frequency of an LC circuit is

$$f_r = \frac{1}{2\pi\sqrt{LC}}$$

where f_r is the resonant frequency. Recall that reactance phasors for inductors and capacitors are drawn in opposite directions because of the opposite phase shift that occurs between inductors and capacitors. At series resonance these two phasors are added and cancel each other. This is illustrated in Figure 1(b). The current in the circuit is limited only by the total resistance of the circuit. The current in this example is 5.0 mA. If each of the impedance phasors is multiplied by this current, the result is the voltage phasor diagram as shown in Figure 1(c). Notice that the voltage across the inductor and the capacitor can be *greater* than the applied voltage!

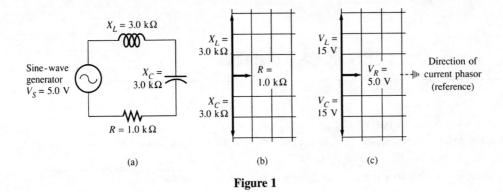

(a)   (b)   (c)

Figure 1

At the resonant frequency, the cancellation of the inductive and capacitive phasors leaves only the resistive phasor to limit the current in the circuit. Therefore, at resonance, the impedance of the circuit is a *minimum* and the current is a *maximum* and equal to V_S/R. The phase angle between the source voltage and current is zero. If the frequency is lowered, the inductive reactance will be smaller and the capacitive reactance will be larger. The circuit is said to be capacitive because the source current leads the source voltage. If the frequency is raised, the inductive reactance increases, and the capacitive reactance decreases. The circuit is said to be inductive.

The *selectivity* of a resonant circuit describes how the circuit responds to a group of frequencies. A highly selective circuit responds to a narrow group of frequencies and rejects other frequencies. The *bandwidth* of a resonant circuit is the frequency range at which the current is 70.7% of the maximum current. A highly selective circuit thus has a narrow bandwidth. The sharpness of the response to the frequencies is determined by the circuit Q. The Q for a series resonant circuit is the reactive power in either the coil or capacitor divided by the true power, which is dissipated in the total resistance of the circuit. The bandwidth and resonant frequency can be shown to be related to the circuit Q by the equation

$$Q = \frac{f_r}{BW}$$

Figure 2 illustrates how the bandwidth can change with Q. Responses 1 and 2 have the same resonant frequency but different bandwidths. The bandwidth for curve 1 is shown. Response curve 2 has a higher Q and a smaller BW. A useful equation that relates the circuit resistance, capacitance, and inductance to Q is

$$Q = \frac{1}{R}\sqrt{\frac{L}{C}}$$

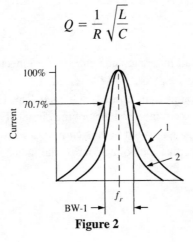

Figure 2

The value of R in this equation is the total equivalent series resistance in the circuit. Using this equation, the circuit response can be tailored to the application. For a highly selective circuit, the circuit resistance is held to a minimum and the L/C ratio is made high.

The Q of a resonant circuit can also be computed from the equation

$$Q = \frac{X_L}{R}$$

where X_L is the inductive reactance and R is again the total equivalent series resistance of the circuit. The result is the same if X_C is used in the equation, since the values are the same at resonance, but usually X_L is shown because the resistance of the inductor is frequently the dominant resistance of the circuit.

PROCEDURE

1. Measure the value of a 100 mH inductor, a 0.1 μF capacitor, a 100 Ω resistor, and a 47 Ω resistor. Enter the measured values in Table 1. If it is not possible to measure the inductor or capacitor, use the listed values.

2. Measure the winding resistance of the inductor, R_W. Enter the measured inductor resistance in Table 1.

Table 1

	Listed Value	Measured Value
L_1	100 mH	
C_1	0.01 μF	
R_1	100 Ω	
R_{S1}	47 Ω	
R_W (L_1 resistance)		

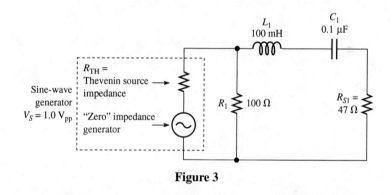

Figure 3

3. Construct the circuit shown in Figure 3. The purpose of the parallel 100 Ω resistor is to reduce the Thevenin driving impedance of the generator and, therefore, the total equivalent series resistance of the circuit.[1] Compute the total resistance of the equivalent series circuit. Note that looking back to the generator, R_{TH} is in parallel with R_1. In equation form, the equivalent series resistance, R_T, is

$$R_T = (R_{TH} \parallel R_1) + R_W + R_{S1}$$

Enter the computed total resistance in Table 2.

---

[1]Some high-quality generators have a Thevenin resistance of 50 Ω. If you are using a 50 Ω generator, it is not necessary to include R_1.

Table 2

	Computed	Measured
R_T		
f_r		
Q		
V_{RS1}		
f_2		
f_1		
BW		

4. Using the measured values from Table 1, compute the resonant frequency of the circuit from the equation:

$$f_r = \frac{1}{2\pi\sqrt{LC}}$$

Record the computed resonant frequency in Table 2.

5. Use the total resistance computed in step 3 and the measured values of L and C to compute the approximate Q of the circuit from the equation:

$$Q = \frac{1}{R_T}\sqrt{\frac{L}{C}}$$

Enter the computed Q in Table 2.

6. Compute the bandwidth from the equation:

$$BW = \frac{f_r}{Q}$$

Enter this as the computed BW in Table 2.

7. Using your oscilloscope, tune for resonance by observing the voltage across the sense resistor, R_{S1}. As explained in Floyd's text, the current in the circuit rises to a maximum at resonance. The sense resistor will have the highest voltage across it at resonance. Measure the resonant frequency with the oscilloscope. Record the measured resonant frequency in Table 2.

8. Check that the voltage across R_1 is 1.0 V_{pp}. Measure the peak-to-peak voltage across the sense resistor at resonance. The voltage across R_{S1} is directly proportional to the current in the series LC branch, so it is not necessary to compute the current. Record in Table 2 the measured peak-to-peak voltage across R_{S1} (V_{RS1}).

9.   Raise the frequency of the generator until the voltage across R_{S1} falls to 70.7% of the value read in step 7. Do not readjust the generator's amplitude in this step; this means that the Thevenin resistance of the generator is included in the measurement of the bandwidth. Measure and record this frequency as f_2 in Table 2.

10.   Lower the frequency to below resonance until the voltage across R_{S1} falls to 70.7% of the value read in step 8. Again, do not adjust the generator amplitude. Measure and record this frequency as f_1 in Table 2.

11.   Compute the bandwidth by subtracting f_1 from f_2. Enter this result in Table 2 as the measured bandwidth.

12.   At resonance, the current in the circuit, the voltage across the capacitor, and the voltage across the inductor are all at a maximum value. Tune across resonance by observing the voltage across the capacitor, then try it on the inductor. Use the oscilloscope difference function technique described in the experiment on Sine Wave Measurements. What is the maximum voltage observed on the capacitor? Is it the same or different than the maximum voltage across the inductor?

V_C (max) = _____ V_L (max) = _____

CONCLUSION

EVALUATION AND REVIEW QUESTIONS

1.   (a)   Compute the percent difference between the computed and measured bandwidth.

      (b)   What factors account for the difference between the computed and measured values?

2.   (a)   What is the total impedance of the experimental circuit at resonance?_____

      (b)   What is the phase shift between the total current and voltage?_____

3.   (a)   In step 12, you measured the maximum voltage across the capacitor and the inductor. The maximum voltage across either one should have been larger than the source voltage. How do you account for this?

      (b)   Is this a valid technique for finding the resonant frequency? _____

4.   (a)   What happens to the resonant frequency, if the inductor is twice as large and the capacitor is half as large? _____

      (b)   What happens to the bandwidth?_____

5.   (a)   Compute the resonant frequency for a circuit consisting of a 50 μH inductor in series with a 1000 pF capacitor. $f_r =$ _____

      (b)   If the total resistance of the above circuit is 10 Ω, what are Q and the bandwidth?
             $Q =$ _____ $BW =$ _____

FOR FURTHER INVESTIGATION

In this experiment, you measured three points on the response curve similar to Figure 1. Using the technique of measuring the voltage across R_{S1}, find several more points on the response curve. Graph your results on Plot 1.

f_r
Frequency

Plot 1

MULTISIM TROUBLESHOOTING

This experiment has four Multisim files on the CD. Three of the four files contain a simulated "fault"; one has "no fault". The file with no fault is named EXP26-3-nf.msm. You may want to open this file to compare your results with the computer simulation. Then open each of the files with faults. Use the simulated instruments to investigate the circuit and determine the problem. The following are the filenames for circuits with troubleshooting problems for this experiment.

EXP26-3-f1.msm
      Fault: _____

EXP26-3-f2.msm
      Fault: _____

EXP26-3-f3.msm
      Fault: _____

Parallel
Resonance

Name _____
Date _____
Class _____

OBJECTIVES

After performing this experiment, you will be able to:

1. Compute the resonant frequency, Q, and bandwidth of a parallel resonant circuit.
2. Measure the frequency response of a parallel resonant circuit.
3. Use the frequency response to determine the bandwidth of a parallel resonant circuit.

MATERIALS NEEDED

One 100 mH inductor
One 0.047 μF capacitor
One 1.0 kΩ resistor

SUMMARY OF THEORY

In an *RLC* parallel circuit, the current in each branch is determined by the applied voltage and the impedance of that branch. For an "ideal" inductor (no resistance), the branch impedance is X_L, and for a capacitor the branch impedance is X_C. Since X_L and X_C are functions of frequency, it is apparent that the currents in each branch are also dependent on the frequency. For any given L and C, there is a frequency at which the currents in each are equal and of opposite phase. This frequency is the resonant frequency and is found using the same equation as was used for series resonance:

$$f_r = \frac{1}{2\pi\sqrt{LC}}$$

The circuit and phasor diagram for an ideal parallel *RLC* circuit at resonance is illustrated in Figure 1. Some interesting points to observe are: The total source current at resonance is equal to the current in the resistor. The total current is actually less than the current in either the inductor or the capacitor. This is because of the opposite phase shift which occurs between inductors and capacitors, causing the addition of the currents to cancel. Also, the impedance of the circuit is solely determined by

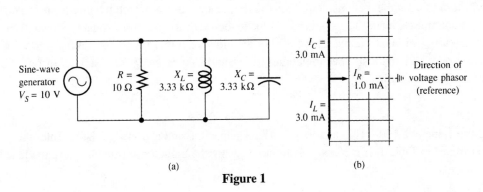

(a)

(b)

Figure 1

R, as the inductor and capacitor appear to be open. In a two-branch circuit consisting of only L and C, the source current would be zero, causing the impedance to be infinite! Of course, this does not happen with actual components that do have resistance and other effects.

In a practical two-branch parallel circuit consisting of an inductor and a capacitor, the only significant resistance is the winding resistance of the inductor. Figure 2(a) illustrates a practical parallel LC circuit containing winding resistance. By network theorems, the practical LC circuit can be converted to an equivalent parallel RLC circuit, as shown in Figure 2(b). The equivalent circuit is easier to analyze. The phasor diagram for the ideal parallel RLC circuit can then be applied to the equivalent circuit as was illustrated in Figure 1. The equations to convert the inductance and its winding resistance to an equivalent parallel circuit are

$$L_{eq} = L\left(\frac{Q^2 + 1}{Q^2}\right) \qquad R_{p(eq)} = R_W(Q^2 + 1)$$

where $R_{p(eq)}$ represents the parallel equivalent resistance, and R_W represents the winding resistance of the inductor. The Q used in the conversion equation is the Q for the inductor:

$$Q = \frac{X_L}{R_W}$$

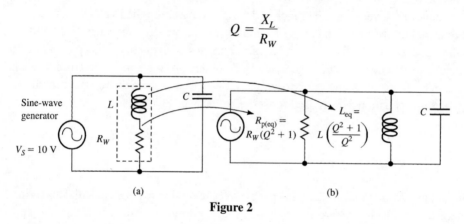

(a)   (b)

Figure 2

The *selectivity* of series circuits was discussed in the experiment on Series Resonance. Parallel resonant circuits also respond to a group of frequencies. In parallel resonant circuits, the impedance as a function of frequency has the same shape as the current versus frequency curve for series resonant circuits. The *bandwidth* of a parallel resonant circuit is the frequency range at which the circuit impedance is 70.7% of the maximum impedance. The sharpness of the response to frequencies is again measured by the circuit Q. The circuit Q will be different from the Q of the inductor if there is additional resistance in the circuit. If there is no additional resistance in parallel with L and C, then the Q for a parallel resonant circuit is equal to the Q of the inductor.

PROCEDURE

1. Measure the value of a 100 mH inductor, a 0.047 μF capacitor, and a 1.0 kΩ resistor. Enter the measured values in Table 1. If it is not possible to measure the inductor or capacitor, use the listed values.

2. Measure the resistance of the inductor. Enter the measured inductor resistance in Table 1.

Table 1		
	Listed Value	Measured Value
L_1	100 mH	
C_1	0.047 µF	
R_{S1}	1.0 kΩ	
R_W (L_1 resistance)		

Table 2		
	Computed	Measured
f_r		
Q		
BW		
$f_i = \dfrac{BW}{4}$		

3. Construct the circuit shown in Figure 3. The purpose of R_{S1} is to develop a voltage that can be used to sense the total current in the circuit. Compute the resonant frequency of the circuit using the equation

$$f_r = \frac{1}{2\pi\sqrt{LC}}$$

Enter the computed resonant frequency in Table 2. Set the generator to the f_r at 1.0 V_{pp} output, as measured with your oscilloscope. Use peak-to-peak values for all voltage measurements in this experiment.

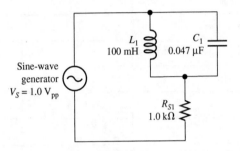

Sine-wave generator
$V_S = 1.0\ V_{pp}$

L_1 100 mH
C_1 0.047 µF
R_{S1} 1.0 kΩ

Figure 3

4. The Q of a parallel LC circuit with no resistance other than the inductor winding resistance is equal to the Q of the inductor. Compute the approximate Q of the parallel LC circuit from

$$Q = \frac{X_L}{R_W}$$

Enter the computed Q in Table 2.

5. Compute the bandwidth from the equation

$$BW = \frac{f_r}{Q}$$

Enter this as the computed BW in Table 2.

6. Connect your oscilloscope across R_{S1} and tune for resonance by observing the voltage across the sense resistor, R_{S1}. Resonance occurs when the voltage across R_{S1} is a minimum, since the impedance of the parallel LC circuit is highest. Measure the resonant frequency (f_r) and record the measured result in Table 2.

7. Compute a frequency increment (f_i) by dividing the computed bandwidth by 4. That is,

$$f_i = \frac{BW}{4}$$

Enter the computed f_i in Table 2.

8. Use the measured resonant frequency (f_r) and the frequency increment (f_i) from Table 2 to compute 11 frequencies according to the Computed Frequency column of Table 3. Enter the 11 frequencies in column 1 of Table 3.

Table 3

Computed Frequency	V_{RS1}	I	Z
$f_r - 5f_i =$			
$f_r - 4f_i =$			
$f_r - 3f_i =$			
$f_r - 2f_i =$			
$f_r - 1f_i =$			
$f_r =$			
$f_r + 1f_i =$			
$f_r + 2f_i =$			
$f_r + 3f_i =$			
$f_r + 4f_i =$			
$f_r + 5f_i =$			

9. Tune the generator to each of the computed frequencies listed in Table 3. At each frequency, check that the generator voltage is still at 1.0 V_{pp}; then measure the peak-to-peak voltage across R_{S1}. Record the voltage in column 2 of Table 3.

10. Compute the total peak-to-peak current, I, at each frequency by applying Ohm's law to the sense resistor R_{S1}. (That is, $I = V_{RS1}/R_{S1}$.) Record the current in column 3 of Table 3.

11. Use Ohm's law with the measured source voltage (1.0 V_{pp}) and source current at each frequency to compute the impedance at each frequency. Complete Table 3 by listing the computed impedances.

12.   On Plot 1, draw the impedance versus frequency curve. From your curve determine the bandwidth. Complete Table 2 with the measured bandwidth.

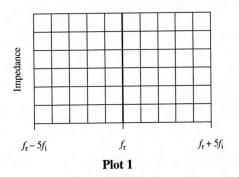

Plot 1

CONCLUSION

EVALUATION AND REVIEW QUESTIONS

1.   (a)   Compare the impedance as a function of frequency for series and parallel resonance.

      (b)   Compare the current as a function of frequency for series and parallel resonance.

2.   What was the phase shift between the total current and voltage at resonance?

3.   At resonance the total current was a minimum, but the branch currents were not. How could you find the value of the current in each branch?

4.   What factors affect the Q of a parallel resonant circuit?

5.   In the circuit of Figure 2(a), assume the inductor is 100 mH with 120 Ω of winding resistance and the capacitor is 0.01 μF. Compute:
       (a)   the resonant frequency _____

       (b)   the reactance, X_L, of the inductor at resonance _____

       (c)   the Q of the circuit _____

       (d)   the bandwidth, BW _____

FOR FURTHER INVESTIGATION

The oscilloscope can be used to display the resonant dip in current by connecting a sweep generator to the circuit. This converts the time base on the oscilloscope to a frequency base. The sweep generator produces an FM (frequency modulated) signal, which is connected in place of the signal generator. In addition, the sweep generator has a synchronous sweep output that should be connected to the oscilloscope on the X channel input. The Y channel input is connected across the 1.0 kΩ sense resistor. The oscilloscope is placed in the XY mode. A diagram of the setup is shown in Figure 4. Build the circuit shown, determine a method to calibrate the frequency base, and summarize your procedure in a report.

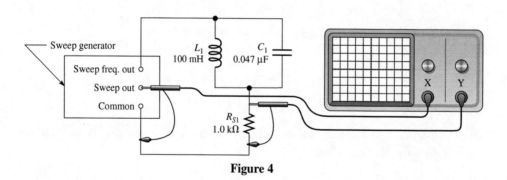

Figure 4

MULTISIM TROUBLESHOOTING

This experiment has four Multisim files on the CD. Three of the four files contain a simulated "fault"; one has "no fault". The file with no fault is named EXP27-3-nf.msm. You may want to open this file to compare your results with the computer simulation. Then open each of the files with faults. Use the simulated instruments to investigate the circuit and determine the problem. The following are the filenames for circuits with troubleshooting problems for this experiment.

EXP27-3-f1.msm

    Fault: _____

EXP27-3-f2.msm

    Fault: _____

EXP27-3-f3.msm

    Fault: _____

| Name _____ |
| Date _____ |
| Class _____ |

Low-Pass and High-Pass Active Filters

Objectives:

After performing this experiment, you will be able to:

1. Specify the components required for a Butterworth low-pass or high-pass filter of a given order.
2. Build and test a Butterworth low-pass active filter for a specific frequency and order.
3. (For Further Investigation) Change the low-pass filter into a high-pass design and test the response.

Summary of Theory:

A filter is a circuit that produces a prescribed frequency response. Passive filters are combination circuits containing only resistors, inductors, and capacitors (*RLC*). Active filters contain these elements and an operational amplifier (or transistor). The major advantage of active filters is that they can achieve frequency response characteristics that are nearly ideal and for reasonable cost for frequencies up to about 100 kHz. Above this, active filters are limited by bandwidth.

Active filters can be designed to optimize any of several characteristics. These include flatness of the response in the passband, steepness of the transition region, or minimum phase shift. The Butterworth form of filter has the flattest passband characteristic, but is not as steep as other filters and has poor phase characteristics. Since a flat passband is generally the most important characteristic, it will be used in this experiment.

The *order* of a filter, also called the number of *poles*, governs the steepness of the transition outside the frequencies of interest. In general, the higher the order, the steeper the response. The roll-off rate for active filters depends on the type of filter but is approximately –20 dB/decade for each pole. (A *decade* is a factor of ten in frequency). A four-pole filter, for example, has a roll-off of approximately –80 dB/decade. A quick way to determine the number of poles is to count the number of capacitors that are used in the frequency-determining part of the filter.

Figure 25-1 illustrates a two-pole active low-pass and a two-pole active high-pass filter. Each of these circuits is a *section*. To make a filter with more poles, simply cascade these sections, but change the gains of each section according to the values listed in Table 25-1. The cutoff frequency will be given by the equation:

$$f_c = \frac{1}{2\pi RC}$$

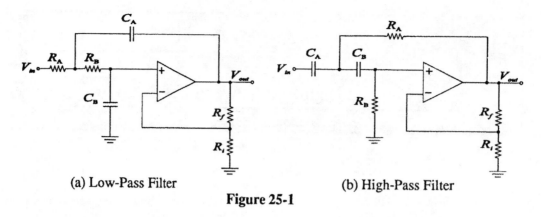

| (a) Low-Pass Filter | (b) High-Pass Filter |

Figure 25-1

You can design your own Butterworth low-pass or high-pass active filter by using the following guidelines:

1. Determine the number of poles necessary based on the required roll-off rate. Choose an even number, as an odd number will require the same number of op-amps as the next highest even number. For example, if the required roll-off is –40 dB/decade, specify a two-pole filter.

2. Choose R and C values for the desired cutoff frequency (R_A, R_B, C_A and C_B). For best results, choose resistors between 1 kΩ and 100 kΩ. The values chosen should satisfy the cutoff frequency as given by the equation:

$$f_c = \frac{1}{2\pi RC}$$

3. Choose resistors R_f and R_i that give the gains for each section according to the values listed in Table 25-1. The gain is controlled only by R_f and R_i. Solving the closed-loop gain of a noninverting amplifier gives the equation for R_f in terms of R_i:

$$R_f = (A_v - 1) R_i$$

Table 25-1
Butterworth Low-Pass and High-Pass Filters

Poles	Gain Required		
	Section 1	Section 2	Section 3
2	1.586		
4	1.152	2.235	
6	1.068	1.586	2.483

Example: A low-pass Butterworth filter with a roll-off of approximately –80 dB/decade and a cutoff frequency of 2.0 kHz is required. Specify the components.

Step 1: Determine the number of poles required. Since the design requirement is for approximately –80 dB/decade, a four-pole (two-section) filter is required.

Step 2: Choose R and C. Try C as 0.01 µF and compute R. Computed $R = 7.96$ kΩ. Since the nearest standard value is 8.2 kΩ, choose $C = 0.01$ µF and $R = 8.2$ kΩ.

Step 3. Determine the gain required for each section and specify R_f and R_i. From Table 25-1, the gain of section 1 is required to be 1.152 and the gain of section 2 is required to be 2.235. Choose resistors that will give these gains for a noninverting amplifier. The choices are determined by again considering standard values and are shown on the completed schematic, Figure 25-2.

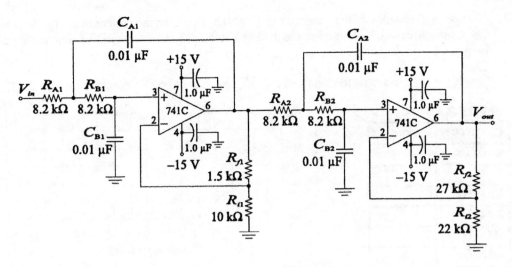

Figure 25-2

Materials Needed:
Resistors: one 1.5 kΩ, four 8.2 kΩ, two 10 kΩ, one 22 kΩ, one 27 kΩ
Capacitors: four 0.01 μF, four 1.0 μF
Two 741C op-amps

For Further Investigation:
   One additional 741C op-amp and components to be specified by student

Procedure:
1. Measure and record the components listed in Table 25-2. If you cannot measure the capacitors, show the listed value.

Table 25-2

Component	Listed Value	Measured Values			
		A1	B1	A2	B2
R_{A1} to R_{B2}	8.2 kΩ				
C_{A1} to C_{B2}	0.01 μF				
R_{i1}	10 kΩ				
R_{f1}	1.5 kΩ				
R_{i2}	22 kΩ				
R_{f2}	27 kΩ				

2. Construct the four-pole low-pass active filter illustrated in Figure 25-2. Install a 10 kΩ load resistor. Connect a sine wave generator to the input. Set it for a 500 Hz sine wave at 1.0 V rms. The voltage should be measured at the generator with the circuit connected. Set the voltage with a voltmeter and check both voltage and frequency with the oscilloscope. Measure V_{RL} at a frequency of 500 Hz, and record it in Table 25-3.

3. Change the frequency of the generator to 1000 Hz. Readjust the generator's amplitude to 1.0 V rms. Measure V_{RL}, entering the data in Table 25-3. Continue in this manner for each frequency listed in Table 25-3.

4. Graph the voltage across the load resistor (V_{RL}) as a function of frequency on Plot 25-1.

Table 25-3

Frequency	V_{RL}
500 Hz	
1000 Hz	
1500 Hz	
2000 Hz	
3000 Hz	
4000 Hz	
8000 Hz	

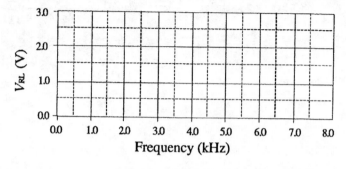

Plot 25-1

5. A Bode plot is a log-log plot of voltage versus frequency. It allows you to examine the data over a larger range than is possible with linear plots. Replot the data from the filter onto the log-log plot shown in Plot 25-2.

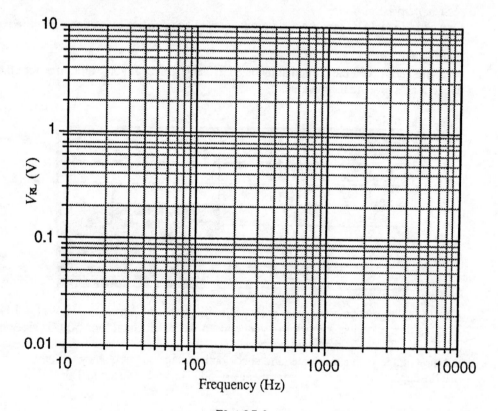

Plot 25-2

Conclusion:

Evaluation and Review Questions:

1. (a) From the frequency response curves, determine the cutoff frequency for the filter in this experiment.

    (b) Compute the average R and C for your active filter (Table 25-1). Use the average values of each to compute the cutoff frequency.

2. (a) What is the measured voltage gain of active filter in the passband?

    (b) What should it be?

3. Using the Bode plot, predict V_{out} at a frequency of 20 kHz.

4. The theoretical roll-off for your filter is –80 dB/decade. How does your actual filter compare to this theoretical roll-off rate?

5. (a) Using the measured values of R_{i1} and R_{f1}, compute the actual gain of the first section. Compare this to the required gain in Table 25-1.

    (b) Repeat for the second section using R_{i2} and R_{f2}.

For Further Investigation:
To convert from a Butterworth low-pass to a high-pass design requires only that the resistors and capacitors that make up the filter be exchanged (see Figure 25-1). Change the filter in the experiment to a high-pass filter and test the response. Submit a report summarizing your findings.

Diode Characteristics

Name _____
Date _____
Class _____

OBJECTIVES

After performing this experiment, you will be able to:
1. Measure and plot the forward- and reverse-biased *IV* characteristics for a diode.
2. Test the effect of heat on a diode's response.
3. Measure the ac resistance of a diode.

MATERIALS NEEDED

Resistors:
> One 330 Ω; one 1.0 MΩ

One signal diode (1N914 or equivalent)

SUMMARY OF THEORY

Semiconductors are certain crystalline materials that can be altered with impurities to radically change their electrical characteristics. The impurity can be an electron donor or an electron acceptor. Donor impurities provide an *extra* electron that is free to move through the crystal at normal temperatures. The total crystal is electrically neutral, but the availability of free electrons in the material causes the material to be classified as an N-type (for negative) semiconductor. Acceptor impurities leave a "hole" (the absence of an electron) in the crystal structure. These materials are called P-type (for positive) semiconductors. They conduct by the motion of shared valence bond electrons moving between the atoms of the crystal. This motion is referred to as hole motion because the absence of an electron from the crystal structure can be thought of as a hole.

When a P-type and an N-type material are effectively made on the same crystal base, a *diode* is formed. The PN junction has unique electrical characteristics. Electrons and holes diffuse across the junction, creating a *barrier potential,* which prevents further current without an external voltage source. If a dc voltage source is connected to the diode, the direction it is connected has the effect of either increasing or decreasing the barrier potential. The effect is to allow the diode to either conduct readily or to become a poor conductor. If the negative terminal of the source is connected to the N-type material and the positive terminal is connected to P-type material, the diode is said to be forward-biased, and it conducts. If the positive terminal of the source is connected to the N-type material and the negative terminal is connected to P-type material, the diode is said to be reverse-biased, and the diode is a poor conductor.

While the actual processes that occur in a diode are rather complex, diode operation can be simplified with three approximations. The first approximation is to consider the diode as a switch. If it is forward-biased, the switch is closed. If it is reverse-biased, the switch is open. The second approximation is the same as the first except it takes into account the barrier potential. For a silicon diode, this is approximately 0.7 V. A forward-biased silicon diode will drop approximately 0.7 V across the diode. The third approximation includes the first and second approximations and adds the small forward *(bulk)* resistance that is present when the diode is forward-biased.

PROCEDURE

1. Measure and record the resistance of the resistors listed in Table 1. Then check your diode with the ohmmeter. Select a low ohm range and measure the forward and reverse resistance by reversing the diode. The diode is good on this test if the resistance is significantly different between the forward and the reverse directions. If you are using an autoranging meter, the meter may not produce enough voltage to overcome the barrier potential. You should select a low ohm range and hold that range. Consult the operator's manual for specific instructions. Record the data in Table 1.

Table 1

Component	Listed Value	Measured Value
R_1	330 Ω	
R_2	1.0 MΩ	
D_1 forward resistance		
D_1 reverse resistance		

2. Construct the forward-biased circuit shown in Figure 1. The line on the diode indicates the cathode side of the diode. Set the power supply for zero volts.

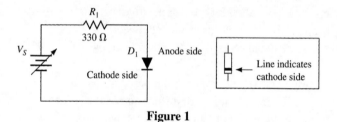

Figure 1

Table 2

V_F (measured)	V_{R1} (measured)	I_F (computed)
0.45 V		
0.50 V		
0.55 V		
0.60 V		
0.65 V		
0.70 V		
0.75 V		

3. Monitor the forward voltage drop, V_F, *across the diode.* Slowly increase V_S to establish 0.45 V across the diode. Measure the voltage across the resistor, V_{R1}, and record it in Table 2.

4.   The diode forward current, I_F, can be found by applying Ohm's law to R_1. Compute I_F and enter the computed current in Table 2.

5.   Repeat steps 3 and 4 for each voltage listed in Table 2.

6.   With the power supply set to the voltage that causes 0.75 V to drop across the diode, bring a hot soldering iron near the diode. Do *not* touch the diode with the iron. Observe the effect of heat on the voltage and current in a forward-biased diode. If you have freeze spray available, test the effect of freeze spray on the diode's operation. Describe your observations.

7.   The data in this step will be accurate only if your voltmeter has a very high input impedance. You can find out if your meter is high impedance by measuring the power supply voltage through a series 1.0 MΩ resistor. If the meter reads the supply voltage accurately, it has high input impedance. Connect the reverse-biased circuit shown in Figure 2. Set the power supply to each reverse voltage listed in Table 3, (V_R). Measure and record the voltage across R_2 (V_{R2}). Use this voltage and Ohm's law to compute the reverse current in each case. Enter the computed current in Table 3.

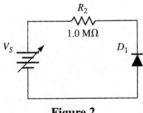

Figure 2

Table 3

V_R (measured)	V_{R2} (measured)	I_R (computed)
5.0 V		
10.0 V		
15.0 V		

8. Graph the forward- and reverse-biased diode curves on Plot 1. The different voltage scale factors for the forward and reverse curves are chosen to allow the data to cover more of the graph. You need to choose an appropriate current scale factor that will put the largest current recorded near the top of the graph.

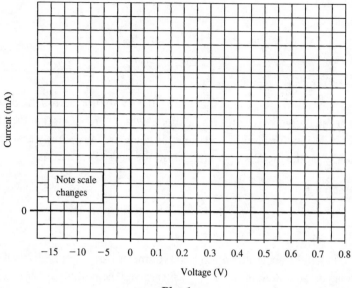

Plot 1

9. With the power supply set to 15 V, bring a hot soldering iron near the diode. Do *not* touch the diode with the iron. Observe the effect of heat on the voltage and current in the reverse-biased diode. If you have freeze spray available, test the effect of freeze spray on the diode's operation. Describe your observations.

CONCLUSION

EVALUATION AND REVIEW QUESTIONS

1. Compute the diode's forward resistance at three points on the forward-biased curve. Apply Ohm's law to the curve in Plot 1 at 0.5 V, 0.6 V, and 0.7 V by dividing a small change in voltage by a small change in current, as illustrated in Figure 3. This result is called the ac resistance (r_{ac}) of the diode.

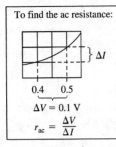

To find the ac resistance:

0.4   0.5

$\Delta V = 0.1$ V

$r_{ac} = \dfrac{\Delta V}{\Delta I}$

Figure 3

r_{ac} (0.5 V) = _____

r_{ac} (0.6 V) = _____

r_{ac} (0.7 V) = _____

2. Does the diode's reverse resistance stay constant? Explain your answer.

3. From the data in Table 2, compute the maximum power dissipated in the diode.

4. Based on your observations of the heating and cooling of a diode, what does heat do to the forward and reverse resistance of a diode?

5. Explain how you could use an ohmmeter to identify the cathode of an unmarked diode. Why is it necessary to know the *actual* polarity of the ohmmeter leads?

6. A student measures the resistance of an unmarked diode with an ohmmeter. When the $(+)$ lead of the ohmmeter is connected to lead 1 of the diode and the $(-)$ lead of the ohmmeter is connected to lead 2 of the diode, the reading is 400 Ω. When the ohmmeter leads are reversed, the reading is ∞. Which lead on the diode is the anode?

FOR FURTHER INVESTIGATION

The theoretical equation for a diode's *I-V* curve shows that the current is an exponential function of the bias voltage.[1] This means that the theoretical forward diode curve will plot as a straight line on semilog paper. Semilog paper contains a logarithmic scale on one axis and a linear scale on the other axis. Graph your data from this experiment (Table 2) onto Plot 2. What conclusion can you make from the data you recorded?

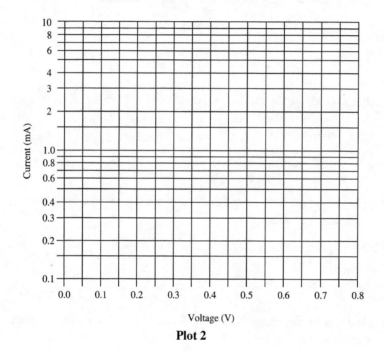

Plot 2

---

[1] A complete discussion of the diode equation can be found in Bogart, *Electronic Devices and Circuits,* 6th edition, 2004, Prentice Hall Publishing Co.

Rectifier Circuits

Objectives:

After performing this experiment, you will be able to:

1. Construct half-wave, full-wave, and bridge rectifier circuits, and compare the input and output voltage for each.
2. Connect a filter capacitor to each circuit in objective 1 and measure the ripple voltage and ripple frequency.

Summary of Theory:

Rectifiers are diodes used to change ac into dc. As you saw in Experiment 1, diodes work like a one-way valve, allowing current in only one direction. When ac is applied to a diode, the diode is forward-biased for one-half of the cycle and reverse-biased for the other half cycle. The output waveform is a pulsating dc waveform (or *half-wave rectified*) as illustrated in Figure 3-1. This pulsating dc waveform can then be filtered to convert it to constant dc.

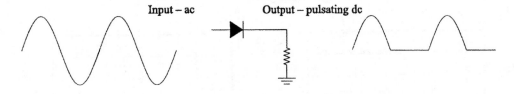

Input – ac   Output – pulsating dc

Figure 3-1

Rectifiers are widely used in power supplies to provide the dc voltage necessary for almost all active devices to work. The three basic rectifier circuits are the half-wave, the center-tapped full-wave, and the full-wave bridge rectifier circuits. The most important parameters for choosing diodes for these circuits are the maximum forward current, I_F, and the peak inverse voltage rating (PIV) of the diode. The peak inverse voltage is the maximum voltage the diode can withstand when it is reverse-biased. The amount of reverse voltage that appears across a diode depends on the type of circuit in which it is connected. Some characteristics of the three rectifier circuits will be investigated in this experiment.

Materials Needed:
Resistors: two 2.2 kΩ resistors
One 12.6 V ac center-tapped transformer with fused line cord
Four diodes 1N4001 (or equivalent)
One 100 μF capacitor
For Further Investigation:
      One 0.01 μF capacitor
      One 7812 or 78L12 regulator

Procedure:
1. Connect the half-wave rectifier circuit shown in Figure 3-2. (**Safety note** – the ac line voltage must not be exposed; the transformer should be fused as shown.) Notice the polarity of the diode. The line indicates the cathode side (the negative side when forward-biased). Connect the oscilloscope so that channel 1 is across the transformer secondary and channel 2 is across the output (load) resistor. The oscilloscope should be set for LINE triggering as the waveforms to be viewed in this experiment are synchronized with the ac line voltage. View the input voltage, V_{sec}, and output voltage, V_{out}, waveforms for this circuit and sketch them on Plot 3-1 below. Label voltage and time on your sketch.

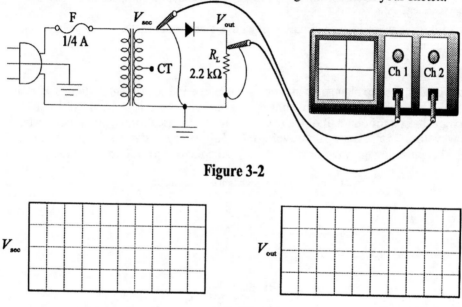

Figure 3-2

Plot 3-1

2. Measure the secondary rms voltage and the output peak voltage. Remember to convert the oscilloscope reading to rms voltage. Record the data in Table 3-1.

3. The output isn't very useful as a dc voltage source because of the pulsating output. Connect a 100 μF filter capacitor in parallel with the load resistor (R_L). Check the polarity of the capacitor; the negative side goes toward ground. Measure the dc load voltage, $V_{out(DC)}$, and the peak-to-peak ripple voltage, $V_{r(pp)}$, in the output. To measure the ripple voltage, switch the oscilloscope to AC COUPLING. This allows you to magnify the small ac ripple voltage without including the much larger dc level. Measure the ripple frequency. The ripple frequency is the frequency at which the waveform repeats. Record all data in Table 3-1.

Table 3-1 Half-Wave Rectifier

Without Filter Capacitor				With Filter Capacitor		
Computed	Measured	Computed	Measured	Measured		
$V_{sec(rms)}$	$V_{sec(rms)}$	$V_{out(p)}$	$V_{out(p)}$	$V_{out(DC)}$	$V_{r(pp)}$	Ripple Frequency
12.6 V ac						

4. Disconnect power and change the circuit to the full-wave rectifier circuit shown in Figure 3-3. Notice that the ground for the circuit has changed. The oscilloscope ground needs to be connected as shown. Check your circuit carefully before applying power. Compute the expected peak output voltage. Then apply power and view the V_{sec} and V_{out} waveforms. Sketch the observed waveforms on Plot 3-2.

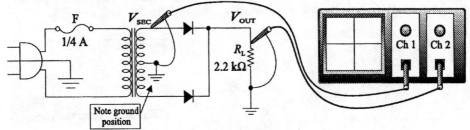

Figure 3-3

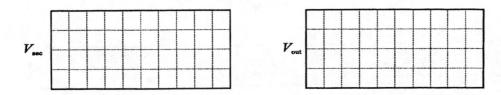

Plot 3-2

5. Measure $V_{sec(rms)}$ and the peak output voltage ($V_{out(p)}$) without a filter capacitor. Record the data in Table 3-2.

6. Now add a 100 µF capacitor in parallel with the load resistor. Measure $V_{out(DC)}$, the peak-to-peak ripple voltage, $V_{r(pp)}$, and the ripple frequency as before. Record the data in Table 3-2.

Table 3-2 Full-Wave Rectifier Circuit

Without Filter Capacitor				With Filter Capacitor		
Computed	Measured	Computed	Measured	Measured		
$V_{sec(rms)}$	$V_{sec(rms)}$	$V_{out(p)}$	$V_{out(p)}$	$V_{out(DC)}$	$V_{r(pp)}$	Ripple Frequency
6.3 V ac						

175

7. Investigate the effect of the load resistor on the ripple voltage by connecting a second 2.2 kΩ load resistor in parallel with R_L in the full-wave circuit in Figure 3-3. The filter capacitor is not shown but should be left in parallel also. Measure the ripple voltage. What can you conclude about the effect of additional load current on the ripple voltage?

---

8. Disconnect power and change the circuit to the bridge rectifier circuit shown in Figure 3-4. Notice that <u>no</u> terminal of the transformer secondary is at ground potential. The input voltage to the bridge, V_{sec}, is not referenced to ground. *The oscilloscope cannot be used to view both the secondary voltage and the output voltage at the same time.* Check your circuit carefully before applying power. Compute the expected peak output voltage. Then apply power and *use a voltmeter* to measure $V_{sec(rms)}$. Use the oscilloscope to measure the peak output voltage ($V_{out(p)}$) without a filter capacitor. Record the data in Table 3-3.

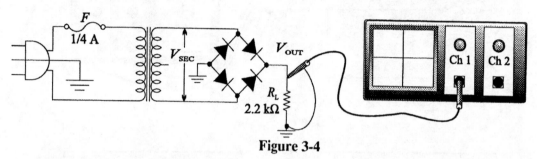

Figure 3-4

Table 3-3 Bridge Rectifier Circuit

Without Filter Capacitor				With Filter Capacitor		
Computed	Measured	Computed	Measured	Measured		
$V_{sec(rms)}$	$V_{sec(rms)}$	$V_{out(p)}$	$V_{out(p)}$	$V_{out(DC)}$	$V_{r(pp)}$	Ripple Frequency
12.6 V ac						

9. Connect the 100 μF capacitor in parallel with the load resistor. Measure $V_{out(DC)}$, the peak-to-peak ripple voltage, and the ripple frequency as before. Record the data in Table 3-3.

10. Simulate an open diode in the bridge by removing one diode from the circuit. What happens to the output voltage? The ripple voltage? The ripple frequency?

Conclusion:

Evaluation and Review Questions:
1. What advantage does a full-wave rectifier circuit have over a half-wave rectifier circuit?

2. Compare a bridge rectifier circuit with a full-wave rectifier circuit. Which has the higher output voltage? Which has the greater current in the diodes?

3. In step 4, you moved the ground reference to the center-tap of the transformer. If you wanted to look at the voltage across the entire secondary, you would need to connect the oscilloscope as shown in Figure 3-5 and *add* the two channels. (Some oscilloscopes do not have this capability.) Why is it necessary to use *two* channels to view the entire secondary voltage?

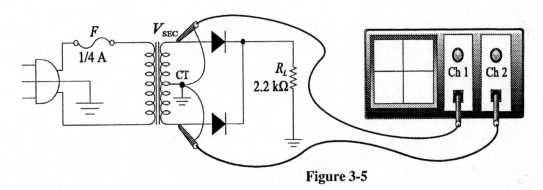

Figure 3-5

4. Explain how you could measure the ripple frequency to determine if a diode were open in a bridge rectifier circuit.

5. (a) What is the maximum dc voltage you could expect to obtain from a transformer with an 18 V rms secondary using a bridge rectifier circuit with a filter capacitor?

   (b) What is the maximum dc voltage you could expect to obtain from the same transformer connected in a full-wave rectifier circuit with a filter capacitor?

For Further Investigation:

The bridge rectifier circuit shown in Figure 3-4 can be readily changed to a +12 V regulated power supply with the addition of a 7812 or 78L12 three-terminal regulator. These three-terminal regulators are easy to use and provide a regulated +12 V output. The 7812 can deliver over 1.0 A of current while the 78L12 can deliver over 100 mA. Add one of the regulators to your bridge rectifier circuit as shown in Figure 3-6. The 100 μF filter capacitor should be connected across the input of the regulator and a 0.01 μF capacitor placed across the ouput as shown. Measure the output ripple from the circuit with the regulator. Compare your results with the unregulated circuit in step 9.

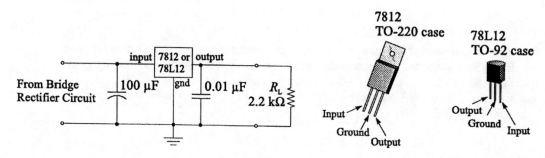

Figure 3-6

Name _____

Date _____

Class _____

Diode Limiting and Clamping Circuits

Objectives:
After performing this experiment, you will be able to:
1. Explain the difference between limiting and clamping circuits.
2. Calculate and measure the voltage limits of both biased and unbiased limiting circuits.
3. Predict and measure the effect of a dc bias voltage on a clamping circuit.

Summary of Theory:
Diodes are frequently used in applications such as waveshaping, mixers, detectors, protection circuits, and switching circuits. In this experiment, you will investigate two widely used applications of diode circuits, diode *limiting* circuits and diode *clamping* circuits. Diode limiting circuits (also called *clipping circuits*) are used to prevent a waveform from exceeding some particular limits, either negative or positive. For example, assume it is desired to remove the portion of sine wave that exceeds +5.0 V. The bias voltage, V_{BIAS}, is set to a voltage 0.7 V less than the desired clipping level. The circuit in Figure 4-1 will limit the waveform because the diode will be forward-biased whenever the signal exceeds +5.0 V. This places V_{BIAS} in parallel with R_L and prevents the input voltage from going above +5.0 V. When the signal is less than +5.0 V, the diode is reverse-biased and appears to be an open circuit. If, instead, it was desired to clip the waveform below some specified level, the diode can be reversed and V_{BIAS} is set to 0.7 V greater than the desired limiting level.

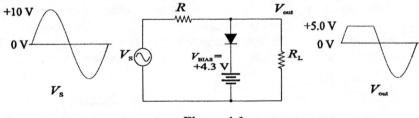

Figure 4-1

Diode clamping circuits are used to shift the dc level of a waveform. If a signal has passed through a capacitor, the dc component is blocked. A clamping circuit can restore the dc level. For this reason these circuits are sometimes called *dc restorers*. Diode clamping action is illustrated in Figure 4-2 for both positive and negative clamping circuits. The diode causes the series capacitor to have a low-resistance charging path and a high-resistance discharge path through R_L. As long as the RC time constant is long compared to the period of the waveform,

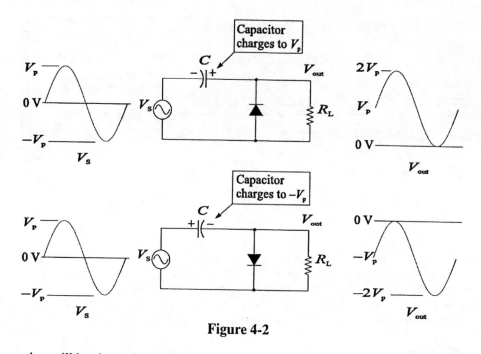

Figure 4-2

the capacitor will be charged to the peak value of the input waveform. This action requires several cycles of the input signal to charge the capacitor. The output load resistor sees the sum of the dc level on the capacitor and the input voltage.

Materials Needed:
Resistors: two 10 kΩ, one 47 kΩ
Two signal diodes: 1N914 (or equivalent)
One 47 μF capacitor
For Further Investigation:
  Three 1.0 kΩ resistors

Procedure:
1. Connect the circuit shown in Figure 4-3. Connect the signal generator to the circuit and set it for a 6.0 V$_{pp}$ sine wave at a frequency of 1.0 kHz with no dc offset. Observe the input and output waveforms on the oscilloscope by connecting it as shown. Notice that R_2 and R_L form a voltage divider, causing the load voltage to be less than the source voltage. R_1 will provide a dc return path in case the signal generator is capacitively coupled.

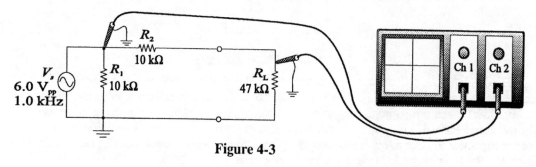

Figure 4-3

2. Add the diode to the circuit as shown in Figure 4-4. Look carefully at the output waveform. Notice the zero volt level. Sketch the input and output waveforms in the space provided. Then measure[1] the waveform across R_2. Sketch the observed waveforms on Plot 4-1.

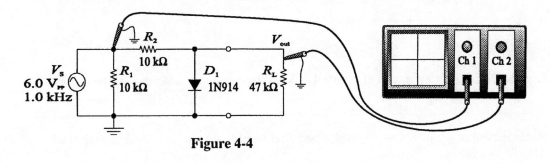

Figure 4-4

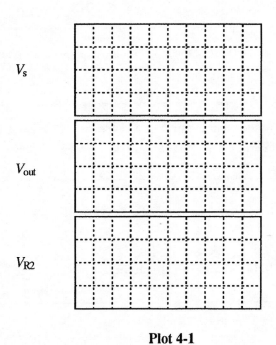

V_s

V_{out}

V_{R2}

Plot 4-1

3. Remove the cathode of the diode from ground and connect it to the power supply as shown in Figure 4-5. Vary the voltage from the supply and describe the results.

---

[1] On the oscilloscope, this is accomplished by placing the probes from each channel on both sides of R_2. The channels are set to the same vertical sensitivity (VOLTS/DIV). For most scopes, you then select the ADD function and INVERT CH-2 . Check with your operator's manual if these functions are not available.

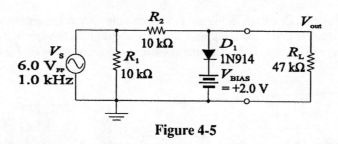

Figure 4-5

4. Reverse the diode in the circuit of Figure 4-5. Vary the dc voltage and describe the results.

_____

5. Replace the positive power supply with a negative supply. Again, vary the dc voltage and describe the results.

_____

6. If you have freeze spray available, test the effect on the clipping level when the diode is cooled. Observations:

_____

7. Connect the clamp circuit shown in Figure 4-6. Couple the oscilloscope with dc coupling and observe the output voltage. Vary the input voltage. Observations:

_____

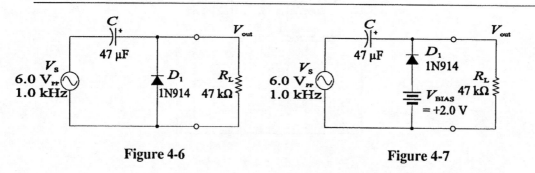

Figure 4-6   **Figure 4-7**

8. Add a dc voltage to the diode by connecting the power supply as shown in Figure 4-7. Sketch the output waveform on Plot 4-2 below. Show the dc level on your sketch:

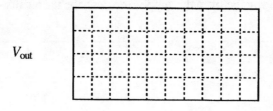

V_{out}

Plot 4-2

9. Find out what happens if the positive dc voltage is replaced with a negative dc source.

Observations:_____

Conclusion:

Evaluation and Review Questions:
1. In step 2, you observed the voltage waveform across the series resistor, R_2. The waveform observed across R_2 could have been predicted by applying Kirchhoff's voltage law to V_s and V_{out}. Explain.

2. For the circuit of Figure 4-6, describe what would happen to the output voltage if the capacitor were shorted.

3. For the circuit of Figure 4-7, what change would you expect in the output if the diode were reversed?

4. Explain the difference between a limiting and a clamping circuit.

5. Sketch the output waveform for the limiting circuit shown in Figure 4-8.

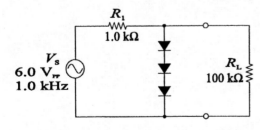

Figure 4-8

For Further Investigation:
Suppose you wanted to set up a limiting circuit that would clip signals above +5.0 V but had only a fixed +10 V supply available. You might try setting up the voltage divider shown in Figure 4-9 to set the limiting level. Build the circuit and drive it with a 20 V_{pp} sinusoidal wave. Can you explain why the output is not flat as in Figure 4-1? Try putting the 47 µF capacitor across R_2. What happens? Why?

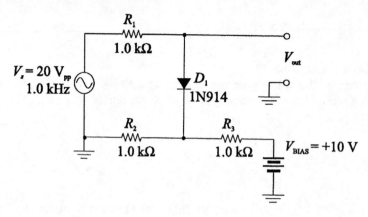

Figure 4-9

Voltage Regulators

Objectives:

After performing this experiment, you will be able to:

1. Construct and test a voltage regulator circuit. From measured voltages, compute the line and load regulation for the circuit.
2. Connect a bridge rectifier and filter to the regulator circuit and measure the input and output ripple voltage.

Summary of Theory:

Virtually all active electronic devices require a stable source of voltage. Most regulated power supplies are designed to provide a constant dc voltage to various loads from a source of alternating current (ac). Good regulation requires that the output voltage be maintained for variation in line voltages, load resistance, or temperature change. The zener regulator studied in Experiment 30 cannot provide sufficient current for most applications; however, it can form the basis of a stable reference voltage for a series regulator. The basic series regulator circuit places the pass transistor in series with the output; hence the term series regulator. The basic circuit was introduced years ago and is still one of the most popular forms of regulators.

For smaller power supplies, three-terminal IC regulators provide a stable output over a wide range of loads (see Experiment 3 – For Further Investigation). These IC regulators are typically within 5% of the nominal voltage – they are available with a limited number of fixed outputs ranging from 5 V to 24 V and can provide up to 1 A output. The 78xx series (positive regulators) and 79xx series (negative regulators) use the last two digits (xx) to represent the output voltage – for example, the 7805 is a +5.0 V regulator. The 7805 regulator can supply 1.0 A with 80 dB of ripple rejection. Integrated circuit regulators can be extended to higher currents by adding external pass transistors. Adjustable regulators allow the power supply to be varied over a wide range of values with a minimum of external components. Adjustable regulators are available with extra features such as adjustable short circuit current limiting. An example of an adjustable IC regulator is the popular LM317, adjustable from 1.2 V to 37 V.

In this experiment, you will test a series regulator constructed from an op-amp, zener reference and a series pass transistor. You will measure the line regulation, load regulation, and ripple voltage. In the For Further Investigation section, a three-terminal regulator used as a current source will be tested.

Materials Needed:
Resistors: four 330 Ω resistors, one 1.0 kΩ, one 1.2 kΩ, one 2.7 kΩ
One 1.0 kΩ potentiometer
Transistors: one 2N3904 *npn* transistor, one SK3024 *npn* power transistor
Diodes: one 1N4733 5 V zener diode, four 1N4001 rectifier diodes
One 1000 μF capacitor

For Further Investigation:
   One 7805 or 78L05 regulator
   One 220 Ω resistor
   One LED
   One 0 – 50 mA ammeter

Procedure:
1. Measure and record the values of the resistors listed in Table 31-1.

Table 31-1

Resistor	Listed Value	Measured Value
R_1	2.7 kΩ	
R_2	330 Ω	
R_3	1.0 kΩ	
R_4*	1.0 kΩ	
R_5	1.2 kΩ	
R_L	330 Ω	

*potentiometer; record maximum resistance

2. Construct the series regulator circuit shown in Figure 31-1. This circuit illustrates the concept of voltage regulation, but it is limited to relatively small power levels unless heat sinking of the pass transistor is provided. (**Caution:** the power dissipated in the pass transistor for this experiment will cause it to become hot, but a heat sink is not required for the loads specified.) Connect the input to a dc power supply set to +18.0 V.

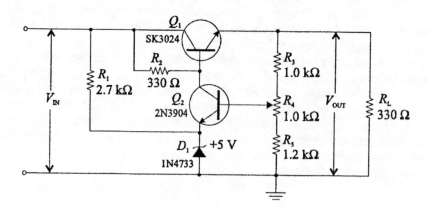

Figure 31-1

186

3. Compute the minimum and maximum output voltage for the regulator. The minimum voltage is found by assuming the $V_{BASE(Q2)}$ is 5.7 V (the zener drop + 0.7 V). This voltage is dropped across R_4 and R_5. Since R_3, R_4, and R_5 are in series, the output can be found by the proportion:

$$\frac{V_{OUT(min)}}{V_{BASE(Q2)}} = \frac{R_3 + R_4 + R_5}{R_4 + R_5}$$

Enter the computed $V_{OUT(min)}$ in Table 31-2. Set up a similar proportion to find $V_{OUT(max)}$. Enter the computed values in Table 31-2.

Table 31-2

Parameter	Computed Value	Measured Value
$V_{OUT(min)}$		
$V_{OUT(max)}$		

4. Maintain the input voltage at +18.0 V. Test the minimum and maximum output voltage by varying R_4 over its range. Enter the measured values in Table 31-2.

5. In this step and step 6, you will measure the variation on the output voltage due to a change in the input voltage and compute the line regulation. With the input voltage at +18 V, adjust R_4 for an output of +10.0 V. (This is shown as the starting value in Table 31-3). Then set the input voltage to each value listed in Table 31-3 and measure the output voltage. (Note that a 4 V variation on the input is more than would be observed in operation).

Table 31-3

V_{IN}	V_{OUT} (measured)
+18.0 V	+10.0 V
+17.0 V	
+16.0 V	
+15.0 V	
+14.0 V	

Table 31-4

Step	Quantity	Measured Value
6	Line regulation	
7	V_{NL}	+10.0 V
	V_{FL}	
	Load regulation	
8	$V_{ripple(in)}$	
	$V_{ripple(out)}$	

6. Compute the line regulation from the data taken in step 5. The line regulation (expressed as percent line regulation per volt) is given by Equation 11-2 in the text and repeated here for convenience:

$$\text{Line Regulation} = \left(\frac{\Delta V_{OUT}/V_{OUT}}{\Delta V_{IN}} \right) 100\%$$

Use the first and last entry of Table 31-3 to compute the line regulation and enter the value in the first row of Table 31-4.

7. The load regulation is found by determining the change in the output voltage between no load and full-load and dividing by the output voltage at full load. It is usually expressed as a percentage. For the purpose of this experiment, we will assume the full-load output current is 90 mA. Remove the 330 Ω load resistor and set the input voltage to +16 V. Adjust the output voltage to +10.0 V (V_{NL}). Then install three parallel 330 Ω resistors across the output and measure the output load voltage (V_{FL}). Compute the load regulation from the equation:

$$\text{Load Regulation} = \left(\frac{V_{NL} - V_{FL}}{V_{FL}} \right) 100\%$$

Enter the measured full-load voltage and the computed load regulation in Table 31-4.

8. In this step, you will determine ripple at the input and output of the regulator. Disconnect the power supply that you have been using as an input device and add the bridge rectifier circuit shown in Figure 31-2. (The bridge rectifier is the same circuit you studied in Experiment 3 plus a filter capacitor). The load consists of the three 330 Ω resistors in parallel from step 7. Measure the peak-to-peak ripple voltage across C_1 ($V_{ripple(in)}$) and across the output load ($V_{ripple(out)}$). Couple your oscilloscope with ac coupling to view the ripple. Record the results in Table 31-4.

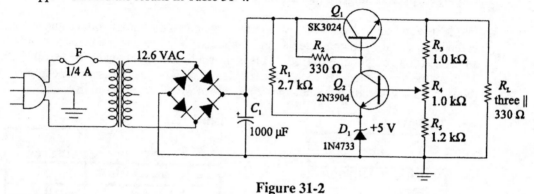

Figure 31-2

Conclusion:

Evaluation and Review Questions:

1. Assume the regulator in Figure 31-1 is designed for a maximum load current of 90 mA at 10 V and the ß of Q_1 is 100. If the input voltage is +18 V,
   (a) What is the power dissipated in the series pass transistor?

   (b) What is the base current in the series pass transistor?

   (c) What is the collector current in Q_2?

2. Assume a student wanted to supply more current than the rated 1 A for the series pass transistor by placing a second identical pass transistor in parallel with the first.
   (a) What problem does this create?

   (b) Why isn't it a problem if MOSFET transistors were used?

3. What change would you suggest to the circuit in Figure 31-2 if you needed to reduce the ripple?

4. The major drawback to a series regulated supply is inefficiency. The efficiency is defined as the percentage of input power that can be delivered to the load. For the circuit in Figure 31-2, assume the input power is 2.01 W (17.5 V at 115 mA). With the output set to 10 V and a 110 Ω load resistance, compute the efficiency of the regulator.

5. Figure 31-3 shows the series regulator from this experiment with the addition of current limiting (Q_3 and R_6). Assume you wanted to set the current limit to 200 mA. Select a value for R_6 that will produce this limit. Show how you obtained the value selected.

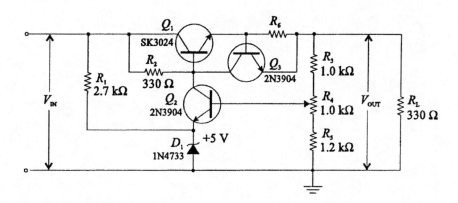

Figure 31-3

189

For Further Investigation:

A three-terminal regulator can be used for a current source by "programming" a current as shown in the circuit in Figure 31-4. Use either a 7805 or 78L05 regulator. The current that is programmed is limited only by the current and power rating of the regulator. Test the circuit by varying the input voltage between +8 V and +18 V and observe the current in the LED. Measure the output current as a function of the input voltage. What current is "programmed" in this circuit? How can you change this current?

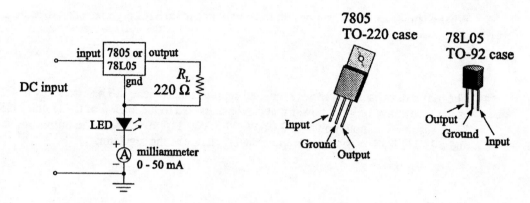

Figure 31-4

The Zener Regulator

Objectives:
After performing this experiment, you will be able to:
1. Use an oscilloscope to plot the characteristic curve of a zener diode.
2. Test a zener regulator circuit for the effect of a changing source and a changing load.
3. From measurements, compute the line and load regulation of a zener regulator circuit.

Summary of Theory:
When a sufficiently large reverse bias voltage is applied to a zener diode, the reverse current will suddenly increase, as illustrated in the characteristic curve in Figure 30-1. This sudden increase happens at a voltage called the zener voltage, V_Z. A zener diode is a special diode designed to operate in this breakdown region. The schematic symbol for a zener diode is shown in Figure 30-2.

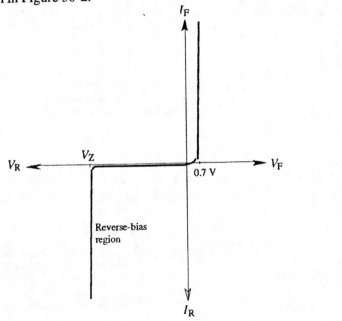

Figure 30-1 Zener characteristic.   **Figure 30-2** Zener symbol.

The zener voltage is a precise voltage that varies according to the type of zener; typically it is a few volts but can be as much as several hundred volts. Although zeners are temperature sensitive, devices have been designed that can compensate for this sensitivity. Zeners are used in applications that require a constant voltage such as voltage regulators and in certain meters where they are used as a reference voltage for comparison. Ideally, the zener breakdown characteristic is a straight vertical line, but in practice, a small ac resistance is present, similar to the ac resistance in the forward-biased diode of Experiment 2. The ac resistance is found by dividing a *change* in voltage by a *change* in current measured in the vertical breakdown region. The ac resistance is typically from 10 Ω to 100 Ω.

In this experiment, you will measure a zener diode's *I-V* characteristic, then use the zener in two regulator circuits. In the first circuit, you will test the effect of a varying voltage and in the second circuit, you will test the effect of a varying load.

Materials Needed:
Resistors: one 220 Ω (1/2 W), one 1.0 kΩ, one 2.2 kΩ
One 1.0 kΩ potentiometer
One center-tapped transformer with fused primary, 12.6 V ac
One 5 V zener, (1N4733 or equivalent)
For Further Investigation:
        Second 5 V zener, (1N4733 or equivalent)

Procedure:
1. Measure and record the values of the resistors listed in Table 30-1.

Table 30-1

Resistor	Listed Value	Measured Value
R_1	220 Ω	
R_2	1.0 kΩ	
R_L	2.2 kΩ	

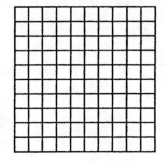

Plot 30-1

2. Observe the zener characteristic curve by setting up the circuit shown in Figure 30-3. Put scope in the X-Y mode. Sketch the *I-V* curve in Plot 30-1. The 1.0 kΩ resistor changes the scope's y-axis into a current axis (1 mA per volt). Label your plot for current and voltage.

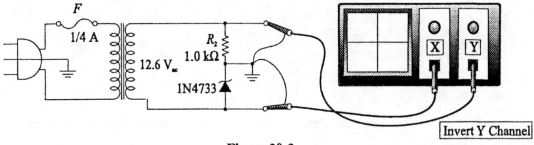

Figure 30-3

192

3. A common application of zener diodes is in regulators. In this step, you will investigate a zener regulator as the source voltage is varied. Connect the circuit shown in Figure 30-4. Set V_s to each voltage listed in Table 30-2 and measure the output (load) voltage, V_{OUT}.

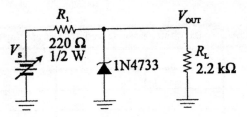

Figure 30-4

Table 30-2

V_s	V_{OUT} (measured)	I_L (computed)	V_{R1} (computed)	I_s (computed)	I_z (computed)
2.0 V					
4.0 V					
6.0 V					
8.0 V					
10.0 V					

4. From the measurements in step 3, complete Table 30-2. Apply Ohm's law to compute the load current, I_L, for each setting of the source voltage. The voltage across R_1 (V_{R1}) can be found by applying Kirchhoff's Voltage Law (KVL) to the outside loop. It is the difference between the source voltage, V_S, and the output voltage, V_{OUT}. Note that I_s is through R_1 and can be found using Ohm's law. Find the zener current, I_Z, by applying Kirchhoff's Current Law (KCL) to the junction at the top of the zener diode.
   What happens to the zener current after the breakdown voltage is reached?

---

5. In this step, you will test the effect of a zener regulator working with a fixed source voltage with a variable load resistance. Often, the load is an active circuit (such as a logic circuit) in which the current changes because of varying conditions. We will simulate this behavior with a potentiometer. Construct the circuit shown in Figure 30-5. Set the power supply to a fixed +12.0 V output and adjust the potentiometer (R_L) for maximum resistance.

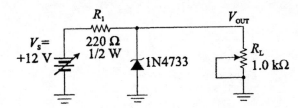

Figure 30-5

6. With the potentiometer set to 1.0 kΩ (maximum), measure the load voltage (V_{OUT}) and record the voltage in Table 30-3. Compute the other parameters listed on the first row as before. (Use Ohm's law for I_L, KVL for V_{R1}, Ohm's law for I_S, and KCL for I_Z).

Table 30-3

R_L	V_{OUT} (measured)	I_L (computed)	V_{R1} (computed)	I_S (computed)	I_Z (computed)
1.0 kΩ					
750 Ω					
500 Ω					
250 Ω					
100 Ω					

7. Set the potentiometer to each value listed in Table 30-3 and repeat step 6.

8. From the data in Table 30-3, plot the output voltage as a function of load resistance in Plot 30-2. Choose a reasonable scale factor for each axis and add labels to the plot.

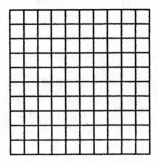

Plot 30-2

From your results, what is the smallest load resistor that can be used and still maintain regulation?

_____

Conclusion:

Evaluation and Review Questions:

1. Observe the characteristic curve for a zener in Plot 30-1.
   (a) What portion of the curve is approximated by an open circuit?

   (b) What portion of the curve is approximated by a short circuit?

2. From the data in Table 30-2, compute the ac resistance of the zener when the source voltage changed from 8.0 V to 10.0 V.

3. Line regulation of a zener regulator is normally expressed as a percentage and is given by the equation:

$$\text{Line regulation} = \frac{\Delta V_{OUT}}{\Delta V_{IN}} \times 100\%$$

Compute the line regulation expressed as a percentage for the circuit in Figure 30-4 using the data for the *last* two rows of Table 30-2. (Note that V_{IN} in the equation is equivalent to V_s in the table.)

4. Load regulation of a zener regulator, expressed as a percentage, is given by the equation:

$$\text{Load regulation} = \frac{V_{NL} - V_{FL}}{V_{FL}} \times 100\%$$

Compute the load regulation for the circuit in Figure 30-5. (Assume V_{OUT} for the 1.0 kΩ resistor $= V_{NL}$ and V_{OUT} for the 100 Ω resistor represents V_{FL}).

5. Assume the potentiometer in Figure 30-5 is set to its maximum value (1.0 kΩ). Predict the output voltage for each of the following faults.

Fault	V_{OUT}
1. Zener diode is open	
2. V_s is +15 V	
3. Zener is reversed	
4. R_1 is 2.2 kΩ	
5. R_L is open	

For Further Investigation:
Modify the regulator circuit tested in this experiment by adding a second zener diode as shown in Figure 30-6 and changing the source to a 15 V_{pp} sine wave at 1.0 kHz. Verify that the source has no dc offset. Set the potentiometer to its maximum resistance. Sketch the output waveform and label voltage and time on your sketch.

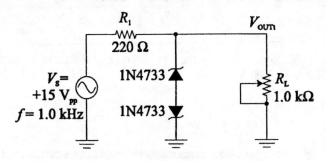

Figure 30-6

Bipolar Junction Transistor Characteristics

Objectives:

After performing this experiment, you will be able to:

1. Measure and graph the collector characteristic curves for a bipolar junction transistor.
2. Use the characteristic curves to determine the β_{DC} of the transistor at a given point.

Summary of Theory:

A bipolar junction transistor (BJT) is a three-terminal device capable of amplifying an ac signal. The three terminals are called the base, emitter, and the collector. BJTs consist of a very thin base material sandwiched in between two of the opposite type materials. They are available in two forms, either *npn* or *pnp*. The middle letter indicates the type of material used for the base, while the outer letters indicate the emitter and collector material. The sandwiched materials produce two *pn* junctions. These two junctions form two diodes – the emitter-base diode and the base-collector diode.

BJTs are current amplifiers. A small base current is amplified to a larger current in the collector-emitter circuit. An important characteristic is the dc current gain, which is the ratio of collector current to base current. This is called the dc beta (β_{DC}) of the transistor. Another useful characteristic is the dc alpha. The dc alpha is the ratio of the collector current to the emitter current and is always less than 1.

For a transistor to amplify, power is required from dc sources. The dc voltages required for proper operation are referred to as bias voltages. The purpose of bias is to establish and maintain the required operating conditions despite variations between transistors or changes in circuit parameters. For normal operation, the base-emitter junction is forward-biased and the base-collector junction is reverse-biased. Since the base-emitter junction is forward-biased, it has characteristics of a forward-biased diode. A silicon bipolar transistor requires approximately 0.7 V of voltage across the base-emitter junction to cause base current.

Materials Needed:

Resistors: One 100 Ω resistor, one 33 kΩ resistor
One 2N3904 *npn* transistor (or equivalent)

For Further Investigation:
Option 1: Transistor curve tracer
Option 2: One rectifier diode (1N4001 or equivalent)
One small power transformer with a 12.6 V ac output

Procedure:

1. Measure and record the resistance of the resistors listed in Table 6-1.

Table 6-1

Resistor	Listed Value	Measured Value
R_1	33 kΩ	
R_2	100 Ω	

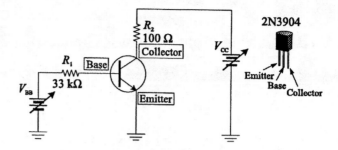

Figure 6-1

2. Connect the common-emitter configuration illustrated in Figure 6-1. Start with both power supplies set to 0 V. The purpose of R_1 is to limit base current to a safe level and to allow indirect determination of the base current. Slowly increase V_{BB} until V_{R1} is 1.65 V. This sets up a base current of 50 μA which can be shown by applying Ohm's law to R_1.

3. Without disturbing the setting of V_{BB}, slowly increase V_{CC} until +2.0 V is measured between the transistor's collector and emitter. This voltage is V_{CE}. Measure and record V_{R2} for this setting. Record V_{R2} in Table 6-2 in the column labeled <u>Base Current = 50 μA</u>.

Table 6-2

V_{CE} (measured)	Base Current = 50 μA		Base Current = 100 μA		Base Current = 150 μA	
	V_{R2} (measured)	I_C (computed)	V_{R2} (measured)	I_C (computed)	V_{R2} (measured)	I_C (computed)
2.0 V						
4.0 V						
6.0 V						
8.0 V						

4. Compute the collector current, I_C, by applying Ohm's law to R_2. Use the measured voltage, V_{R2}, and the measured resistance, R_2, to determine the current. Note that the current in R_2 is the same as I_C for the transistor. Enter the computed collector current in Table 6-2 in the column labeled <u>Base Current = 50 μA</u>.

5. Without disturbing the setting of V_{BB}, increase V_{CC} until 4.0 V is measured across the transistor's collector to emitter. Measure and record V_{R2} for this setting. Compute the collector current by applying Ohm's law as in step 4. Continue in this manner for each of the values of V_{CE} listed in Table 6-2.

6. Reset V_{CC} for 0 V and adjust V_{BB} until V_{R1} is 3.3 V. The base current is now 100 μA.

7. Without disturbing the setting of V_{BB}, slowly increase V_{CC} until V_{CE} is 2.0 V. Measure and record V_{R2} for this setting in Table 6-2 in the column labeled <u>Base Current = 100 μA</u>. Compute I_C for this setting by applying Ohm's law to R_2. Enter the computed collector current in Table 6-2.

8. Increase V_{CC} until V_{CE} is equal to 4.0 V. Measure and record V_{R2} for this setting. Compute I_C as before. Continue in this manner for each value of V_{CC} listed in Table 6-2.

9. Reset V_{CC} for 0 V and adjust V_{BB} until V_{R1} is 4.95 V. The base current is now 150 μA.

10. Complete Table 6-2 by repeating steps 7 and 8 for 150 μA of base current.

11. Plot three collector characteristic curves using the data tabulated in Table 6-2. The collector characteristic curve is a graph of V_{CE} versus I_C for a constant base current. Choose a scale for I_C that allows the largest current observed to fit on the graph. Label each curve with the base current it represents. Graph the data on Plot 6-1 below.

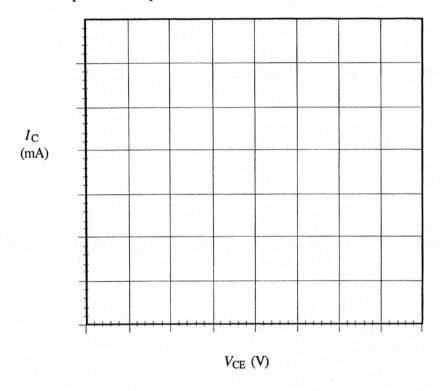

I_C
(mA)

V_{CE} (V)

Plot 6-1

12. Use the characteristic curve you plotted to determine the $β_{DC}$ for the transistor at a V_{CE} of 3.0 V and a base current of 50 μA, 100 μA, and 150 μA. Then repeat the procedure for a $β_{DC}$ at a V_{CE} of 5.0 V. Tabulate your results in Table 6-3.

Table 6-3

	Current Gain, $β_{DC}$		
V_{CE}	$I_B = 50$ μA	$I_B = 100$ μA	$I_B = 150$ μA
3.0 V			
5.0 V			

Conclusion:

Evaluation and Review Questions:

1. Does the experimental data indicate that β_{DC} is a constant at all points? Does this have any effect on the linearity of the transistor?

2. What effect would a higher β_{DC} have on the characteristic curves you measured?

3. What is the maximum power dissipated in the transistor for the data taken in the experiment?

4. (a) The dc alpha of a bipolar transistor is the collector current, I_C, divided by the emitter current, I_E. Using this definition and $I_E = I_C + I_B$, show that dc alpha can be written as:

$$\alpha_{DC} = \frac{\beta_{DC}}{\beta_{DC} + 1}$$

(b) Compute dc alpha for your transistor at $V_{CE} = 4.0$ V and $I_B = 100$ μA.

5. What value of V_{CE} would you expect if the base terminal of a transistor were open? Explain your answer.

For Further Investigation:

Option 1:

If you have a transistor curve tracer available, you can use it to check the data taken in this experiment. A transistor curve tracer has a step generator that generates a staircase set of current or voltage steps. Set the step generator to 50 μA per step. Select positive steps to apply to the base with the emitter grounded. Select a positive sweep voltage of approximately +20 V with a series limiting resistance of several hundred ohms. Select a horizontal display of 1 V/div and a vertical display of about 10 mA/div. (If your transistor has a very high or low β_{DC}, you may need to change these settings.) The curve tracer will show the collector characteristic curves. Test the effect of heating or cooling the transistor on the β_{DC}.

Option 2:

If you do not have a transistor curve tracer available, you can still observe the collector curves, one at a time, on an oscilloscope. The circuit is a modification of the one used in the experiment and is shown in Figure 6-2. The collector supply is replaced with a low voltage transformer and diode. Start with V_{BB} set to 1.65 V as before (I_B = 50 μA).

Put the oscilloscope in X-Y mode and put both channels to the GND (ground) position. Keep the intensity low and position the dot in the lower left corner of the screen. Adjust the oscilloscope Y channel to 0.1 V/div (equivalent to 1.0 mA/div) and the X channel to 1 V/div and invert the Y channel.[1] Couple the signal to the scope and raise the intensity; you should see the first collector curve that you measured in the experiment. You can adjust V_{BB} to observe the other curves.

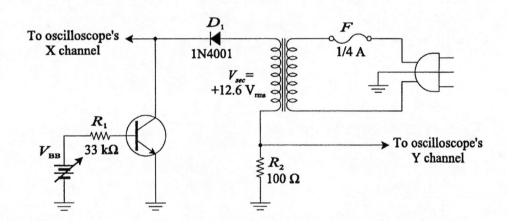

Figure 6-2

---

[1] If you cannot invert the Y channel, position the trace at the top of the screen. Increasing current will be toward the bottom of the screen.

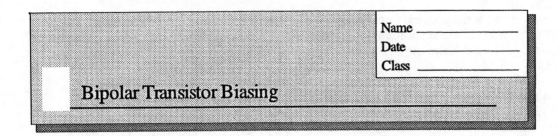

Bipolar Transistor Biasing

Name _____

Date _____

Class _____

Objectives:
After performing this experiment, you will be able to:
1. Construct and analyze three types of transistor bias circuits: base bias, voltage-divider bias, and collector-feedback bias. Compare the stability of the bias with different transistors.
2. Select appropriate bias resistors for each type of bias.
3. *For Further Investigation:* Construct and analyze an emitter-bias circuit.

Summary of Theory:
For a transistor to amplify signals, it is necessary to forward-bias the base-emitter junction and to reverse-bias the base-collector junction. The purpose of bias is to provide dc voltages to set up the proper quiescent (no signal) conditions for circuit operation.

There are four common bias circuits for bipolar transistors. You should be familiar with the advantages and disadvantages of each. The four circuits are: (1) base bias, (2) emitter bias, (3) voltage-divider bias, and (4) collector-feedback bias. These basic bias circuits are illustrated in Figure 7-1 for *npn* transistors. These bias methods apply to *pnp* transistors by reversing voltage polarities. The key for either type of transistor is that the base-emitter junction is forward-biased and the base-collector junction is reverse-biased.

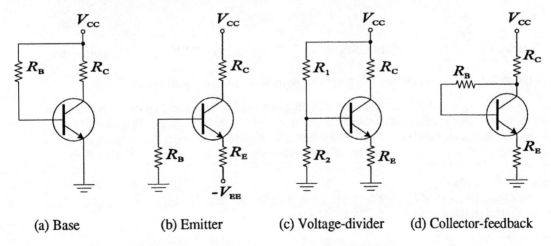

(a) Base   (b) Emitter   (c) Voltage-divider   (d) Collector-feedback

Figure 7-1 Types of bias for bipolar transistors.

Base bias is the simplest form because it uses a single power supply and resistor. It is satisfactory for switching applications but is generally unsatisfactory for linear circuits due to ß dependency. Normal variations in transistors greatly affect the operating point of base-biased circuits.

Emitter bias overcomes the difficulty of ß dependency, but requires a positive and a negative power supply. The dc conditions can be found by writing Kirchhoff's Voltage Law (KVL) around the base-emitter circuit and solving for the emitter current. The emitter current is approximately equal to the collector current, and voltages can be found by applying Ohm's law. Emitter bias is discussed on page 143 of the text.

Voltage-divider bias is widely used because it is stable yet requires only one power supply. When the divider current is much larger than the base current, the small base current can be ignored, simplifying the analysis. This is called "stiff" bias. The steps to solve for the dc parameters for the CE amplifier with stiff voltage-divider bias are given as follows:

1. Mentally remove the capacitors from the circuit since they appear open to dc. For this circuit, this causes the load resistor, R_L, to be removed (see Figure 7-2(a)).
2. Solve for the base voltage, V_B, by applying the voltage-divider rule to R_1 and R_2 as illustrated in Figure 7-2(b).
3. Subtract the 0.7 V forward-bias drop across the base-emitter diode from V_B to obtain the emitter voltage, V_E, as illustrated in Figure 7-2(c).
4. The dc current in the emitter circuit is found by applying Ohm's law to R_E. The emitter current, I_E, is approximately equal to the collector current, I_C. The transistor appears to be a current source of approximately I_E into the collector circuit as shown in Figure 7-2(d).

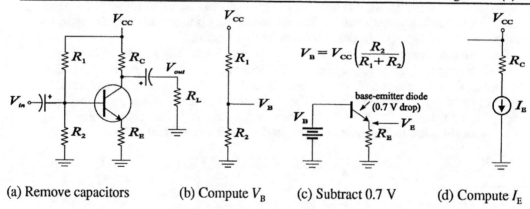

(a) Remove capacitors   (b) Compute V_B (c) Subtract 0.7 V   (d) Compute I_E

Figure 7-2 Steps in solving a CE amplifier with stiff voltage-divider bias.

Collector-feedback bias uses a form of negative feedback to stabilize the Q-point. The analysis of collector-feedback bias can be done by writing KVL through the base circuit and finding the emitter (or collector) current. Note that for this form of biasing, the *collector* resistor actually has the *emitter* current! The derivation is given in step 8 of the Procedure.

Materials Needed:
Resistors (one of each): 470 Ω, 2.0 kΩ, 6.8 kΩ, 33 kΩ, 360 kΩ, 1.0 MΩ
Three small signal *npn* transistors, (2N3904 or equivalent)

For Further Investigation:
Resistors: one 3.6 kΩ, one 100 kΩ

Procedure:

1. Measure and record the values of the resistors listed in Table 7-1.

Table 7-1

Resistor	Listed Value	Measured Value
R_B	1.0 MΩ	
R_C	2.0 kΩ	

2. You will test each of the three transistors, one at a time, in a base bias circuit. The manufacturer's specification sheet for a 2N3904 transistor indicates that $ß_{DC}$ can range from 100 to 400. Assuming the $ß_{DC}$ is 200, compute the parameters listed in Table 7-2 for the base bias circuit shown in Figure 7-3. Start by computing the voltage across the base resistor, V_{RB}, and the current in this resistor, I_B. Using $ß_{DC}$ find the collector current, I_C, the voltage across the collector resistor, V_{RC}, and the voltage from collector to ground, V_C.

Table 7-2

DC Parameter	Computed Value	Measured Value		
		Q_1	Q_2	Q_3
V_{RB}				
I_B				
I_C				
V_{RC}				
V_C				

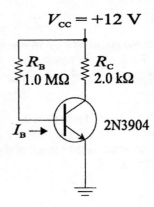

$V_{cc} = +12$ V

R_B 1.0 MΩ R_C 2.0 kΩ

$I_B \rightarrow$ 2N3904

Figure 7-3

3. Label each of three *npn* transistors as Q_1, Q_2, and Q_3. Construct the circuit shown in Figure 7-3 using Q_1. Measure the voltages listed in Table 7-2 for Q_1. Then remove Q_1 from the circuit and test the other two transistors in the same circuit. Record all measurements in Table 7-2.

4. Test voltage-divider bias for the same three transistors. Start by measuring and recording the values of the resistors listed in Table 7-3.

Table 7-3

Resistor	Listed Value	Measured Value
R_1	33 kΩ	
R_2	6.8 kΩ	
R_E	470 Ω	
R_C	2.0 kΩ	

5. Compute the parameters listed in Table 7-4 for the circuit shown in Figure 7-4. The method is outlined in the box shown in the Summary of Theory. Note that the bias is relatively "stiff" so the approximations given in the Summary of Theory are reasonable.

Table 7-4

DC Parameter	Computed Value	Measured Value Q_1	Q_2	Q_3
V_B				
V_E				
$I_E \approx I_C$				
V_{RC}				
V_C				

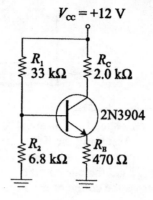

$V_{CC} = +12$ V

R_1 33 kΩ R_C 2.0 kΩ

2N3904

R_2 6.8 kΩ R_B 470 Ω

Figure 7-4

6. Construct the circuit shown in Figure 7-4 using transistor Q_1. Measure the voltages listed in Table 7-4 for Q_1. Then remove Q_1 from the circuit and test the other two transistors in the same circuit. Record all measurements in Table 7-4.

7. In this step, you will compare the same three transistors in a collector-feedback circuit. Measure and record the values of the resistors listed in Table 7-5.

Table 7-5

Resistor	Listed Value	Measured Value
R_B	360 kΩ	
R_C	2.0 kΩ	

8. Compute the parameters listed in Table 7-6 for the circuit shown in Figure 7-5. To find the approximate collector and emitter currents, you can write Kirchhoff's voltage law around the base path as follows:

$$-V_{CC} + I_E R_C + I_B R_B + V_{BE} = 0$$

Substituting for I_B, $I_B \cong \dfrac{I_E}{\beta_{DC}}$

And solving for I_E, we obtain: $I_E \cong I_C = \dfrac{V_{CC} - V_{BE}}{R_C + \dfrac{R_B}{\beta_{DC}}}$

Assume the β_{DC} is 200 for the calculation. Then find the voltage across the collector resistor, V_{RC}, and the collector voltage, V_C.

9. Construct the circuit shown in Figure 7-5 using transistor Q_1. Measure the voltages listed in Table 7-6 for Q_1. Then remove Q_1 from the circuit and test the other two transistors in the same circuit. Record all measurements in Table 7-6.

Table 7-6

DC Parameter	Computed Value	Measured Value Q₁	Q₂	Q₃
I_C				
V_{RC}				
V_C				

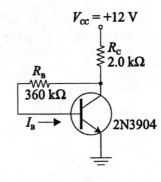

$V_{CC} = +12$ V

R_C
2.0 kΩ

R_B
360 kΩ

$I_B \rightarrow$ 2N3904

Figure 7-5

Conclusion:

Evaluation and Review Questions:

1. Compare your observations of the three bias methods tested in the experiment. Which showed the *least* variation between the transistors?

2. Draw each of the three bias circuits tested in the experiment for the case of a *pnp* transistor. Assuming the same resistors as used in the experiment, compute the base, emitter and collector voltages. Show these voltages on your drawing.

   (a) base bias   (b) voltage-divider bias   (c) collector-feedback bias

3. Assume you need to bias the amplifier shown in Figure 7-6. It is desired to have the Q-point set to approximately 20 mA of collector current. Choose bias resistors for voltage-divider bias that will provide reasonably stiff bias. Show your work.

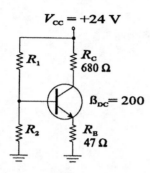

Figure 7-6

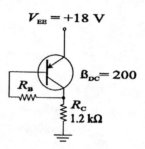

Figure 7-7

4. Assume you need to bias the amplifier shown in Figure 7-7. It is desired to have the Q-point set to approximately 5.0 mA of collector current. Choose a base resistor for collector-feedback bias that will provide reasonably stiff bias. Show your work.

5. For the circuit in Figure 7-6, predict the effect of each of the following problems on the collector voltage:

(a) R_1 opens

(b) Base is shorted to ground through a solder bridge

(c) R_E is 470 Ω instead of 47 Ω

(d) V_{CC} drops to +15 V

For Further Investigation:
As discussed in the Summary of Theory, emitter bias is an excellent way of obtaining stable bias, however, it requires both a positive and negative power supply. Figure 7-8 shows a transistor with emitter bias. Compute the dc parameters for the circuit, then build and test it. Compare the measured dc parameters for each of the three transistors you used in this experiment. Summarize your findings in a short report.

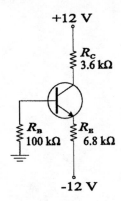

Figure 7-8

The Common-Emitter Amplifier

Objectives:

After performing this experiment, you will be able to:

1. Compute the dc and ac parameters for a common-emitter (CE) amplifier.
2. Build a CE amplifier circuit and measure the dc parameters, the ac input resistance, and the voltage gain. Observe the phase relationship between the input and output signals.
3. Predict and test the effects of certain faults in a CE amplifier.

Summary of Theory:

In a common-emitter (CE) amplifier, the input signal is applied between the base and emitter and output signal is developed between the collector and emitter. The transistor's *emitter* is common to both the input and output circuits, hence, the term *common emitter*. A CE amplifier is illustrated in Figure 8-1(a). This is the basic circuit that will be tested in this experiment. It will be used again in the Further Investigation of Experiment 9 to drive a common-collector (CC) amplifier.

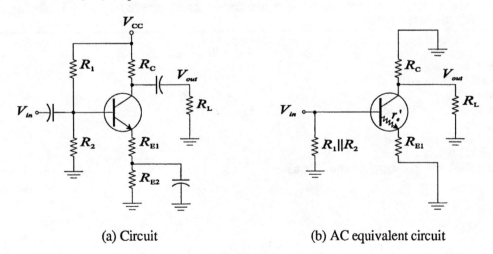

(a) Circuit   (b) AC equivalent circuit

Figure 8-1

To amplify ac signals, the base-emitter junction must be forward-biased and the base-collector junction must be reverse-biased. The bias establishes and maintains the proper dc operating conditions for the transistor. The dc parameters are analyzed first as described in Experiment 7 and the text.

After analyzing the dc conditions, the ac parameters for the amplifier can be evaluated. The equivalent ac circuit is drawn in Figure 8-1(b). The capacitors appear to be an ac short. Thus, the ac equivalent circuit does not contain R_{E2} in this example. Using the superposition theorem, V_{CC} is replaced with a short, placing it at ac ground. The analysis steps are:

---

1. Replace all capacitors with a short and place V_{CC} at ac ground. Compute the ac resistance of the emitter, r_e', from the equation:

$$r_e' = \frac{25 \text{ mV}}{I_E}$$

2. Compute the amplifier's voltage gain. Voltage gain is the ratio of the output voltage divided by the input voltage. The input voltage is across the ac emitter resistance to ground which, in this example, is $r_e' + R_{E1}$. The output voltage is taken across the ac resistance from collector to ground. Looking from the transistor's collector, R_L appears to be in parallel with R_C. Also, I_c is approximately equal to I_e. For the circuit in Figure 8-1(b), the output voltage divided by the input voltage can be written:

$$A_v = \frac{V_{out}}{V_{in}} = \frac{I_c \left(R_C \parallel R_L \right)}{I_e \left(r_e' + R_{E1} \right)} \cong \frac{\left(R_C \parallel R_L \right)}{\left(r_e' + R_{E1} \right)}$$

3. Compute the total input resistance seen by the ac signal:

$$R_{in(tot)} = R_1 \parallel R_2 \parallel \beta_{ac}(r_e' + R_{E1})$$

Notice that the ac resistance of the emitter circuit is multiplied by β_{ac} when it is brought into the base circuit.

Materials Needed:

Resistors:
   one 100 Ω, one 330 Ω, two 1.0 kΩ, one 4.7 kΩ, two 10 kΩ

Capacitors:
   two 1.0 μF, one 47 μF

One 10 kΩ potentiometer

One 2N3904 *npn* transistor (or equivalent)

Procedure:

1. Measure and record the resistance of the resistors listed in Table 8-1.

Table 8-1

Resistor	Listed Value	Measured Value
R_1	10 kΩ	
R_2	4.7 kΩ	
R_{E1}	100 Ω	
R_{E2}	330 Ω	
R_C	1.0 kΩ	
R_L	10 kΩ	

Table 8-2

DC Parameter	Computed Value	Measured Value
V_B		
V_E		
I_E		
V_C		
V_{CE}		

2. Compute the dc parameters listed in Table 8-2 for the CE amplifier shown in Figure 8-2. (Review Experiment 7 for the method.) Note that V_B, V_E, and V_C are with respect to circuit ground. Use the sum of R_{E1} and R_{E2} times I_E to compute the dc emitter voltage, V_E. Compute V_C by subtracting V_{RC} from V_{CC}. Enter your computed values in Table 8-2.

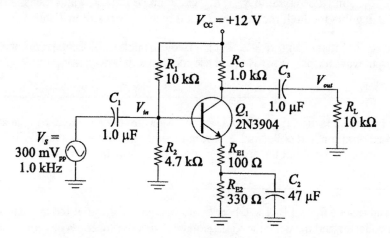

Figure 8-2

3. Construct the amplifier shown in Figure 8-2. The signal generator should be turned off. Measure and record the dc voltages listed in Table 8-2.

4. Compute the ac parameters listed in Table 8-3. The input signal, V_{in}, is set for 300 mV$_{PP}$. This is both V_{in} and the ac base voltage, V_b. Multiply V_{in} by the computed voltage gain to calculate the ac voltage at the collector; this is both V_c and V_{out}. If you do not know the β_{ac} for the input resistance calculation, assume a value of 100.

5. Turn on the signal generator and set V_{in} for 300 mV$_{PP}$ at 1.0 kHz with the generator connected to the circuit. Use the oscilloscope to set the proper voltage and check the frequency. Measure the ac signal voltage at the transistor's emitter and at the collector. Note that the signal at the emitter is less than the base (why?). Use V_{in} and the ac collector voltage (V_{out}) to determine the measured voltage gain, A_v. The measurement of $R_{in(tot)}$ is explained in step 6. Record the ac measurements in Table 8-3.

Table 8-3

AC Parameter	Computed Value	Measured Value
$V_{in} = V_b$	300 mV$_{pp}$	
V_e		
r_e'		
A_v		
$V_{out} = V_c$		
$R_{in\,(tot)}$		

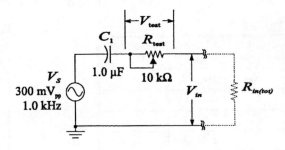

Figure 8-3 Indirect measurement of $R_{in\,(tot)}$.

6. The measurement of $R_{in\,(tot)}$ is done indirectly since it is an ac resistance that cannot be measured with an ohmmeter. The output signal (V_{out}) is measured with an oscilloscope and recorded with the amplifier operating normally (no clipping or distortion). A rheostat (R_{test}) is then inserted in series with the source as shown in Figure 8-3. The rheostat is varied until V_{out} drops to one-half the value prior to inserting R_{test}. With this condition, $V_{in} = V_{test}$ and $R_{in\,(tot)}$ must be equal to R_{test}. R_{test} can then be removed and measured with an ohmmeter. Using this method, measure $R_{in\,(tot)}$ and record the result in Table 8-3.

7. Restore the circuit to that of Figure 8-2. With a two-channel oscilloscope, compare the input and output waveforms. What is the phase relationship between V_{in} and V_{out}?

_____

8. Remove the bypass capacitor, C_2, from the circuit. Measure the ac signal voltage at the transistor's base, emitter, and collector. Measure the voltage gain of the amplifier. What conclusion can you make about the amplifier's performance with C_2 open?

_____

9. Replace C_2 and reduce R_L to 1.0 kΩ. Observe the ac signal voltage at the transistor's base, emitter, and collector and measure the voltage gain of the amplifier. What conclusion can you make about the amplifier's performance with R_L reduced to 1.0 kΩ?

_____

10. Replace R_L with the original 10 kΩ resistor and open R_{E1}. Measure the dc voltages at the base, emitter, and collector. Is the transistor in cutoff or in saturation? Explain.

_____

11. Replace R_{E1} and open R_2. Measure the dc voltages at the base, emitter and collector. Is the transistor in cutoff or saturation? Explain.

_____

Note: The amplifier from this experiment is used again in the For Further Investigation section of Experiment 9. You may want to save the circuit from this experiment.

Conclusion:

Evaluation and Review Questions:

1. When the bypass capacitor, C_2, is open, you found that the gain is affected. Explain.

2. In step 6, you were instructed to measure the input resistance while monitoring the output voltage. Why is this procedure better than monitoring the base voltage?

3. Assume the amplifier shown in Figure 8-2 has +1.8 V dc measured on the base, 1.1 V dc measured on the emitter, and +1.1 V dc measured on the collector.

   (a) Is this normal?

   (b) If not, what is the most likely cause of the problem?

4. If C_2 were shorted,

   (a) what dc base voltage would you expect? _____

   (b) what dc collector voltage would you expect? _____

5. Explain a simple test to determine if a transistor is in saturation or in cutoff.

For Further Investigation:
The low frequency response of the CE amplifier in this experiment is determined by the coupling and bypass capacitors, C_3 and C_2, respectively. The upper frequency response is determined by the unseen interelectrode and stray circuit capacitances. Using the oscilloscope to view the output waveform, set the generator for a midband frequency of 1.0 kHz. Use a sine wave with a convenient level (not clipped) across the load resistor. Raise the generator frequency until the output voltage falls to 70.7% of the midband level. This is the upper cutoff frequency. Then lower the generator frequency until the output voltage falls to 70.7% of the midband level. This is the lower cutoff frequency. Try switching C_1 with C_2 in the circuit of Figure 8-2. What effect does this have on the lower cutoff frequency? Does it have an effect on the upper cutoff frequency? Summarize your investigation in a short report.

The Common-Collector Amplifier

Objectives:

After performing this experiment, you will be able to:

1. Compute the dc and ac parameters for a common-collector amplifier.
2. Build the amplifier from objective 1 and measure the dc and ac parameters including input resistance and power gain.
3. Test the effect of different load resistors on the ac parameters.
4. Predict the effect of faults in a common-collector amplifier.

Summary of Theory:

The common-collector (CC) amplifier (also called the *emitter-follower*) has the input signal applied to the base and the output signal is taken from the emitter. Figure 9-1(a) illustrates a CC amplifier using a *pnp* transistor with voltage-divider bias. The ac output voltage almost perfectly duplicates the input voltage waveform. While this implies that the voltage gain is approximately 1, the current gain is not; hence, it can deliver increased signal power to a load. The CC amplifier is characterized by a high input resistance and a low output resistance.

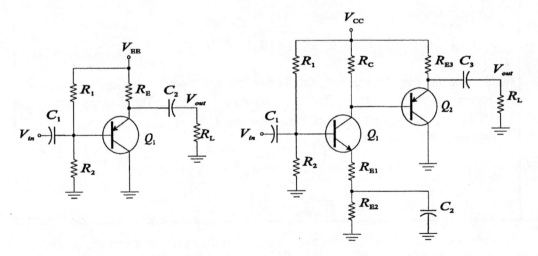

    (a) CC amplifier with *pnp* transistor   (b) CE and CC amplifiers

Figure 9-1

Frequently, a CC amplifier follows a voltage amplifier. Instead of having separate bias resistors, bias may be obtained through a dc path connected from the previous stage as illustrated in Figure 9-1(b). This technique is common in power amplifiers. It will be investigated in the For Further Investigation for this experiment.

Analysis of the amplifier begins with the **dc** parameters. These procedures are described in Experiment 7 and summarized here for the *pnp* transistor shown in Figure 9-1(a).

---

1. Mentally remove the capacitors from the circuit since they appear open to dc. This causes the load resistor, R_L, to be removed.

2. Solve for the base voltage, V_B, by applying the voltage-divider rule to R_1 and R_2.

3. *Add* the 0.7 V forward-bias drop across the base-emitter diode from V_B to obtain the emitter voltage, V_E. (Note that the emitter is at a higher voltage in the *pnp* case.)

4. The dc current in the emitter circuit is found by applying Ohm's law to R_E. The voltage across the emitter resistor is the difference between the supply voltage (V_{EE}) and V_E. The collector current is nearly equal to the emitter current, and the collector voltage is zero.

The **ac** parameters for the amplifier can now be analyzed. The equivalent ac circuit is illustrated in Figure 9-2. The analysis steps are:

---

1. Replace all capacitors with a short. Compute the ac resistance of the emitter, r_e', from the equation:

$$r_e' = \frac{25 \text{ mV}}{I_E}$$

2. Compute the amplifier's voltage gain. Voltage gain is the ratio of the output voltage divided by the input voltage. The input voltage is applied across r_e' and the ac emitter resistance, whereas the output voltage is taken only across the ac emitter resistance. Thus, the voltage gain is based on the voltage divider equation:

$$A_v = \frac{V_{out}}{V_{in}} = \frac{I_e(R_E \parallel R_L)}{I_e(r_e' + R_E \parallel R_L)} = \frac{R_E \parallel R_L}{r_e' + R_E \parallel R_L}$$

3. Compute the total input resistance seen by the ac signal:

$$R_{in(tot)} = R_1 \parallel R_2 \parallel \left\{ \beta_{ac}(r_e' + R_E \parallel R_L) \right\}$$

4. Compute the amplifier's power gain. In this case, we are only interested in the power delivered to the load resistor. The output power is V_{out}^2 / R_L. The input power is $V_{in}^2 / R_{in(tot)}$. Since the voltage gain is approximately 1, the power gain can be expressed as a ratio of $R_{in(tot)}$ to R_L:

$$A_p = \frac{\dfrac{V_{out}^2}{R_L}}{\dfrac{V_{in}^2}{R_{in(tot)}}} = A_v^2 \left\{ \frac{R_{in(tot)}}{R_L} \right\} = \frac{R_{in(tot)}}{R_L}$$

These formulas were derived for the particular CC amplifier given in the example. You should <u>not</u> assume that these equations are valid for other configurations.

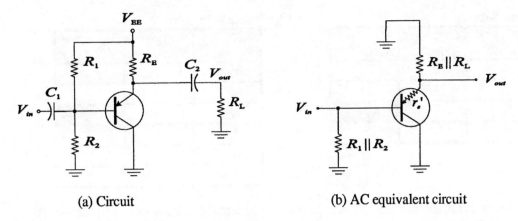

(a) Circuit (b) AC equivalent circuit

Figure 9-2

Materials Needed:
Resistors:
    two 1.0 kΩ, one 10 kΩ, one 33 kΩ
Capacitors:
    one 1.0 μF, one 10 μF
One 10 kΩ potentiometer
One 2N3906 *pnp* transistor (or equivalent)

For Further Investigation:
    One 2N3906 *pnp* transistor (or equivalent)
    Three 330 Ω resistors

Procedure:
1. Measure and record the resistance of the resistors listed in Table 9-1.

Table 9-1

Resistor	Listed Value	Measured Value
R_1	33 kΩ	
R_2	10 kΩ	
R_E	1.0 kΩ	
R_L	1.0 kΩ	

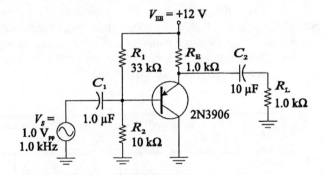

Figure 9-3

2. Compute the dc parameters listed in Table 9-2 for the CC amplifier shown in Figure 9-3. (See Summary of Theory for method.) Enter your computed values in Table 9-2.

Table 9-2

DC Parameter	Computed Value	Measured Value
V_B		
V_E		
I_E		
V_{CE}		

Table 9-3

AC Parameter	Computed Value	Measured Value
V_b	$1.0\ V_{pp}$	
V_e		
r_e'		
A_v		
$R_{in\,(tot)}$		
A_p		

3. Construct the amplifier shown in Figure 9-3. The signal generator should be turned off. With the power supply on, measure and record the dc voltages listed in Table 9-2. Your measured and computed values should agree within 10%.

4. Compute the ac parameters listed in Table 9-3. Assume V_b is the same as the source voltage, V_s. If you do not know the ß for your transistor, assume it is 100. Use the procedure outlined in the Summary of Theory to compute the parameters.

5. Turn on the signal generator and set V_s for 1.0 V_{pp} at 1.0 kHz. Use the oscilloscope to set the proper voltage and check the frequency. Measure the ac signal voltage at the transistor's emitter, V_{out}, and determine the voltage gain, A_v. Measure $R_{in\,(tot)}$ using the method employed for the CE amplifier in Experiment 8. Use the measured $R_{in\,(tot)}$ and R_L to determine the measured power gain.

6. With a two-channel oscilloscope, compare the input and output waveforms. What is the phase relationship between V_{in} and V_{out}?

---

7. Table 9-4 lists some possible troubles with the CC amplifier. For each trouble listed, predict the effect on the dc voltages. Then insert the trouble into the circuit and test your prediction. Insert the open collector and open emitter troubles by removing the transistor lead and measuring the voltages at the circuit. For each fault, describe the effect on the ac output waveform (clipped, no output, etc.).

Table 9-4

Trouble	DC Predictions			DC Measurements			Effect of Trouble on V_{out}
	V_B	V_E	V_{CE}	V_B	V_E	V_{CE}	
R_1 open							
R_2 open							
R_1 shorted							
R_E open							
open collector							
open emitter							

8. Replace R_L with a 10 kΩ variable resistor set to 1.0 kΩ. Connect an oscilloscope probe to the emitter. Raise the signal amplitude until you just begin to observe clipping. If the positive peaks are clipped, you are observing *cutoff* clipping because the transistor is turned off. If the negative peaks are clipped, this is called *saturation* clipping because the transistor is fully conducting. What type of clipping is first observed?

_____

9. Vary R_L while observing the output waveform. Describe your observations.

_____

_____

Conclusion:

Evaluation and Review Questions:
1. In step 6, you observed the phase relationship between the input and output waveforms. Is the phase relationship you observed the same for an *npn* circuit? Explain.

2. In step 8, you observed the effect of clipping due to saturation or cutoff of the transistor. The statement was made that if the positive peaks are clipped, you are observing *cutoff* clipping because the transistor is turned off. Is this statement true if the CC circuit had been constructed with an *npn* transistor? Why or why not?

3. The circuit used in this experiment used voltage-divider bias.
   (a) Compared to base bias, what is the advantage?

   (b) What disadvantage does it have?

4. Common-collector amplifiers do not have voltage gain but still provide power gain. Explain.

5. Figure 9-4 shows a CC amplifier with voltage-divider bias. Assume $\beta_{ac} = \beta_{dc} = 100$. Compute the dc and ac parameters listed below for the circuit.

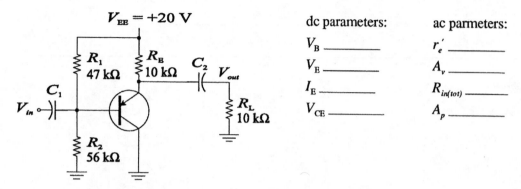

dc parameters:

V_B _____

V_E _____

I_E _____

V_{CE} _____

ac parmeters:

r_e' _____

A_v _____

$R_{in(tot)}$ _____

A_p _____

Figure 9-4

For Further Investigation:
As mentioned in the Summary of Theory, the CC amplifier is frequently used after a voltage amplifier and may derive its bias from the voltage amplifier. The circuit shown in Figure 9-5 uses the CE amplifier from Experiment 8 to drive the CC amplifier. Notice that the CC amplifier is dc coupled so it does not require bias resistors. Construct the circuit and measure the dc and ac parameters. Summarize your findings in a short report.

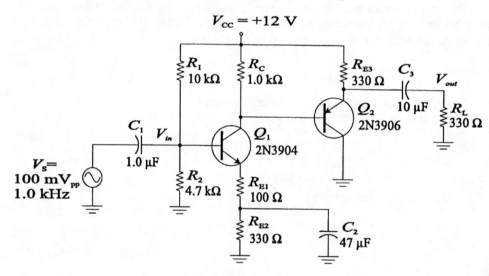

Figure 9-5

Name _____
Date _____
Class _____

Multistage Amplifiers

Objectives:

After performing this experiment, you will be able to:

1. Construct a two-stage transistor amplifier and measure the dc and ac parameters including the input resistance, output resistance, voltage gain, and power gain.

2. *For Further Investigation:* Add automatic gain control to the amplifier in objective 1 and plot the gain characteristic of the amplifier as a function of the amplitude of the input signal.

Summary of Theory:

A single stage of amplification is often not enough for a particular application. The overall gain can be increased by using more than one stage. Frequently, the first stage is a low-noise voltage amplifier which is followed by additional voltage or power amplification. An example of this was given in the For Further Investigation section of Experiment 9 where a CE stage was followed by a dc coupled CC stage to form a two stage amplifier.

Sometimes the input signal is not a fixed quantity. An example is in communication receivers, where the signal strength varies for a number of reasons such as the signal path, weather conditions, time of day or night, etc. In cases like this, a compensation circuit, called automatic gain control (AGC), is useful to decrease the gain when the signal rises and increase the gain when the signal falls. In the For Further Investigation section of this experiment, you will add a field-effect transistor to the circuit to provide AGC.

The two-stage linear amplifier is shown in Figure 15-1. It uses two common emitter (CE) circuits, with the *pnp* and *npn* transistors connected in a cascade amplifier. R_A and R_B are not considered part of the amplifier, but are only used to attenuate the input signal from the function generator by a known factor. To analyze the amplifier, start with the dc parameters. Use measured values of components in your calculations. The steps to solve for the dc parameters for this amplifier are:

1. Mentally remove (open) capacitors from the circuit since they appear open to dc. Solve for the base voltage, V_B of Q_1. By inspection, the dc base voltage is zero; however if the resistors are not equal, the base voltage can be found by applying the voltage-divider rule and the superposition theorem to R_1 and R_2.

2. Add the 0.7 V forward-bias drop across the base-emitter diode of Q_1 from V_B to obtain the emitter voltage, V_E, of Q_1.

3. Find the voltage across the emitter resistors and apply Ohm's law to solve for the emitter current, I_E, of Q_1.

4. Assume the emitter current (step 3) is equal to the collector current, I_C, of Q_1. Find the voltage across R_{C1} and the voltage drop across Q_1. Solve for the dc voltage drop across this equivalent resistance to find the voltage at the collector of Q_1.

5. Compute the base voltage of Q_2 by applying the superposition theorem and voltage divider rule to R_3 and R_4. Subtract 0.7 V from the base voltage of Q_2 to find the emitter voltage of Q_2. Find the voltage across the emitter resistors and apply Ohm's law to determine the emitter current in Q_2.

6. Assume the emitter current (step 5) is equal to the collector current, I_C, of Q_2. Find the voltage across R_{C2} and the voltage drop across Q_2.

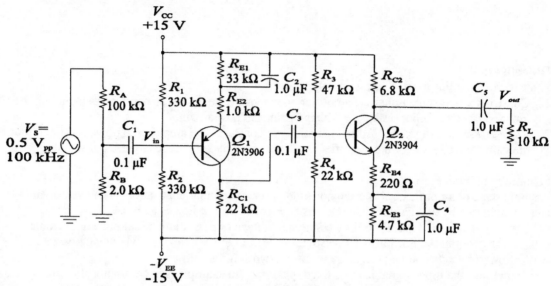

Figure 15-1

The **ac** parameters for the amplifier can now be analyzed. The ac analysis steps are:

1. Replace all capacitors with a short. The ac resistance in the emitter circuit includes the unbypassed emitter resistor and the ac resistance of the transistor. Compute the ac emitter resistance of each transistor, r'_e, from the equation:

$$r'_e = \frac{25 \text{ mV}}{I_E}$$

2. Compute the input and output resistance of Q_1. The input resistance includes the bias resistors in parallel with the ac resistance of the emitter circuit reflected into the base circuit. The output resistance is simply the value of the collector resistor.

$$R_{in(Q1)} = R_1 \| R_2 \| \{\beta_{ac}(r'_e + R_{E2})\}$$

3. Compute the input and output resistance of Q_2. As before, the input resistance includes the bias resistors and the ac emitter resistance reflected to the base circuit. The output resistance is again the collector resistor.

$$R_{in(Q2)} = R_3 \| R_4 \| \{\beta_{ac}(r'_e + R_{E4})\}$$

4. Compute the unloaded gain, $A_{v(NL)}$, of each stage. The unloaded voltage gain for the common-emitter transistors can be written:

$$A_{v(NL)} = \frac{V_{out}}{V_{in}} = \frac{I_c R_C}{I_e \left(r'_e + R_{e(ac)} \right)} = \frac{R_C}{\left(r'_e + R_{e(ac)} \right)}$$

5. Compute the overall gain of the amplifier. It is easier to calculate the voltage gain of a multistage amplifier by computing the *unloaded* voltage gain for each stage, then including the loading effect by computing voltage dividers for the output resistance and input resistance of the following stage. This idea is illustrated in Figure 15-2. Each transistor is drawn as an amplifier consisting of an input resistance, R_{in}, an output resistance, R_{out}, along with its unloaded gain, A_v. Then, the overall loaded gain, A'_v, of this amplifier can be found by:

$$A'_v = A_{v1} \left(\frac{R_{in2}}{R_{out1} + R_{in2}} \right) A_{v2}$$

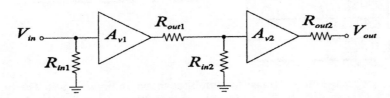

Figure 15-2

Note that if a load resistor was added across the output, an additional voltage divider consisting of the output resistance of the second stage and the added load resistor is used to compute the new gain.

Materials Needed:
One 2N3904 *npn* transistor (or equivalent)
One 2N3906 *pnp* transistor (or equivalent)
Capacitors: two 0.1 µF, three 1.0 µF
Resistors: one of each: 220 Ω, 1.0 kΩ, 2.0 kΩ, 4.7 kΩ, 6.8 kΩ, 10 kΩ, 33 kΩ, 47 kΩ
Resistors: two of each 22 kΩ, 100 kΩ, 330 kΩ
One 100 kΩ potentiometer

For Further Investigation:
   One MPF102 *n*-channel JFET
   One 1N914 signal diode (or equivalent)
   Resistors: one 100 Ω, one 220 kΩ
   Capacitors: one additional 1.0 µF capacitor

Procedure:

1. Measure and record the values of the resistors listed in Table 15-1. Compute the dc parameters for the amplifier listed in Table 15-2.

Table 15-1

Resistor	Listed Value	Measured Value
R_A	100 kΩ	
R_B	2.0 kΩ	
R_1	330 kΩ	
R_2	330 kΩ	
R_{E1}	33 kΩ	
R_{E2}	1.0 kΩ	
R_{C1}	22 kΩ	
R_3	47 kΩ	
R_4	22 kΩ	
R_{E3}	4.7 kΩ	
R_{E4}	220 Ω	
R_{C2}	6.8 kΩ	
R_L	10 kΩ	

Table 15-2

DC Parameter	Computed Value	Measured Value
$V_{B(Q1)}$		
$V_{E(Q1)}$		
$I_{E(Q1)}$		
$V_{C(Q1)}$		
$V_{CE(Q1)}$		
$V_{B(Q2)}$		
$V_{E(Q2)}$		
$I_{E(Q2)}$		
$V_{C(Q2)}$		
$V_{CE(Q2)}$		

2. Construct the two stage bipolar transistor amplifier shown in Figure 15-1. The function generator should be turned off. Measure and record the dc voltages listed in Table 15-2. Your measured and computed values should agree within 10%.

3. Compute the ac parameters listed in Table 15-3. The gains for each stage are not loaded. The output resistance of Q_1 ($R_{out(Q1)}$) is simply the collector resistor; the input resistance of Q_2 is determined by the procedure given in the Summary of Theory.

4. Compute the overall gain of the amplifier using the computed gains from Table 15-3 and the input and output resistance between the stages (see step 5 of the ac analysis in the Summary of Theory). Enter the computed overall gain, A_v', on the first line of Table 15-4. Using this value, compute the expected output voltage; enter the computed output voltage on the last line of Table 15-4.

5. Connect the function generator voltage to the divider composed of R_A and R_B as shown in Figure 15-1. (*Note*: The purpose of these resistors is to attenuate the generator signal by a known amount; they will not be considered part of the amplifier.) Turn on the function generator and set V_s for a 0.5 V_{pp} sine wave at 100 kHz. (Check voltage and frequency with the oscilloscope.) The ac base voltage of Q_1 is V_{in}; it is shown as 10 mV$_{pp}$ (based on the voltage divider). Measure the ac signal voltage at the amplifier's output ($V_{out(Q2)}^{pp}$) and record the value on the last line of Table 15-4. Then use V_{in} and V_{out} to find the measured overall gain, A_v'. Record the measured overall gain in the first line of Table 15-4.

Table 15-3

AC Parameter	Computed Value
$r'_{e\,(Q1)}$	
$r'_{e\,(Q2)}$	
$A_{v\,(NL)(Q1)}$	
$A_{v(NL)(Q2)}$	
$R_{out\,(Q1)}$	
$R_{in\,(Q2)}$	

Table 15-4

AC Parameter	Computed Value	Measured Value
A_v		
$R_{in(Q1)}$		
$R_{out\,(Q2)}$		
$V_{in\,(Q1)}$	10 mV	
$V_{out\,(Q2)}$		

6. The measurement of the total input resistance, $R_{in(tot)}$, is done indirectly by the method shown in Experiment 8 (step 6) using a variable test resistor. The method is repeated here. The output signal (V_{out}) set by V_s to a convenient level with the amplifier operating normally (no clipping or distortion). The output is observed (with an oscilloscope) and the amplitude noted. A variable test resistor (R_{test}) is then inserted in series with the source as shown in Figure 15-3. Because of the higher input resistance of this amplifier, a 100 kΩ test resistor is shown. The resistance of R_{test} is increased until V_{out} drops to one-half the value prior to inserting R_{test}. With this condition, $V_{in} = V_{test}$ and $R_{in(tot)}$ must be equal to R_{test}. R_{test} can then be removed and measured with an ohmmeter. The total input resistance, $R_{in(tot)}$, is the same as the ac input resistance to Q_1 ($R_{in(Q1)}$). Using this method, measure $R_{in(Q1)}$ and record the result in Table 15-4.

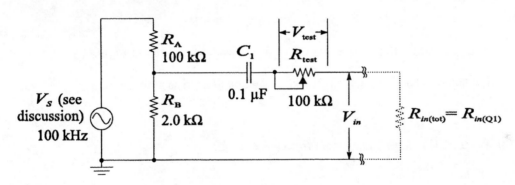

Figure 15-3 Measurement of $R_{in(tot)}$.

7. In this step you will measure the output resistance of the amplifier. The computed output resistance is the same as R_{C2}, the load resistor of Q_2. You can measure the output resistance of any amplifier by measuring the loading effect caused by adding a load resistor. It is not necessary that the load resistor be equal to the output resistance. Consider the model of an amplifier shown in Figure 15-2. Assume that you want to indirectly measure R_{out2}. Think of the amplifier as a Thevenin source with the Thevenin resistance represented by the output resistance. You can find this resistance by measuring the unloaded output voltage and the new output voltage when a known load resistor is placed on the output. Use this idea to develop the equation for the output resistance of the amplifier. Then make the measurements and solve for the output resistance.

Conclusion:

Evaluation and Review Questions:

1. Explain why it is necessary to measure the input resistance indirectly.

2. When you calculated the ac parameters, you were instructed to consider the capacitors as *shorts*. Under what conditions is this assumption *not* warranted?

3. For the circuit in the experiment, the output resistance of both transistors was considered to be the individual collector resistor. Explain.

4. Assume you wanted to use base bias for Q_2 as shown in the circuit of Figure 15-1.

   (a) Explain the changes you would make to the amplifier to accomplish this.

   (b) What disadvantage would result from this change?

5. What is the phase between the input and output signal? Explain your answer.

For Further Investigation:

Add the Automatic Gain Control (AGC) shown in Figure 15-4. The AGC circuit consists of transistor Q_3, diode D_1, capacitors C_2 and C_6 and resistors R_5 and R_6. (Note that C_2, which served as a bypass capacitor in Figure 15-1, has been moved and is now a coupling capacitor for the AGC circuit.) This AGC will limit the gain moderately because control is applied to only one stage, whereas in many applications, the gain control voltage is applied to several stages. Test the gain of the amplifier with the input signals listed in Table 15-5. The input signal is computed from the function generator setting and assumed to be 2% of the function generator value due to the input voltage divider. Graph the overall gain versus the input signal amplitude with AGC on Plot 15-1. Label your graph.

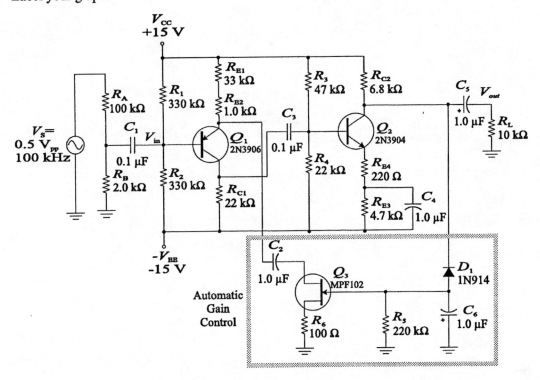

Figure 15-4

Table 15-5

Generator Setting	V_{in}	V_{out}	A_v
0.5 V	10 mV		
1.0 V	20 mV		
2.0 V	40 mV		
4.0 V	80 mV		
6.0 V	120 mV		
8.0 V	160 mV		
10.0 V	200 mV		
20.0 V	400 mV		

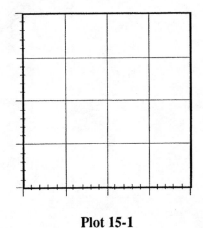

Plot 15-1

Field-Effect Transistors

Name _____

Date _____

Class _____

OBJECTIVES

After performing this experiment, you will be able to:

1. Measure and graph the drain characteristic curves for a junction field-effect transistor (JFET).
2. Use the characteristic drain curves to determine the transconductance of the JFET.
3. Explain how a JFET can be used as a two-terminal constant-current source.

MATERIALS NEEDED

Resistors:

      One 100 Ω, one 33 kΩ

One 2N5458 N-channel JFET transistor (or equivalent)

SUMMARY OF THEORY

The field-effect transistor (FET) is a voltage-controlled transistor that uses an electrostatic field to control current rather than a base current. Instead of a sandwich of materials as in the bipolar junction transistor, the FET begins with a doped piece of silicon called a *channel*. On one end of the channel is a terminal called the *source* and on the other end of the channel is a terminal called the *drain*. Current in the channel is controlled by a voltage applied to a third terminal called the *gate*. Field-effect transistors are classified as either junction-gate (JFET) or insulated-gate (IGFET) devices. Insulated gate devices are also called MOSFETs (for *M*etal *O*xide *S*emiconductor FETs). The major difference between bipolar and field-effect transistors is that BJTs use a small base *current* to control a larger current, but the FET uses a gate *voltage* to control the current. Since the input of a FET draws virtually no current, the input impedance is extremely high; however, the sensitivity to input voltage change is much greater in the bipolar junction transistor than in the FET. Both the JFET and MOSFET have similar ac characteristics; however, in this experiment, we will concentrate on the JFET to simplify the discussion.

      The gate of a JFET is made of the opposite type of material from that of the channel, forming a PN diode between the gate and channel. Application of a reverse bias on this junction decreases the conductivity of the channel, reducing the source-drain current. The gate diode is never forward-biased and hence draws almost no current. The JFET comes in two forms, N-channel and P-channel. The N-channel is distinguished on drawings by an inward drawn arrow on the gate connection, while the P-channel has an outward pointing arrow on the gate.

      The characteristic drain curves for a JFET exhibit several important differences from the BJT. Besides being a voltage-controlled device, the JFET is a normally ON device. In other words, a reverse-bias voltage must be applied to the gate-source diode in order to close off the channel and stop drain-source current. When the gate is shorted to the source, there is a maximum allowable drain-source current. This current is called I_{DSS} for *D*rain-*S*ource current with gate *S*horted. The JFET exhibits a region on its characteristic curve where drain current is proportional to the drain-source voltage. This region, called the ohmic region, has important applications as a voltage-controlled resistance.

A useful specification for estimating the gain of a JFET is called the *transconductance,* which is abbreviated g_m. Recall that conductance is the reciprocal of resistance. Since the output current is controlled by an input voltage, it is useful to think of FETs as transconductance amplifiers. The transconductance can be found by dividing a small change in the *output current* by a small change in the *input voltage;* that is,

$$g_m = \frac{\Delta I_D}{\Delta V_{GS}}$$

PROCEDURE

1. Measure and record the resistance of the resistors listed in Table 1.

2. Construct the circuit shown in Figure 1. Start with V_{GG} and V_{DD} at zero volts. Connect a voltmeter between the drain and source of the transistor. Keep V_{CC} at 0 V and slowly increase V_{DD} until V_{DS} is 1.0 V. (V_{DS} is the voltage between the transistor's drain and source.)

Table 1

	Listed Value	Measured Value
R_1	33 kΩ	
R_2	100 Ω	

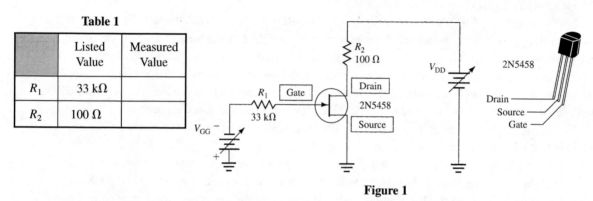

Figure 1

3. With V_{DS} at 1.0 V, measure the voltage across R_2 (V_{R2}). Compute the drain current, I_D, by applying Ohm's law to R_2. Note that the current in R_2 is the same as I_D for the transistor. Enter the computed I_D in Table 2 under the columns labeled Gate Voltage = 0 V.

4. Without disturbing the setting of V_{GG}, slowly increase V_{DD} until V_{DS} is 2.0 V. Then measure and record V_{R2} for this setting. Compute I_D as before and enter the computed current in Table 2 under the columns labeled Gate Voltage = 0 V.

Table 2

V_{DS} (measured)	Gate Voltage = 0 V		Gate Voltage = -1.0 V		Gate Voltage = -2.0 V	
	V_{R2} (measured)	I_D (computed)	V_{R2} (measured)	I_D (computed)	V_{R2} (measured)	I_D (computed)
1.0 V						
2.0 V						
3.0 V						
4.0 V						
6.0 V						
8.0 V						

5. Repeat step 4 for each value of V_{DS} listed in Table 2.

6. Adjust V_{GG} for -1.0 V. This applies -1.0 V between the gate and source because there is almost no gate current into the JFET and almost no voltage drop across R_1. Reset V_{DD} until $V_{DS} = 1.0$ V. Measure V_{R2} and enter it in Table 2. Compute I_D and enter the computed current in Table 2 under the columns labeled Gate Voltage = -1.0 V.

7. Without changing the setting of V_{GG}, adjust V_{DD} for each value of V_{GS} listed in Table 2 as before. Compute the drain current at each setting and enter it in Table 2 under the columns labeled Gate Voltage = -1.0 V.

8. Adjust V_{GG} for -2.0 V.[1] Repeat steps 6 and 7, entering the data under the columns labeled Gate Voltage = -2.0 V.

9. The data in Table 2 represent three drain characteristic curves for your JFET. The drain characteristic curve is a graph of V_{DS} versus I_D for a constant gate voltage. Plot the three drain characteristic curves on Plot 1. Choose a scale for I_D that allows the largest current observed to fit on the graph. Label each curve with the gate voltage it represents.

---

[1]The gate-source cutoff voltage for the 2N5458 can vary from -1.0 V to -7.0 V. You may find that -2.0 V turns off the transistor. If the transistor is turned off, try testing it with a gate voltage of -0.5 V.

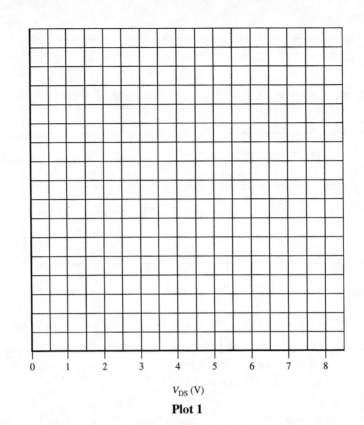

I_D (mA)

0   1   2   3   4   5   6   7   8

V_{DS} (V)

Plot 1

10.   Determine the approximate transconductance (g_m) of your JFET at $V_{DS} = 6$ V. Do this by observing the change in drain current between two of the characteristic curves at $V_{DS} = 6$ V and dividing it by a change in the gate-source voltage. Note that the change in the gate-source voltage is 1.0 V between each plotted curve. You should be able to find a transconductance that agrees with the specified range for the JFET you are using, typically 1000 μS to several thousand μS.

$g_m = $ _____

CONCLUSION

EVALUATION AND REVIEW QUESTIONS

1.   (a)   Explain how to find I_{DSS} from the characteristic curves of a JFET.

      (b)   From your data, what is the I_{DSS} for your JFET? _____

2. Using the data when the gate voltage is 0 V, explain how you could use your JFET as a two-terminal current source that gives a current of I_{DSS}.

3. (a) Does the experimental data indicate that the transconductance is a constant at all points?

    (b) From your experimental data, what evidence indicates that a JFET is a nonlinear device?

4. Look up the meaning of pinch-off voltage when $V_{GS} = 0V$. Note that the *magnitude* of V_{GS} is equal to the *magnitude* of V_p, so we can use the characteristic curve for $V_{GS} = 0$ to determine V_p. Using the data from this experiment, determine the pinch-off voltage for your JFET.

5. Why should a JFET be operated with only reverse bias on the gate source?

FOR FURTHER INVESTIGATION
Using the test circuit shown in Figure 1, test the effect of varying V_{GS} with V_{DD} held at a constant $+10$ V. Tabulate a set of data of I_D as a function of V_{GS} (Table 3). Start with $V_{GS} = 0.0$ V and take data every -5.0 V until there is no appreciable drain current. Then graph the data on Plot 2. This curve is the transconductance curve for your JFET. The data you obtain are nonlinear because the gate-source voltage is proportional to the square root of the drain current. To illustrate this, compute the square root of I_D and plot the square root of the drain current as a function of the gate-source voltage on Plot 3.

Table 3

V_{GS} (measured)	I_D (measured)	$\sqrt{I_D}$ (computed)
0.0 V		
−0.5 V		
−1.0 V		
−1.5 V		
−2.0 V		
−2.5 V		
−3.0 V		
−3.5 V		
−4.0 V		
−4.5 V		
−5.0 V		

I_D (mA)

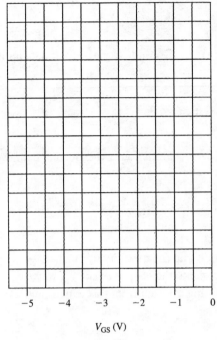

V_{GS} (V)

Plot 2

$\sqrt{I_D}$ ($\sqrt{mA}$)

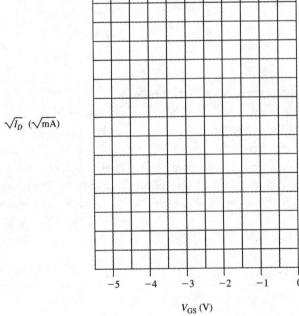

V_{GS} (V)

Plot 3

The Differential Amplifier

Objectives:

After performing this experiment, you will be able to:
1. Compute and measure the basic dc and ac parameters for a differential amplifier.
2. Measure the differential and common-mode gain for a differential amplifier and compute the CMRR′.

Summary of Theory:

The differential amplifier has two inputs and amplifies the *difference* signal applied between the two inputs but ignores any *common* signal applied to the inputs. A difference signal is said to be a normal mode signal, while a signal that is the same on both inputs is said to be a common-mode signal. The ability to amplify a normal mode signal while rejecting a common-mode signal is an important advantage in instrumentation systems, where a small signal may be contaminated by common-mode noise pickup in cabling.

Figure 18-1(a) shows an emitter-biased differential amplifier constructed with two *npn* transistors. The emitter currents for each transistor combine to form the current in the tail resistor, R_T. The signal is applied between the bases and is removed between the collectors. Since there are two inputs and two outputs, this mode of operation is referred to

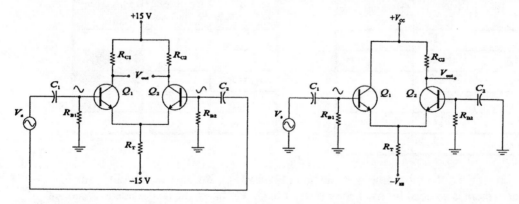

(a) Double-ended input and output   (b) Single-ended input and output

Figure 18-1

as a double-ended input and double-ended output. If the input is applied to only one side, as in Figure 18-1(b), and the output is taken from only one side (output is taken from only one of the collectors), then the mode of operation is referred to as a single-ended input and single-ended output.

The dc conditions for the differential amplifier are computed by finding the tail current and splitting it for the two transistors. Because it uses emitter bias, you can approximate the emitter voltage as -1 V and determine the tail current by applying Ohm's law to R_T. The dc emitter current in each transistor is one-half the tail current.

In this experiment, you will construct and test a differential amplifier. First you will compute the dc conditions; then you will compute the ac conditions. You will then measure the differential-mode and common-mode gains and use these gains to compute the common mode rejection ratio (CMRR). In the For Further Investigation section, you will test a current source biasing circuit and observe how it can improve the CMRR.

Materials Needed:
Resistors: two 100 Ω, two 10 kΩ, one 33 kΩ, two 100 kΩ
Capacitors: two 10 µF
Transistors: two 2N3904 (or equivalent)
For Further Investigation:
    one additional 2N3904 transistor
    two additional 10 kΩ resistors and one 4.7 kΩ resistor

Procedure:
1. Measure and record the values of the resistors listed in Table 18-1. Best results (for maximum CMRR) can be obtained if R_{B1} and R_{B2} are matched and R_{E1} and R_{E2} are also matched.

Table 18-1

Resistor	Listed Value	Measured Value
R_{B1}	100 kΩ	
R_{B2}	100 kΩ	
R_{E1}	100 Ω	
R_{E2}	100 Ω	
R_T	10 kΩ	
R_{C2}	10 kΩ	

Table 18-2

DC Parameter	Computed Value	Measured Value
V_A	-1 V	
I_T		
$I_{E1} = I_{E2}$		
$V_{C(Q1)}$		
$V_{C(Q2)}$		

2. Construct the differential amplifier shown in Figure 18-2. Because the output is single ended, there is no need for a collector resistor in Q_1. Compute the dc parameters listed in Table 18-2. The voltage at point A is approximated as -1 V for the calculations as shown in the table. I_T is found by applying Ohm's law to the tail resistor, R_T.

3. Measure and record the dc parameters listed in Table 18-2.

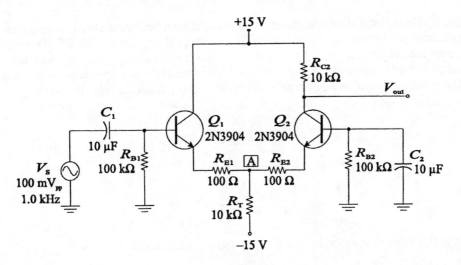

Figure 18-2

4. Compute the ac parameters given in Table 18-3. The differential amplifier can be thought of as a common-collector amplifier (Q_1) driving a common-base amplifier (Q_2). For the single-ended input signal, the overall differential voltage gain is given by:

$$A_{v(d)} = \frac{R_{C2}}{2(R_{E2} + r'_e)}$$

Except for the 2 in the denominator, this equation is equivalent to the gain of a CB amplifier. The reduction by a factor of 2 is due to the attenuation of the signal to point A by the CC amplifier. To compute $R_{in(tot)}$, begin by assuming $r'_{e(Q2)}$ is in series with R_{E2}, R_{E1}, and $r'_{e(Q1)}$. Move this resistance into the base circuit of Q_1 by multiplying by β_{Q1}. This result is then seen to be in parallel with the Q_1 base resistor, R_{B1}. Writing this in equation form:

$$R_{in(tot)} = R_{B1} \parallel \{\beta_{Q1}(r'_{e(Q1)} + R_{E1(Q1)} + R_{E1(Q2)} + r'_{e(Q2)})\}$$

If you don't know β_{Q1}, assume a nominal value of 200 for the 2N3904.

Table 18-3

AC Parameter	Computed Value	Measured Value
$V_{b(Q1)}$	100 mV$_{pp}$	
V_A		
$r'_{e\,(Q1)} = r'_{e\,(Q2)}$		
$A_{v(d)}$		
$V_{c(Q2)}$		
$R_{in\,(tot)}$		
$A_{v(cm)}$		
CMRR$'$		

5. Add the single-ended differential mode ac signal as shown in Figure 18-2 (previous page) and measure the ac parameters listed in Table 18-3 (except $A_{v(cm)}$ and CMRR′). To measure $R_{in(tot)}$, note the output voltage, V_c, then add a 33 kΩ test resistor, R_{test}, in series with the input signal and observe the reduced output V_c'. (V_c' should drop to approximately one-half V_c). The measured value of $R_{in(tot)}$ is determined by solving for $R_{in(tot)}$ from the ratio:

$$\frac{V_c'}{R_{in(tot)}} = \frac{V_c}{R_{test} + R_{in(tot)}}$$

Solving for $R_{in(tot)}$:

$$R_{in(tot)} = \left(\frac{V_c'}{V_c - V_c'} \right) R_{test}$$

Notice that if the output drops in half after inserting the test resistor, $R_{test} = R_{in(tot)}$.

6. In this step, you will find the common-mode gain, $A_{v(cm)}$. The common-mode gain can be approximated from the formula:

$$A_{v(cm)} \cong \frac{R_C}{2R_T}$$

This formula assumes the two sides of the differential amplifier are balanced. Enter the computed common-mode gain in Table 18-3.

7. The common-mode gain is the gain observed when the same signal is applied to both sides of the differential amplifier. Remove the test resistor from step 5 and connect the circuit shown in Figure 18-3. In order to measure the common-mode gain, raise the input signal level from the signal generator until a 1 V_{pp} output is observed. Then measure the ratio of the output to input signal and record the measured $A_{v(cm)}$ in Table 18-3.

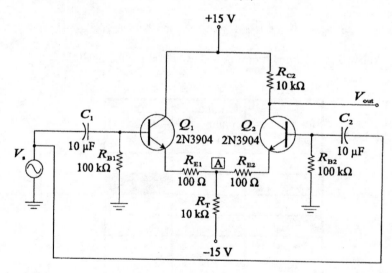

Figure 18-3 Applying a common-mode signal to the differential amplifier.

8. The CMRR′ is 20 times the logarithmic ratio of the absolute value of the ratio of $A_{v(d)}$ to $A_{v(cm)}$, expressed in dB. Expressed as an equation,

$$\text{CMRR}' = 20 \log \left| \frac{A_{v(d)}}{A_{v(cm)}} \right|$$

Compute the CMRR′ for your differential amplifier and record the value in Table 18-3.

Conclusion:

Evaluation and Review Questions:

1. There is no collector resistor for Q_1 in the circuit of Figure 18-2. Why doesn't this have any effect on the dc collector current in either transistor?

2. In step 5, you were directed to measure the input resistance while observing the output voltage, V_c, instead of the input voltage, V_b. Explain what advantage this has to assure a good measurement.

3. Assume the following troubles are associated with the differential amplifier in Figure 18-2. What effect would you expect for each problem on the output signal? Assume only one problem occurs at a time.

   (a) Capacitor C_2 is open:

   (b) Resistor R_{E1} is shorted:

   (c) The transistors have ß's at the opposite extremes of the specified range (one 100, the other 300).

   (d) The negative power supply drops to –10 V.

   (e) The base of Q_2 is shorted to ground.

4. What is the phase relationship of the output signal compared to the input signal?

5. Assume you wanted a higher CMRR′ for the differential amplifier. What improvements to the circuit would you suggest?

For Further Investigation:
The CMRR′ can be improved by reducing the common-mode gain. The internal resistance of a current source is very high. By replacing the tail resistor with a current source, the common-mode gain is reduced and the CMRR′ is made higher. Connect the current-source shown in Figure 18-4 to the circuit in the experiment. Compare the differential and common-mode gains and compute the increased CMRR′. Summarize your results.

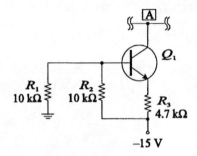

Figure 18-4

Op-Amp Characteristics

Objectives:

After performing this experiment, you will be able to:

1. Explain the meaning of common op-amp specifications.
2. Use IC op-amp specification sheets to determine op-amp characteristics.
3. Measure the input offset voltage, input bias current, input offset current, CMRR', and slew rate for a 741C op-amp.

Summary of Theory:

An operational amplifier (*op-amp*) is a linear integrated circuit that incorporates a dc-coupled, high-gain differential amplifier and other circuitry that gives it specific characteristics. The ideal op-amp has certain unattainable specifications, but hundreds of types of operational amplifiers are available, which vary in specific ways from the ideal op-amp. Important specifications are reviewed in the experiment and include open-loop gain, input impedance, output impedance, input offset voltage and current, bias current, and slew rate. Slew rate is defined as the maximum rate of change of the output voltage under large signal conditions. A higher slew rate implies a better frequency response of the op-amp. Other characteristics important in certain applications include CMRR, current and voltage noise level, maximum output current, roll-off characteristics, and voltage and power requirements. The data sheet for a specific op-amp contains these specifications, a description of the op-amp, the device pin-out, internal schematic, maximum ratings, suggested applications, and performance curves.

Because the input stage of all op-amps is a differential amplifier, there are two inputs marked with the symbols (+) and (−). These symbols refer to the phase of the output signal compared to the input signal and should be read as noninverting (+) and inverting (−) rather than "plus" or "minus". If the noninverting input is more positive than the inverting input, the output will be positive. If the inverting input is more positive, then the output will be negative. The symbol for an op-amp is shown in Figure 19-1.

The power supply connections are not always shown but must be connected for proper operation. In addition, power supply bypass capacitors are frequently placed near the power connections as shown. Be careful to observe the polarity of electrolytic capacitors when bypassing the power supplies.

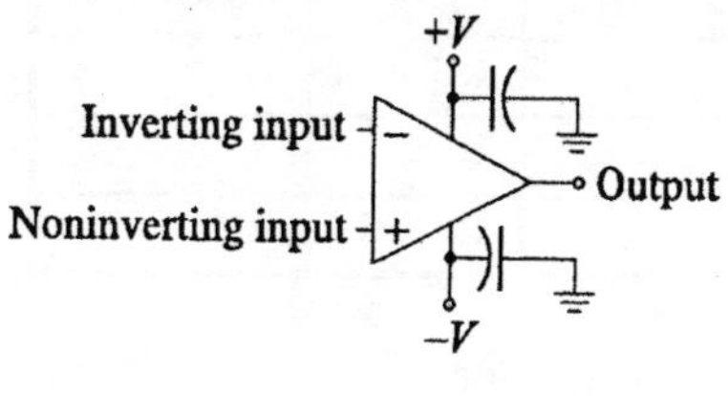

Figure 19-1

Materials Needed:
Resistors: two 100 Ω, two 10 kΩ, two 100 kΩ, one 1.0 MΩ
Two 1.0 µF capacitors
One 741C op-amp

For Further Investigation:
    One 10 Ω resistor

Procedure:
1. Examine the specification sheet for the 741C op-amp (Appendix A). From the specification sheet, determine the typical and maximum values for each quantity listed in Table 19-1. Record the specified values for $T_A = 25°C$. Note the measurement units which are listed on the right side of the specification sheet. (Slew rate is provided because it is not shown in the shortened data sheet in Appendix A.)

Table 19-1

Step	Parameter	Specified Value			Measured Value
		Minimum	Typical	Maximum	
2d	Input Offset Voltage, V_{OS}				
3d	Input Bias Current, I_{BIAS}				
3e	Input Offset Current, I_{OS}				
4b	Differential Gain, $A_{v(d)}$				
4c	Common-Mode Gain, A_{cm}				
4d	CMRR$'$				
5	Slew Rate		0.5 V/µs		

2. In this step, you will measure the input offset voltage, V_{OS}, of a 741C op-amp. The input offset voltage is the amount of voltage that must be applied between the *input* terminals through two equal resistors to give zero *output* voltage. It is a dc parameter.
    a. Measure and record the resistors listed in Table 19-2. R_C is for bias compensation.
    b. Connect the circuit shown in Figure 19-2. Install 1 µF bypass capacitors on the power supply leads as shown. Note the polarities of the capacitors.
    c. Measure the output voltage, V_{OUT}. The input offset voltage is found by dividing the output voltage by the closed loop gain. The closed-loop gain is: $A_{v(cl)} = R_f/R_i + 1$ (assuming a noninverting amplifier for the purpose of the offset calculation).
    d. Record the measured V_{OS} in Table 19-1.

Table 19-2

Resistor	Listed Value	Measured Value
R_f	1.0 MΩ	
R_i	10 kΩ	
R_C	10 kΩ	

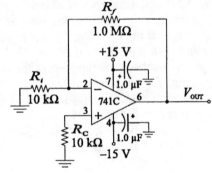

Figure 19-2

244

3. In this step, you will measure the input bias current, I_{BIAS}, and the input offset current, I_{os}, of a 741C op-amp. The input bias current is the average of the input currents at each input terminal. The input offset current is a measure of how well these two currents match. The input offset current is the difference in the two bias currents when the output voltage is 0 V. The input bias current and input offset current are dc parameters.
    a. Measure and record the resistors listed in Table 19-3.
    b. Connect the circuit shown in Figure 19-3.
    c. Measure the voltage across R_1 and R_2 of Figure 19-3. Use Ohm's law to calculate the current in each resistor.
    d. Record the *average* of these two currents in Table 19-1 as the input bias current, I_{BIAS}.
    e. Record the *difference* in these two currents in Table 19-1 as the input offset current, I_{os}.

Table 19-3

Resistor	Listed Value	Measured Value
R_1	100 kΩ	
R_2	100 kΩ	

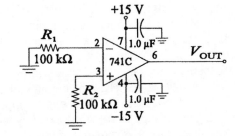

Figure 19-3

4. In this step, you will measure the common-mode rejection ratio, CMRR, of a 741C op-amp. The basic CMRR is the ratio of the op-amp's differential gain ($A_{v(d)}$) divided by the common-mode gain ($A_{v(cm)}$). Because it is a ratio of gains, CMRR is an ac parameter. It is frequently expressed in decibels (indicated with a prime symbol) according to the definition:

$$CMRR' = 20 \log \frac{A_{v(d)}}{A_{v(cm)}}$$

    a. Measure and record the resistors listed in Table 19-4. For an accurate measurement of CMRR', resistors R_A and R_B should be closely matched as should R_C and R_D.
    b. It is more accurate to compute the differential gain, $A_{v(d)}$, based on the resistance ratio than to measure it directly. Determine the differential gain by dividing the measured value of R_C by R_A. Enter the differential gain, $A_{v(d)}$, in Table 19-1.
    c. Connect the circuit shown in Figure 19-4. Set the signal generator for 1.0 V_{pp} at 1 kHz. Measure the output voltage, $V_{out(cm)}$. Determine the common-mode gain, $A_{v(cm)}$, by dividing $V_{out(cm)}$ by $V_{in(cm)}$. Record the result in Table 19-1.
    d. Determine the CMRR', in decibels, for your 741C op-amp. Record the result in Table 19-1.

Table 19-4

Resistor	Listed Value	Measured Value
R_A	100 Ω	
R_B	100 Ω	
R_C	100 kΩ	
R_D	100 kΩ	

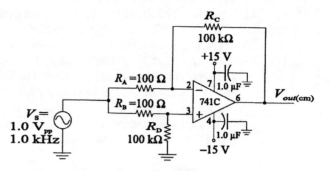

Figure 19-4

5. In this step, you will measure the slew rate of your op-amp. Slew rate is the internally limited rate of change in output voltage with a large-amplitude step function applied to the input. It is usually specified for a unity-gain voltage-follower with a fast rising input pulse. It is usually expressed in units of volts/microsecond (V/μs).

Connect the unity gain circuit shown in Figure 19-5. Set the signal generator for a 10 V_{pp} square wave at 10 kHz. The output voltage will be slew-rate limited and will not respond instantaneously to the change in the input voltage. The slew rate can be measured by observing the change in voltage divided by the change in time at any two points on the rising output waveform as shown in Figure 19-6. Record the measured value in Table 19-1.

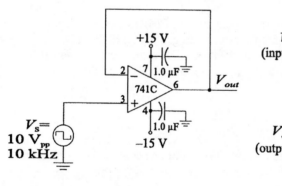

Figure 19-5

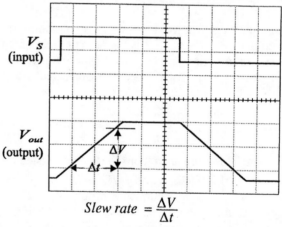

$$Slew\ rate = \frac{\Delta V}{\Delta t}$$

Figure 19-6

Conclusion:

246

Evaluation and Review Questions:

1. What is the meaning of the (+) and (−) terminals on the op-amp symbol?

2. Explain the meaning of input offset voltage.

3. What is the difference between the input bias current and the input offset current?

4. (a) What is the difference between differential gain and common-mode gain?

    (b) Explain how you measured the CMRR$'$ of the 741C.

    (c) What is the advantage of a high CMRR?

5. What is the advantage of a fast slew rate for an op-amp?

For Further Investigation:
Although the output impedance of an op-amp is low, it does not follow that an op amp can drive a very small load impedance. Op-amps have a current-limiting circuit to protect the output when it is short circuited or when the load is too small. Test the current limit of your op-amp using the voltage-follower circuit you constructed in step 5. Reduce the input frequency until you observe no slew rate limiting on the output. While observing, connect a 10 Ω resistor between the output and ground. Sketch the input and output signals and determine the current limit for both the positive and negative excursion of the signal. Compare the measured current limit with the specified current limit. For the signal observed, what is the *smallest* resistor you could use without having current limiting?

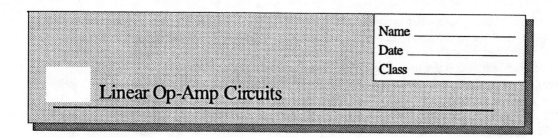

Name _____

Date _____

Class _____

Linear Op-Amp Circuits

Objectives:

After performing this experiment, you will be able to:
1. Construct and test inverting and noninverting amplifiers using op-amps.
2. Specify components for inverting and noninverting amplifiers using op-amps.

Summary of Theory:

One of the most important ideas in electronics incorporates the idea of *feedback*, where a portion of the output is returned to the input. If the return signal tends to decrease the input amplitude, it is called *negative feedback*. Negative feedback produces a number of desirable qualities in an amplifier, increasing its stability and its frequency response. It also allows the gain to be controlled independently of the device parameters, temperature, or other variables.

Operational amplifiers are almost always used with external, negative feedback. The feedback circuit determines the specific characteristics of the amplifier. By itself, an op-amp has an extremely high voltage gain called the *open-loop* gain, A_{ol}. When negative feedback is added, the overall gain of the amplifier is determined by the feedback circuit. This gain, including the feedback circuit, is called the *closed-loop* gain, A_{cl}.

Figure 20-1 illustrates a noninverting amplifier with negative feedback. The input is applied to the noninverting terminal and a fraction (B) of the output is returned to the inverting input by the voltage divider. The very high gain of the amplifier forces the two inputs to be very nearly the same voltage; therefore, the input voltage is across R_i and the output voltage is across $R_i + R_f$. The closed-loop gain of this noninverting amplifier is given as $A_{cl(NI)}$. The closed-loop gain is the reciprocal of the feedback fraction as shown with Figure 20-1.

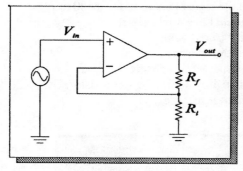

$$\text{feedback fraction} = B = \frac{R_i}{R_i + R_f}$$

$$A_{cl(NI)} = \frac{1}{B} = \frac{R_i + R_f}{R_i} = 1 + \frac{R_f}{R_i}$$

Figure 20-1

An inverting amplifier is shown in Figure 20-2. In this amplifier, the output voltage is the opposite phase to the input voltage. The noninverting input is grounded and the input signal is applied through a resistor to the inverting terminal. A feedback resistor is connected between the output and the inverting input. This amplifier can be analyzed by assuming the input current is same as the current in the feedback resistor, $I_{in} = I_f$ and that the open-loop gain of the amplifier is very high. From these assumptions, the closed loop gain can be calculated quite accurately as the ratio of the feedback resistor to the input resistor. The basic equations for the inverting amplifier are shown with Figure 20-2. The minus sign indicates inversion between the input and output. $V_{(-)}$ refers to the inverting input on the op-amp.

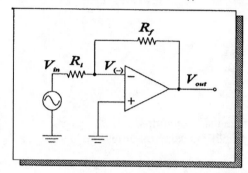

$$I_{in} = I_f$$

A_{ol} is very large, therefore

$$V_{(-)} = -\frac{V_{out}}{A_{ol}} \cong 0$$

$$\frac{V_{in}}{R_i} = -\frac{V_{out}}{R_f}$$

$$\frac{V_{out}}{V_{in}} = A_{cl(I)} = -\frac{R_f}{R_i}$$

Figure 20-2

Materials Needed:
Resistors: two 1.0 kΩ, one 10 kΩ, one 470 kΩ, one 1.0 MΩ
Two 1.0 µF capacitors
One 741C op-amp

For Further Investigation:
    One 1.0 kΩ potentiometer, one 100 kΩ resistor, assorted resistors to test

Procedure:
1. The circuit to be tested in this step is the noninverting amplifier illustrated in Figure 20-3.
    a. Measure a 10 kΩ resistor for R_f and a 1.0 kΩ resistor for R_i. Record the measured value of resistance in Table 20-1.
    b. Using the measured resistances, compute the closed-loop gain of the noninverting amplifier. The closed-loop gain equation is given next to Figure 20-1.
    c. Calculate V_{out} using the computed closed-loop gain.
    d. Connect the circuit shown in Figure 20-3. Set the signal generator for a 500 mV$_{pp}$ sinusoidal wave at 1.0 kHz. The generator should have no dc offset.
    e. Measure the output voltage, V_{out}. Record the measured value.
    f. Measure the feedback voltage at pin 2. Record the measured value.
    g. Place a 1.0 MΩ test resistor in series with the generator. Measure the input resistance of the circuit, R_{in}, based on the voltage drop across the test resistor. Use the voltage divider rule to indirectly find the input resistance.

Table 20-1

R_f Measured	R_i Measured	V_{in} Measured	$A_{cl(NI)}$ Computed	V_{out} Computed	V_{out} Measured (pin 6)	$V_{(-)}$ Measured (pin 2)	R_{in} Measured
		500 mV$_{pp}$					

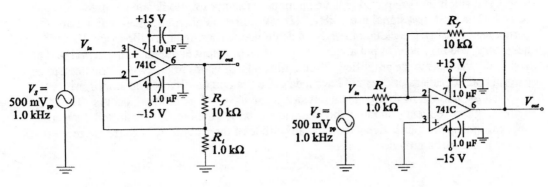

Figure 20-3   Figure 20-4

2. In this step you will test an inverting amplifier. All data are to be recorded in Table 20-2. The circuit is illustrated in Figure 20-4. The closed-loop gain is:

$$A_{cl(I)} = -\frac{R_f}{R_i}$$

a. Use the same resistors for R_f and R_i as in step 1. Record the measured value of resistance in Table 20-2.
b. Using the measured resistance, compute and record the closed-loop gain of the inverting amplifier.
c. Calculate V_{out} using the computed closed-loop gain.
d. Connect the circuit shown in Figure 20-4. Set the signal generator for a 500 mV$_{pp}$ sine wave at 1 kHz. The generator should have no dc offset.
e. Measure and record the output voltage, V_{out}.
f. Measure and record the voltage at pin 2. This point is called a *virtual ground* because of the effect of negative feedback.
g. Place a 1.0 kΩ test resistor in series with the generator and R_i. Measure the input resistance of the circuit, R_{in}, based on the voltage drop across the test resistor. In this case, you should observe that the drop across the test resistor is about the same as the drop across R_i.

Table 20-2

R_f Measured	R_i Measured	V_{in} Measured	$A_{cl(I)}$ Computed	V_{out} Computed	V_{out} Measured (pin 6)	$V_{(-)}$ Measured (pin 2)	R_{in} Measured
		500 mV$_{pp}$					

3. In this step you will specify the components for an inverting amplifier using a 741C op-amp. The amplifier is required to have an input resistance of 10 kΩ and a closed-loop gain of –47. The input test signal is a 1 kHz, 100 mV$_{pp}$ sinusoidal wave signal with no dc component (offset). Check that there is no dc component using an oscilloscope. If necessary, you may need to put a voltage divider on the input to attenuate the signal to the 100 mV level. Draw the amplifier. Then build and test your circuit. *Note:* You need to be careful that the generator does not have a dc offset; remember this is a dc amplifier!

   Find the maximum voltage the input signal can have before clipping occurs. Try increasing the frequency and note the frequency at which the output is distorted. Does the upper frequency response depend on the amplitude of the waveform? Summarize your results in the space provided.

Conclusion:

Evaluation and Review Questions:
1. Express the gain of the amplifiers tested in steps 1 and 2 in dB.

2. It was correct to talk about a *virtual ground* for the inverting amplifier. Why isn't it correct to refer to a virtual ground for the noninverting amplifier?

3. If $R_f = R_i = 10$ kΩ, what gain would you expect for:
   (a) a noninverting amplifier?

   (b) an inverting amplifier?

4. (a) For the noninverting amplifier in Figure 20-3, if $R_f = 0$ and R_i is infinite, what is the gain?

(b) What is this type of amplifier called?

5. What output would you expect in the inverting amplifier of Figure 20-4 if R_f were open?

For Further Investigation:
An interesting application of an inverting amplifier is to use it as the basis of an ohmmeter for high value resistors. The circuit is shown in Figure 20-5. The unknown resistor, labeled R_x, is placed between the terminals. The output voltage is proportional to the unknown resistance. Calibrate the meter by placing a known 10 kΩ resistor in place of R_x and adjusting the potentiometer for exactly 100 mV output. The output then represents 10 mV/1000 Ω. By reading the output voltage, and moving the decimal point, you can directly read resistors from several thousand ohms to over 1 MΩ.

Construct the circuit and test it using different resistors. Calibrate output voltage against resistance and compare with theory. Find the percent error for a 1 MΩ resistor using a lab meter as a standard. Summarize your results in a short report.

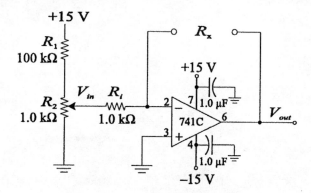

Figure 20-5

Nonlinear Op-Amp Circuits

OBJECTIVES

After performing this experiment, you will be able to:
1. Construct and test an op-amp comparator, an integrator, and a differentiator circuit.
2. Determine the response of the circuits listed in objective 1 to various waveforms.
3. Troubleshoot faults in op-amp circuits.

MATERIALS NEEDED

Resistors:

One 330 Ω, one 1.0 kΩ, four 10 kΩ, three 22 kΩ, one 330 kΩ

Capacitors:

One 2200 pF, one 0.01 μF, two 1.0 μF

Three 741C op-amps

One 1 kΩ potentiometer

Two LEDs (one red, one green)

SUMMARY OF THEORY

The basic op-amp is a linear device; however, many applications exist in which the op-amp is used in a nonlinear circuit. One of the most common nonlinear applications is the comparator. A comparator is used to detect which of two voltages is larger and to drive the output into either positive or negative saturation. Comparators can be made from ordinary op-amps (and frequently are), but there are special ICs designed as comparators. They are designed with very high slew rates and frequently have open-collector outputs to allow interfacing to logic or bus systems.

Other uses of op-amps include a variety of signal processing applications. Op-amps are ideally suited to make precise integrators. Integration is the process of finding the area under a curve, as shown in the Summary of Theory for the experiment on Integrating and Differentiating Circuits. An integrator produces an output voltage that is proportional to the *integral* of the input voltage waveform. The opposite of integration is differentiation. Differentiation circuits produce an output that is proportional to the *derivative* of the input voltage waveform. The basic op-amp comparator, integrator, and differentiator circuits with representative waveforms are illustrated in Figure 1.

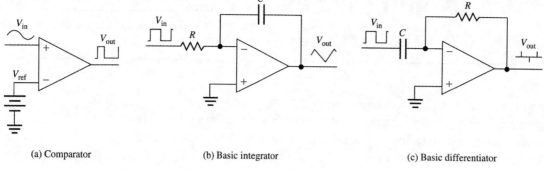

(a) Comparator   (b) Basic integrator   (c) Basic differentiator

Figure 1

PROCEDURE

1. In this step you will construct and test an op-amp circuit connected as a comparator. Construct the circuit shown in Figure 2. Vary the potentiometer. Measure the output voltage when the red LED is on and then when the green LED is on. The 741C has current-limiting circuitry that prevents excessive current from destroying the LEDs. Record the output voltages, V_{OUT}, in Table 1. Notice that the LEDs prevent the output from going into positive and negative saturation. Then set the potentiometer to the threshold point. Measure and record V_{ref} at the threshold.

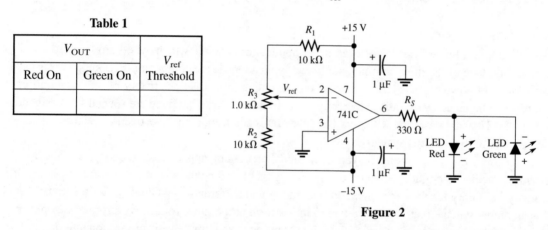

Table 1

V_{OUT}		V_{ref}
Red On	Green On	Threshold

Figure 2

2. In this step, you will test the effects of the comparator on a sine wave input and add an integrating circuit to the output of the comparator. Connect the circuit shown in Figure 3 and add a sine wave generator to the comparator as illustrated. Set the output for a 1.0 V_{pp} at 1.0 kHz with no dc offset. Observe the waveforms from the comparator (point **A**) and from the integrator (point **B**). Adjust R_3 so that the waveform at **B** is centered about zero volts. Sketch the observed waveforms in the correct time relationship on Plot 1. Show the voltages and time on your plot.

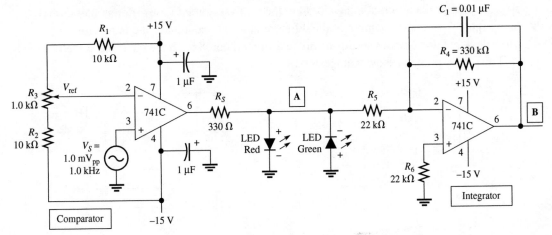

Figure 3

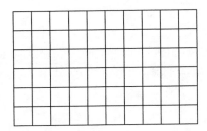

Plot 1

3.   Vary R_3 while observing the output of the comparator and the integrator. Observations:

4.   For each of the troubles listed in Table 2, see if you can predict the effect on the circuit. Then insert the trouble and check your prediction. At the end of this step, restore the circuit to normal operation.

Table 2

Trouble	Symptoms
No negative power supply	
Red LED open	
C_1 open	
R_4 open	

257

5.   In this step, you will add a differentiating circuit to the previous circuit. The differentiator circuit is shown in Figure 4. Connect the input of the differentiator to the output of the integrator (point **B**). Observe the input and output waveforms of the differentiator. Sketch the observed waveforms on Plot 2. Label your plot and show voltage and time.

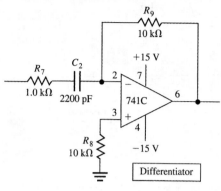

Figure 4

Plot 2

6.   Remove the input from the differentiator and connect it to the output from the comparator (point **A**). Observe the new input and output waveforms of the differentiator. Sketch the observed waveforms on Plot 3. Label your plot.

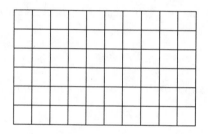

Plot 3

CONCLUSION

EVALUATION AND REVIEW QUESTIONS

1.   Compute the minimum and maximum V_{ref} for the comparator in Figure 2.

$V_{ref(min)} = $ _____ $V_{ref(max)} = $ _____

2.   The comparator output did not go near the power supply voltages. Explain why not.

3. (a)   For the integrator circuit in Figure 3, what is the purpose of R_4?

    (b)   What happened when it was removed?

4. What type of circuit will produce leading- and trailing-edge triggers from a square wave input?

5. What effect would you expect on the output of the integrator in Figure 3 if the frequency used were 100 Hz instead of 1.0 kHz?

FOR FURTHER INVESTIGATION

A useful variation of the comparator is the Schmitt trigger circuit shown in Figure 5. This circuit is basically a comparator that uses *positive* feedback to change the threshold voltage when the output switches. The trip point is dependent on whether the output is already saturated high or low. This effect is called *hysteresis*. Construct the circuit, test its operation, and summarize your findings in a short report.

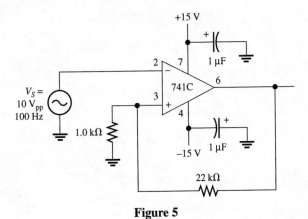

Figure 5

MULTISIM TROUBLESHOOTING

This experiment has four Multisim files on the CD. Three of the four files contain a simulated "fault"; one has "no fault". The file with no fault is named EXP40-3-nf.msm. You may want to open this file to compare your results with the computer simulation. Then open each of the files with faults. Use the simulated instruments to investigate the circuit and determine the problem. The following are the filenames for circuits with troubleshooting problems for this experiment.

EXP40-3-f1.msm

    Fault: _____

EXP40-3-f2.msm

    Fault: _____

EXP40-3-f3.msm

    Fault: _____

Op-Amp Frequency Response

Objectives:

After performing this experiment, you will be able to:

1. Compute and measure the bandwidth of noninverting op-amp circuits as a function of gain.
2. Compute and measure the bandwidth of inverting op-amp circuits as a function of gain.
3. Compare the bandwidth of noninverting op-amp circuits with inverting op-amps circuits.

Summary of Theory:

The typical single-pole frequency response for a 741C op-amp is shown as the curve marked open-loop gain in Figure 21-1. The plot shows the gain plotted as a function of frequency in kHz. The op-amp's cutoff frequency, $f_{c(ol)}$, is the frequency at which the gain is 0.707 of the value at dc. For the 741C, this is typically only about 10 Hz. As with all one-pole RC filters, the response rolls off at –20 dB/decade above f_c. This roll-off has a constant slope of –1 (on the log-log plot). This implies that the open-loop gain times the bandwidth is a constant for frequencies above f_c.

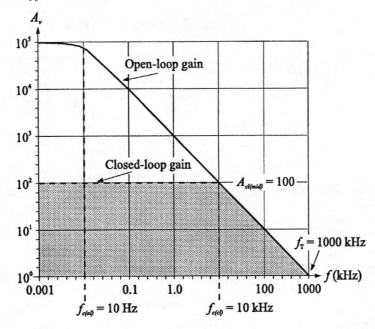

Figure 21-1

Closed-loop refers to the circuit with negative feedback present to control the gain and other parameters. When an op-amp is configured as a noninverting amplifier, the closed-loop gain is $1/B$ as discussed in Experiment 20 (recall that B is the feedback fraction). If the closed-loop gain of a noninverting amplifier is 1.0, the bandwidth is given by f_T, the unity-gain frequency (see Figure 21-1). For other gains, the closed-loop bandwidth (equivalent to the cutoff frequency for any dc amplifier) can be determined graphically from the frequency response curve by noting the intersection of the closed-loop gain line with the open-loop response. An example is shown in Figure 21-1. For a closed-loop gain of 100 (shaded area) the bandwidth is observed to be 10 kHz. The same result can be obtained from the equation

$$BW_{cl} = f_T B \hspace{3cm} Equation\ 21\text{-}1$$

where:

BW_{cl} = closed-loop bandwidth
f_T = unity-gain frequency
B = feedback fraction

The bandwidth for an inverting amplifier is not as high as a comparable noninverting amplifier. The difference is small for high-gain circuits but is more pronounced for lower gain circuits or with certain applications such as a summing amplifier. To compute the bandwidth for the inverting configuration, assume all signal sources are at ground and calculate the feedback fraction, B, *as if the noninverting input were driven*. Use this B in Equation 21-1 to find the bandwidth.

For example, consider the inverting amplifier in Figure 21-2(a) with a unity-gain frequency of 1.0 MHz and a gain of –2.0. To compute the bandwidth, mentally move the input to the noninverting terminal as in (b) and compute the feedback fraction. In this case, $B = 1/3$. Substituting into Equation 21-1,

$$BW_{cl} = f_T B$$
$$= (1.0\ MHz)(1/3) = 333\ kHz$$

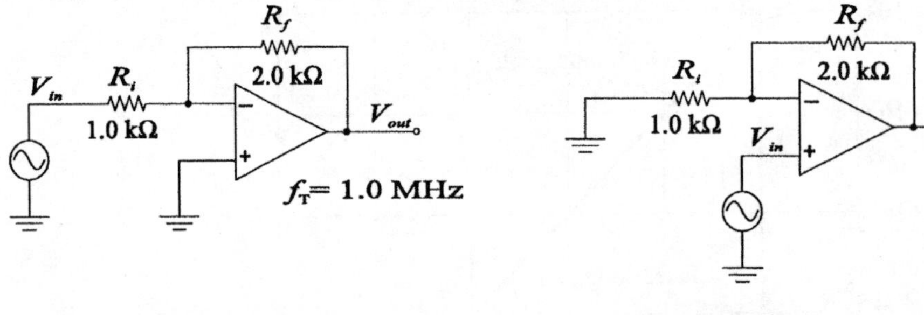

(a) Inverting amplifier with a gain of –2   (b) Calculate frequency response based on driving noninverting input

Figure 21-2

Materials Needed:
Resistors: one 620 Ω, two 1.0 kΩ, one 2.0 kΩ, one 3.3 kΩ, one 10 kΩ, one 18 kΩ, one 100 kΩ
Two 1.0 µF capacitors
One 741C op-amp

For Further Investigation:
One 100 Ω resistor

Procedure:
Frequency Response of the Noninverting Amplifier
1. Measure and record the values of the resistors listed in Table 21-1.

2. Construct a noninverting voltage-follower as in Figure 21-3 with the power supplies set to ±15 V. Connect 1.0 µF bypass capacitors near the power connections to the op-amp. The purpose of R_A and R_B is to attenuate the generator voltage; they are not necessary if you can set your generator to a 50 mV$_{pp}$ sine wave.

Table 21-1

Step	Resistor	Listed Value	Measured Value
4	$R_{i\text{-}1}$	2.0 kΩ	
4	$R_{f\text{-}1}$	18 kΩ	
5	$R_{i\text{-}2}$	1.0 kΩ	
5	$R_{f\text{-}2}$	100 kΩ	

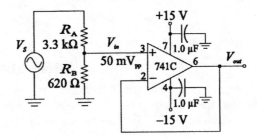

Figure 21-3

3. (a) To measure the unity-gain frequency (or unity-gain bandwidth), a very small signal must be used to avoid slew rate limitations. Adjust the generator for a 50 mV$_{pp}$ sine wave at the noninverting input terminal of the op-amp at a frequency of 10 kHz. Measure the output voltage and record the gain in Table 21-2.

   (b) Increase the frequency until the output amplitude falls to 70.7% of the output amplitude observed for the gain measurement. Adjust the generator as necessary to maintain the input signal at 50 mV$_{pp}$. Since this is a dc amplifier, the closed-loop bandwidth is equal to the unity-gain frequency. Measure and record the bandwidth in Table 21-2.

Table 21-2 Data for Noninverting Amplifiers

Step	Computed Gain	Measured Gain	Closed-loop Bandwidth Computed	Measured
3	1.0			
4	10			
5	101			

4. (a) Change the circuit to a noninverting amplifier with a gain of 10 as shown in Figure 21-4. Set the frequency to 10 kHz with a 50 mV$_{pp}$ input signal. Measure the output voltage and compute the gain. Enter the measured gain in Table 21-2.

   (b) Compute the closed-loop bandwidth for this configuration by dividing the unity-gain bandwidth (step 3) by the measured gain (step 4(a)). Now measure the bandwidth by increasing the generator's frequency until the output amplitude falls to 70.7% of the output amplitude that was measured at 10 kHz. Again, the input signal should be maintained at 50 mV$_{pp}$. Record the data in Table 21-2.

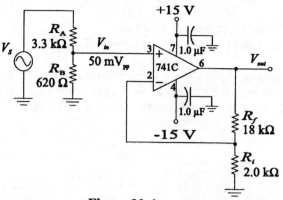

Figure 21-4

5. Change R_f to 100 kΩ and R_i to 1.0 kΩ, resulting in a computed gain of 101. Repeat step 4 but start the frequency at 1.0 kHz with a 50 mV$_{pp}$ input signal. Measure the gain and the bandwidth as before. Record the values in Table 21-2.

Frequency Response of the Inverting Amplifier
6. Measure and record the values of the resistors listed in Table 21-3.

Table 21-3

Step	Resistor	Listed Value	Measured Value
7	R_{i-3}	1.0 kΩ	
7	R_{f-3}	1.0 kΩ	
8	R_{f-4}	10 kΩ	
9	R_{f-5}	100 kΩ	

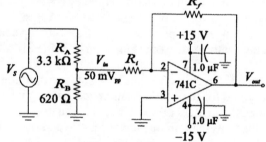

Figure 21-5

7. Refer to Figure 21-5. Using 1.0 kΩ resistors for both (R_{i-3} and R_{f-3}), construct an inverting amplifier with a gain of –1.0. Compute the closed-loop bandwidth using Equation 21-1. Assume the unity-gain frequency is the same as you found in step 3 and the feedback fraction is 0.5 (why?). Measure the gain and bandwidth as before using a 50 mV$_{pp}$ signal as the input. Record computed and measured values in Table 21-4.

8. Form an inverting amplifier with a gain of –10 by changing R_f equal to 10 kΩ (Use R_{f-4}). Compute the bandwidth for this configuration. Repeat the measurements of gain and bandwidth, and record these values in Table 21-4.

Table 21-4 Data for Inverting Amplifiers

Step	Computed Gain	Measured Gain	Closed-loop Bandwidth Computed	Measured
7	–1.0			
8	–10			
9	–100			

9. Form an inverting amplifier with a gain of –100. (Use $R_{f\text{-}5}$). Compute the bandwidth for this configuration. Repeat step 7 but start the frequency at 1.0 kHz with a 50 mV$_{pp}$ input signal. Record the data in Table 21-4.

Conclusion:

Evaluation and Review Questions:

1. (a) From your data for the noninverting amplifier (Table 21-2), determine if the gain-bandwidth product was constant.

   (b) Should it be?

2. (a) From your data for the inverting amplifier (Table 21-4), determine if the gain-bandwidth product was constant.

   (b) Should it be?

3. In step 5, you were directed to start the gain and bandwidth measurements using a 1.0 kHz signal instead of a 10 kHz signal as before. Explain why this was necessary.

4. (a) How would you expect the bandwidth of the amplifiers in this experiment to affect the rise time of a square wave input?

(b) What factor, other than bandwidth, can also affect the rise time of a square wave?

5. Is it possible to increase the bandwidth of a high-gain amplifier by substituting two lower gain amplifiers? Explain.

For Further Investigation:
The bandwidth can be controlled for an inverting amplifier by connecting a resistor from the inverting input to ground. Investigate this effect by testing the circuit shown in Figure 21-6. The circuit is essentially the same as Figure 21-5 but with the addition of R_C. Find the gain at a low frequency; then find the bandwidth. Consider the feedback fraction as seen from the noninverting terminal. Compare your results with those in Table 21-4. Can you explain the significance of the reduced bandwidth? Can you think of an application where a reduced bandwidth like this is desirable?

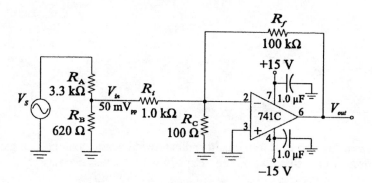

Figure 21-6

Summing Amplifiers

Objectives:

After performing this experiment, you will be able to:

1. Construct and test a digital-to-analog converter (DAC) from a summing amplifier. Apply a binary count sequence to form a step generator, and explain the waveforms observed.
2. Test various precision diode circuits including a noninverting half-wave rectifier, an inverting half-wave rectifier, and a full-wave rectifier that uses a summing amplifier.
3. Explain the operation of these circuits.

Summary of Theory:

The summing amplifier, illustrated in Figure 23-1, is essentially a multiple input version of an inverting amplifier. The current into the feedback resistor, R_f, is the sum of the current in each input resistor. Since the inverting input is at virtual ground, the total input current is $V_1/R_1 + V_2/R_2 + V_3/R_3$. The virtual ground has the advantage of isolating the various inputs from each other. In addition, the gain of each input can be set differently. Variable gain is useful for mixing several audio sources at different levels (such as microphones) into a single channel.

Another application of a summing amplifier is the notch or band-reject filter illustrated in Figure 23-2. In this circuit, the outputs of a low-pass and a high-pass filter are combined in a summing amplifier. Typically, the low-pass and high-pass filters are designed with operational amplifiers to form the filter elements (this defines an *active filter*). Designs based on this idea are called state-variable filters and they are the most versatile type of active filter. Outputs could be taken from both the low-pass and high-pass filter sections in addition to the output of the summing amplifier. (Active filters are studied in Chapter 9 of the text.)

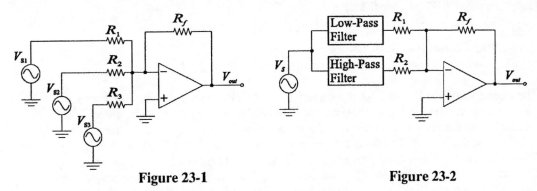

Figure 23-1   **Figure 23-2**

The ability of a summing amplifier to combine multiple inputs while maintaining isolation between them leads to a number of other interesting applications. One circuit that you will investigate is a precision full-wave rectifier. (Precision refers to the fact that the output is not offset by any diode drops.) The full-wave circuit contains a precision inverting half-wave rectifier and a summing amplifier.

A *noninverting* precision half-wave circuit is shown in Figure 23-3, formed by simply inserting a diode into the feedback path of a voltage-follower. When the diode is forward-biased, it closes the feedback loop, giving an output that follows the input exactly. When the diode is reverse-biased, the output essentially disconnects the op-amp from the load, causing the output to be zero. Instead of this noninverting configuration, the full-wave circuit requires an *inverting* rectifier circuit which is introduced in the Procedure section.

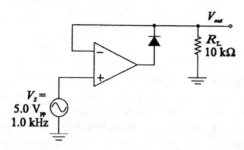

Figure 23-3 Noninverting precision half-wave rectifier.

A summing amplifier can also be used as a basic digital-to-analog converter (DAC) by weighting the inputs according to a binary sequence. Adding a counter to the input results in a step-generator that produces a series of steps by the weighted addition of the outputs of the counter for applications such as a transistor curve tracer. This experiment starts with this circuit, as an interface between the digital and analog world.

Materials Needed:
Resistors: one 3.9 kΩ, one 5.1 kΩ, four 10 kΩ, one 20 kΩ
Capacitors: two 1.0 μF
Two signal diodes, 1N914 (or equivalent)
Two op-amps: LM741C
One 7493A 4-bit ripple counter

For Further Investigation:
Resistors: two 4.7 kΩ, three 100 kΩ
Capacitors: one 0.01 μF, one 0.1 μF

Procedure:
DAC and Step Generator
1. Measure and record the values of the resistors listed in Table 23-1.

2. The circuit shown in Figure 23-4 is a summing amplifier connected to the outputs of a binary counter. The counter outputs are weighted differently by resistors R_A through R_C, and added by the summing amplifier. The resistors and summing amplifier form a basic DAC. Note that the 7493A counter is powered from a +5.0 V supply. The input to the 7493A is a logic pulse (approximately 0 to 4 V) at 1.0 kHz from a function generator. Construct the circuit. Observe V_{out} from the 741C. You should observe a series of steps. Sketch the output in Plot 23-1. Label the voltage and time on your plot.

Table 23-1

Resistor	Listed Value	Measured Value
R_A	20 kΩ	
R_B	10 kΩ	
R_C	5.1 kΩ	
R_f	3.9 kΩ	

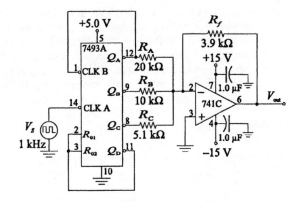

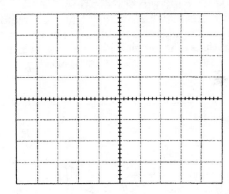

Figure 23-4

3. To see how the steps are formed, observe the Q_A, Q_B, and Q_C outputs from the 7493A. To see the correct time relationship between the signals, put Q_C on channel 1 of your oscilloscope; trigger the scope from this channel. Keep channel 1 in place while moving the channel 2 probe. Sketch the waveforms in the correct time relation in Plot 23-2.

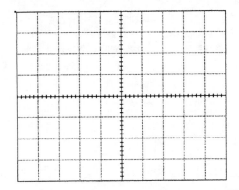

Plot 23-1   **Plot 23-2**

Precision Noninverting Half-wave Rectifier

4. A precision noninverting half-wave rectifier was shown in Figure 23-3 and discussed in the Summary of Theory. Construct the circuit; set the input waveform for a 5.0 V_{pp} sinusoidal wave with no dc offset at a frequency of 1.0 kHz. The power connections on this and remaining circuits in this experiment are not shown explicitly – connect the 741C the same as before including the bypass capacitors. Observe the output waveform. You should see that the output follows the input almost exactly except for a small "jump" on the leading edge. (This jump is more pronounced if you raise the frequency). The reason for the jump is the time required (slew rate) for the output to go from negative saturation to +0.7 V (the voltage required to turn on the diode).

Observations:_____

_____

Precision Inverting Half-wave Rectifier

5. A precision inverting half-wave rectifier is shown in Figure 23-5. The diode between the op-amp output and the inverting input (D_1) prevents the output from saturating, allowing the output to change immediately after the diode starts conducting. The circuit can be recognized as an inverting amplifier with a diode added to the feedback path and the clamping diode. Construct the circuit with the input set as before and observe the output. Look at pin 6 and momentarily pull D_1 from the circuit.

Observations:_____

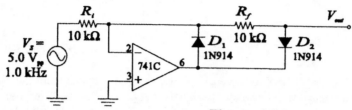

Figure 23-5

Precision Full-wave Rectifier

6. By combining the inverting half-wave rectifier from step 5 with a summing amplifier, a precision full-wave rectifier can be constructed. The circuit is shown in Figure 23-6. Construct the circuit with the input set as before. On Plot 23-3, sketch the waveforms at the left side of R_{i2} and R_{i3} (inputs) and V_{out}.

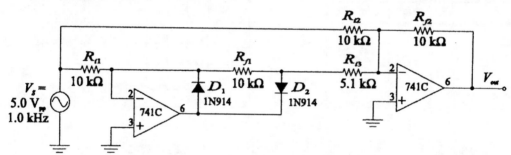

Figure 23-6

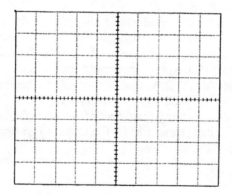

Plot 23-3

270

Conclusion:

Evaluation and Review Questions:

1. (a) The step generator in Figure 23-4 forms negative falling steps starting at zero volts and going to a negative voltage (approximately –4.4 V). Explain why.

   (b) How could you modify the circuit to produce positive, rising steps at the output?

2. Assume that all three inputs to the summing amplifier (Q_A, Q_B, and Q_C) in Figure 23-4 are 4.5 V. Compute the output voltage from the summing amplifier.

3. Assume you have a function generator that does not have a dc offset control. Show how you could use a summing amplifier to add or subtract a dc offset from the output.

4. The gain for the summing amplifier in the full-wave rectifier circuit (Figure 23-6) is not the same for both inputs. Explain why.

5. The word *operational amplifier* originated from mathematical operations that could be performed with it. Assume you wanted to produce a circuit for which the output voltage was given by the expression $V_{out} = -3A - 2B$ (A and B are variable input voltages). Show how this operation could be accomplished with a summing amplifier by drawing the circuit. Show values for resistors.

- - -

For Further Investigation:

As discussed in the Summary of Theory, a notch filter can be constructed by summing the outputs of a low-pass and a high-pass filter in a summing amplifier. Designs based on this idea are called state-variable filters and they are the most versatile of active filters. The particular filter shown in Figure 23-7 replaces the normal active filters with passive ones to give you an idea of the process. Start with the generator set to a 300 mV$_{pp}$ sine wave at 100 Hz. Then investigate the response of the circuit by varying the frequency across the audio band while you monitor the output on an oscilloscope. Summarize your findings.

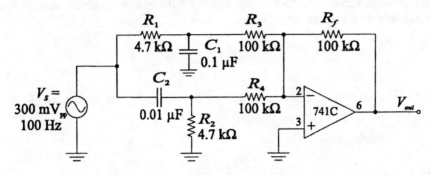

Figure 23-7

Feedback Oscillators

Name _____

Date _____

Class _____

OBJECTIVES

After performing this experiment, you will be able to:

1. Connect a class A amplifier; calculate and measure the dc and ac parameters.
2. Modify the amplifier with a feedback circuit that forms two versions of *LC* oscillators—the Colpitts and the Hartley.
3. Compare the computed and measured performance of the oscillators.

MATERIALS NEEDED

2N3904 NPN transistor (or equivalent)

One 100 Ω potentiometer

Resistors:

    One 1.0 kΩ, one 2.7 kΩ, one 3.3 kΩ, one 10 kΩ

Capacitors:

    Two 1000 pF, one 0.01 μF, three 0.1 μF

Inductors:

    One 2 μH (can be wound quickly from #22 wire), one 25 μH

For Further Investigation:

    One 1 MHz crystal, one 2N5458 N-channel JFET, one 10 MΩ resistor

SUMMARY OF THEORY

In electronic systems, there is almost always a requirement for one or more circuits that generate a continuous waveform. The output voltage can be a square wave, sine wave, sawtooth, or other periodic waveform. A free-running oscillator is basically an amplifier that generates a continuous alternating voltage by feeding a portion of the output signal back to the input. This type of oscillator is called a feedback oscillator; two types will be investigated in this experiment. A second type of oscillator is called a relaxation oscillator. Relaxation oscillators typically charge a capacitor to some point, then switch it to a discharge path. They are useful for generating sawtooth, triangle, and square waves.

Feedback oscillators are classified by the networks used to provide feedback. To sustain oscillations, the amplifier must have sufficient gain to overcome the losses in the feedback network. In addition, the feedback must be of the proper phase to ensure that the signal is reinforced at the output—in other words, there must be *positive* feedback. Feedback networks can be classified as *LC, RC,* or by a *crystal,* a special piezoelectric resonant network.

LC circuits have a parallel resonant circuit, commonly referred to as the *tank* circuit, that determines the frequency of oscillation. A portion of the output is returned to the input causing the amplifier to conduct only during a very small part of the total period. This means that the amplifier is actually run in class C mode. *LC* circuits are generally preferred for frequencies above 1 MHz, whereas *RC* oscillators are usually limited to frequencies below 10 MHz, where stability is not as critical. In applications where frequency stability is important, crystal oscillators have the advantage. In this experiment, you will test two *LC* oscillators, and in the For Further Investigation section, you will test a crystal oscillator.

PROCEDURE

1.   Measure and record the value of the resistors listed in Table 1.

2.   Observe the class A amplifier shown in Figure 1. Using your measured resistor values, compute the dc parameters for the amplifier listed in Table 2. R_{E1} is a 100 Ω potentiometer that you should set to 50 Ω. Then construct the circuit and verify that your computed dc parameters are as expected.

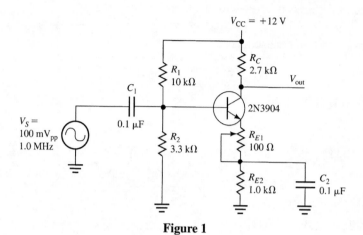

Figure 1

Table 1

Resistor	Listed Value	Measured Value
R_1	10 kΩ	
R_2	3.3 kΩ	
R_{E1}	50 Ω*	
R_{E2}	1.0 kΩ	
R_C	2.7 kΩ	

*Set potentiometer for 50 Ω

3.   Compute the ac parameters listed in Table 3. After you find r_e, find the gain by dividing the collector resistance by the sum of the unbypassed emitter resistance and r_e. (Assume that the potentiometer remains set to 50 Ω.) Find the ac voltage at the collector by multiplying the gain by the ac base voltage. Set the generator for a 100 mV$_{pp}$ sine wave at 1.0 MHz and measure the peak-to-peak collector voltage. Your computed quantities should agree with the measured values within experimental uncertainty. Record the measured ac parameters in Table 3.

Table 2

DC Parameter	Computed Value	Measured Value
V_B		
V_E		
I_E		
V_C		

Table 3

AC Parameter	Computed Value	Measured Value
V_b	100 mV$_{pp}$	
r_e		
A_v		
V_c		

4. Remove the generator and add the feedback network for a Colpitts oscillator, as shown in Figure 2. Adjust R_{E1} for the best output sine wave. Compute the frequency of the Colpitts oscillator and record the computed frequency in Table 4. Then, measure the frequency and the peak-to-peak voltage V_{pp} at the output and record them in Table 4.

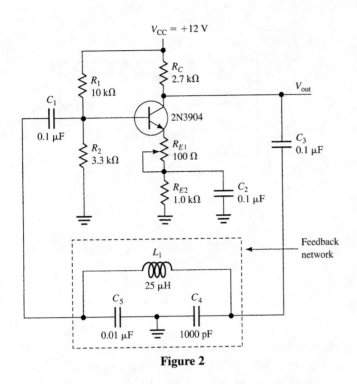

Table 4

Colpitts Oscillator	Computed Value	Measured Value
Frequency		
V_{pp}		

Figure 2

5. Observe what happens to the frequency and amplitude of the output signal when another 1000 pF capacitor is placed in parallel with C_4.

6. Observe the effect of freeze spray on the stability of the oscillator.

7. Replace the feedback network with the one shown in Figure 3. (L_2 can be wound by wrapping about 40 turns of #22 wire on a pencil.) Adjust R_{E1} for a good sine wave output. This configuration is that of a Hartley oscillator. Compute the frequency of the Hartley oscillator, and record the computed frequency in Table 5. Then, measure the frequency and the peak-to-peak voltage at the output and record them in Table 5.

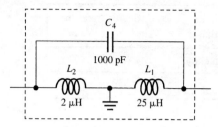

Figure 3

Table 5

Hartley Oscillator	Computed Value	Measured Value
Frequency		
V_{pp}		

CONCLUSION

EVALUATION AND REVIEW QUESTIONS

1. In step 5, you observed a change in the amplitude of the output signal when a capacitor was placed in parallel with C_4. Since the gain of the class A amplifier remained the same, what conclusion can you draw about the effect of the change on the amount of feedback?

2. What are the two conditions required for oscillation to occur in an LC oscillator?

3. Give a reason that an oscillator might drift from its normal frequency.

4. Summarize the difference between a Colpitts and a Hartley oscillator.

5.   For the circuit in Figure 2, predict the outcome in each case.
      (a) R_{E1} is shorted.

      (b) C_4 and C_5 are reversed.

      (c) C_2 is open.

      (d)   The power supply voltage is 6 V.

FOR FURTHER INVESTIGATION

When it is necessary to have high stability in an oscillator, the crystal oscillator is superior. For high-frequency crystal oscillators, FETs have advantages over bipolar transistors because of their high input impedance. This allows the tank circuit to be unloaded, resulting in a high Q. The circuit shown in Figure 4 has the advantage of being simple, yet very stable. Construct the circuit and observe the waveform at the drain. Compare the frequency with that stamped on the crystal case (to do this requires a frequency counter). Test the effect of freeze spray on the frequency and amplitude. Summarize your results.

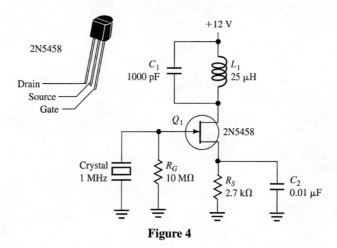

Figure 4

The Colpitts and Hartley Oscillator

Objectives:
After performing this experiment, you will be able to:
1. Connect a class-A amplifier; calculate and measure the dc and ac parameters.
2. Modify the amplifier with a feedback circuit that forms two versions of *LC* oscillators – the Colpitts and the Hartley.
3. Compare the computed and measured performance of the oscillators.

Summary of Theory:
In electronic systems, there are many requirements for one or more circuits that generate a continuous waveform. Several of these circuits are discussed in the text. A free-running oscillator is basically an amplifier that generates a continuous alternating voltage by feeding a portion of the output signal back to the input. The circuit in this experiment is based on the principles of a feedback oscillator, but introduces two other ways of obtaining the feedback, not discussed in the text.

Sinusoidal oscillators are classified by the networks used to provide feedback. To sustain oscillations, the amplifier must have sufficient gain to overcome the losses in the feedback network. In addition, the feedback must be of the proper phase to ensure that the signal is reinforced at the output – in other words, there must be *positive* feedback. One example is the phase shift oscillator that uses an *RC* network to produce the proper feedback (see Section 10-3 of the text). Feedback networks can be classified as *LC*, *RC* or by a *crystal*, a special piezoelectric resonant network. In the previous experiment, you generated a sine wave with a Wien bridge that uses an *RC* feedback network. The Wien bridge is an excellent choice for frequencies below 1 MHz. For higher frequencies, *LC* circuits and crystal oscillators are generally preferred.

LC circuits have a parallel resonant circuit, commonly referred to as the *tank* circuit, that determines the frequency of oscillation. A portion of the output is returned to the input causing the amplifier to conduct only during a very small part of the total period. This means that the amplifier is actually running in class C mode. In applications where frequency stability is important, crystal oscillators have the advantage. In this experiment, you will test two *LC* oscillators and, in the For Further Investigation section, you will test a crystal oscillator.

Materials Needed:
One 2N3904 *npn* transistor (or equivalent)
One 100 Ω potentiometer
Resistors: one 1.0 kΩ, one 2.7 kΩ, one 3.3 kΩ, one 10 kΩ
Capacitors: two 1000 pF, one 0.01 μF, three 0.1 μF
Inductors: one 2 μH (can be wound quickly from #22 wire), one 25 μH

For Further Investigation:
> One 1.0 MHz crystal
> One 2N5458 *n*-channel JFET
> One 1.0 MΩ resistor

Procedure:
1. Measure and record the value of the resistors listed in Table 28-1.

2. Observe the class A amplifier shown in Figure 28-1. Using your measured resistor values, compute the dc parameters for the amplifier listed in Table 28-2. R_{E1} is a 100 Ω potentiometer that you should set to 50 Ω. Then construct the circuit and verify that your computed dc parameters are as expected. Record the measured values in Table 28-2.

Table 28-1

Resistor	Listed Value	Measured Value
R_1	10 kΩ	
R_2	3.3 kΩ	
R_{E1}	50 Ω *	
R_{E2}	1.0 kΩ	
R_C	2.7 kΩ	

* set potentiometer for 50 Ω

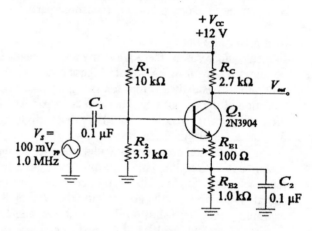

Figure 28-1

3. Compute the ac parameters listed in Table 28-3. After you find r_e', the gain is found by dividing the collector resistance by the sum of the unbypassed emitter resistance and r_e'. (Assume that the potentiometer remains set to 50 Ω.) The ac voltage at the collector is found by multiplying the gain by the ac base voltage. Set the function generator for a 100 mV$_{pp}$ signal at 1.0 MHz and measure the peak-to-peak collector voltage. Your computed and measured values should agree within normal experimental uncertainty.

Table 28-2

DC Parameter	Computed Value	Measured Value
V_B		
V_E		
I_E		▓▓▓▓
V_C		

Table 28-3

AC Parameter	Computed Value	Measured Value
V_b		
r_e'		▓▓▓▓
A_v		
V_c		

4. Remove the signal generator and add the feedback network for a Colpitts oscillator as shown in Figure 28-2. Adjust R_{E1} for the best sine wave. Compute the frequency of the Colpitts oscillator and record the computed frequency in Table 28-4. Then, measure the frequency and the peak-to-peak voltage at the output and record them in Table 28-4.

Table 28-4

Colpitts Oscillator	Computed Value	Measured Value
frequency		
amplitude	▓▓▓▓	

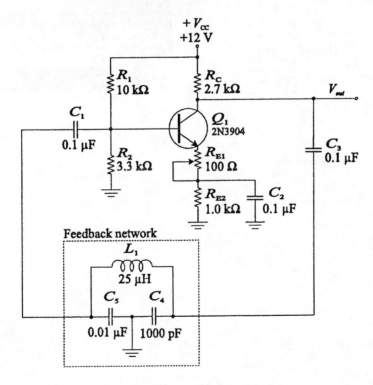

Figure 28-2

5. Observe what happens to the frequency and amplitude of the output signal when another 1000 pF capacitor is placed in parallel with C_4.

_____

_____

6. Observe the effect of freeze spray on the stability of the oscillator.

_____

_____

7. Replace the feedback network with the one shown in Figure 28-3. (L_2 can be wound by wrapping about 40 turns of #22 wire on a pencil). Adjust R_{E1} for a good sine wave output. This configuration is that of a Hartley oscillator. Compute the frequency of the Hartley oscillator, and record the computed frequency in Table 28-5. Then, measure the frequency and the peak-to-peak voltage at the output and record them in Table 28-5.

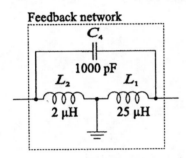

Figure 28-3

Table 28-5

Hartley Oscillator	Computed Value	Measured Value
frequency		
amplitude		

Conclusion:

Evaluation and Review Questions:

1. In step 5, you observed a change in the amplitude of the output signal when a capacitor was placed in parallel with C_4. Since the gain of the class A amplifier remained the same, what conclusion can you draw about the effect of the change on the amount of feedback?

2. What are the two conditions required for oscillation to occur in an *LC* oscillator?

3. Give a reason that an oscillator might drift from its normal frequency.

4. Summarize the difference between a Colpitts and Hartley oscillator.

5. For the circuit in Figure 28-2, predict the outcome in each case.

   (a) R_{E1} is shorted:

   (b) C_3 and C_4 are reversed:

   (c) C_2 is open:

   (d) The power supply voltage is +6 V:

For Further Investigation:

When it is necessary to have high stability in an oscillator, a crystal oscillator is superior. For high-frequency crystal oscillators, FETs have advantages over bipolar transistors because of their high input impedance. This allows the tank circuit to be unloaded, resulting in a high Q. The circuit shown in Figure 28-4 has the advantage of being simple, yet very stable. Construct the circuit and observe the waveform at the drain. Compare the frequency with that stamped on the crystal case (to do this requires a frequency counter). Test the effect of freeze spray on the frequency and amplitude. Summarize your results.

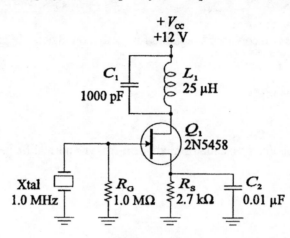

Figure 28-4

The Wien-Bridge Oscillator

Objectives:
After performing this experiment, you will be able to:
1. Explain the requirements for a Wien bridge to oscillate, predict the feedback voltages and phases, and compute the frequency of oscillation.
2. Construct and test a FET stabilized Wien-bridge oscillator.

Summary of Theory:
The Wien bridge is a bridge-type circuit that is widely used as a sinusoidal oscillator for frequencies below about 1 MHz. Oscillation occurs when a portion of the output is returned to the input in the proper amplitude and phase to reinforce the input signal. This type of feedback is called *regenerative* or *positive* feedback. All regenerative oscillators require amplification to overcome the loss in the feedback network. For the Wien bridge, the feedback network returns 1/3 of the output signal to the noninverting input. Therefore, the amplifier must provide a gain of 3 to overcome this attenuation and prevent oscillations from dying out.

The basic Wien-bridge circuit is shown in Figure 27-1(a). The gain is controlled by the resistors connected to the inverting input of the op-amp (R_f and R_i). The frequency of oscillation is determined by the lead-lag network connected to the noninverting input of the op-amp. The frequency of oscillation is found from the equation:

$$f_r = \frac{1}{2\pi RC}$$

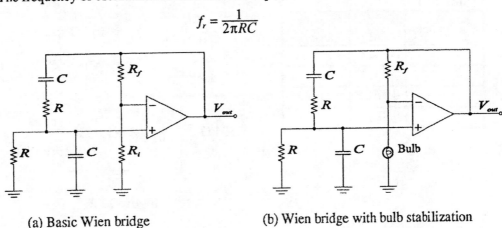

(a) Basic Wien bridge   (b) Wien bridge with bulb stabilization

Figure 27-1

The gain must be at least 3 to maintain oscillations but too much gain causes the output to saturate. Too little gain causes oscillations to cease. Various circuits have been designed to stabilize loop gain at the required 3. The basic requirement is to provide *automatic gain control*, or AGC for short. One common technique is to use a light bulb that has a positive temperature coefficient for AGC as illustrated in Figure 27-1(b). As the bulb's filament warms, its resistance increases and reduces the gain. Other more sophisticated techniques use the ohmic region of a FET as a variable resistor to control gain. You will investigate a FET stabilized Wien bridge in this experiment.

Materials Needed:
Resistors: one 1.0 kΩ, three 10 kΩ
Capacitors: two 0.01 μF, three 1.0 μF
Two 1N914 signal diodes (or equivalent)
One 741C op-amp
One 2N5458 N-channel JFET transistor (or equivalent)
One 10 kΩ potentiometer

For Further Investigation:
    One type #1869 or type #327 bulb

Procedure:
1. Measure R_1, R_2, C_1, and C_2 for this experiment. These components determine the frequency of the Wien bridge. Record the measured values in Table 27-1. If you cannot measure the capacitors, record the listed value.

2. Construct the basic Wien bridge illustrated in Figure 27-2. Adjust R_f so that the circuit just oscillates. You will see that it is nearly impossible to obtain a clean sine wave as the control is too sensitive. With the bridge oscillating, try spraying some freeze spray on the components and observe the result.

    Observations:_____

Table 27-1

Component	Listed Value	Measured Value
R_1	10 kΩ	
R_2	10 kΩ	
C_1	0.01 μF	
C_2	0.01 μF	

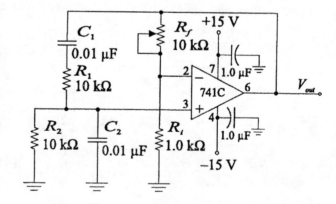

Figure 27-2

286

3. The bridge in step 2 has the problem of unstable gain and requires some form of automatic gain control to work properly. Field-effect transistors are frequently used for AGC circuits because they can be used as voltage-controlled resistors for small applied voltages (see text discussion on page 206). The circuit illustrated in Figure 27-3 is a FET-stabilized Wien bridge. Compute the expected frequency of oscillation from the equation:

$$f_r = \frac{1}{2\pi RC}$$

Use the <u>average</u> measured value of the resistance and capacitance listed in Table 27-1 to calculate f_r. Record the computed f_r in Table 27-2.

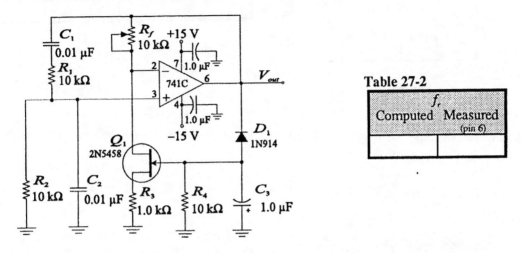

Table 27-2

	f_r	
	Computed	Measured (pin 6)

Figure 27-3

4. Construct the FET-stabilized Wien bridge shown in Figure 27-3. The diode causes negative peaks to charge C_3 and bias the FET. C_3 has a relatively long time constant discharge path (through R_4) so the bias does not change rapidly. Note the polarity of C_3. Adjust R_f for a good sine wave output. Measure the frequency and record it in Table 27-2.

5. Measure the peak-to-peak output voltage, $V_{out(pp)}$. Then measure the peak-to-peak positive and negative feedback voltages, $V_{(+)(pp)}$ and $V_{(-)(pp)}$ and the dc voltage on the gate of the FET (V_G). Use two channels and observe the phase relationship of the waveforms. Record voltages in Table 27-3.

Table 27-3

Measured Voltages			
$V_{out(pp)}$ (pin 6)	$V_{(+)(pp)}$ (pin 3)	$V_{(-)(pp)}$ (pin 2)	V_G

What is the phase shift from the output voltage to the positive feedback voltage? _____

6. Try freeze spray on the various components while observing the output.

Observations:_____

7. Add a second diode in series with the first one between the output and the gate of the FET (See Figure 27-4). You may need to readjust R_f for a good sine wave. Measure the voltages as before and record in Table 27-4.

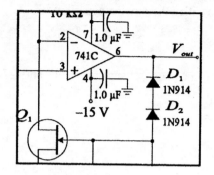

Figure 27-4

Table 27-3

	Measured Voltages		
$V_{out(pp)}$ (pin 6)	$V_{(+)(pp)}$ (pin 3)	$V_{(-)(pp)}$ (pin 2)	V_G

Conclusion:

Evaluation and Review Questions:
1. In step 5, you measured the positive feedback voltage.
   (a) What fraction of the output voltage did you find?

   (b) Is this what you expect from theory?

2. Explain why adding a second diode in series with the first caused the output voltage to increase.

3. For the circuit in Figure 27-3, why is the positive side of C_3 shown on ground?

4. What frequency would the Wien bridge of Figure 27-3 oscillate if R_1 and R_2 were doubled?

5. How could you make a Wien bridge tune to different frequencies?

For Further Investigation:
Investigate the light bulb stabilized Wien bridge shown in Figure 27-1(b). A good bulb to try is a type #1869 or type #327. Other bulbs will work, but low-resistance filaments are not good. You can use the same components as in Figure 27-2 except replace R_3 with the bulb. Summarize your results in a short lab report.

Class A Power Amplifiers

Objectives:

After performing this experiment, you will be able to:
1. Calculate the dc and ac parameters for a multistage class A power amplifier.
2. Construct the circuit in Objective 1 and measure the dc and ac parameters.
3. Predict and test the effect of troubles in a two-stage amplifier.
4. Determine the ac power dissipated in the load (speaker) and the power gain of the circuit.

Summary of Theory:

The common-emitter (CE) amplifier provides high voltage gain with moderate input resistance whereas the common collector (CC) amplifier provides current gain and low output resistance. Combining the two amplifiers gives the advantages of each, allowing the amplifier to drive a relatively low resistance load such as a speaker.

In all amplifiers, some power from the supply is wasted – that is, it does not show up as signal power in the load. In class A power amplifiers, the transistor is biased on at all times, causing power to be dissipated in the transistor, even when no signal is present. Because of this, class A amplifiers are not as efficient as class B designs. For low power applications, this reduced efficiency is not a major problem. Further, the power dissipated in the transistor is highest when no signal is present, so it is simple to compute the worst case power dissipated in the transistor - it is simply $V_{CEQ}I_{CQ}$.

In this experiment, you will combine a CE and CC amplifier to form an amplifier that will be used for driving a small speaker. Most speakers are low resistance devices, requiring the driving amplifier to have a low output resistance. Because the CE amplifier typically has relatively high output resistance, a Darlington CC amplifier is selected to minimize the loading effect. In the For Further Investigation section, you can complete the amplifier by adding a common base (CB) driver and microphone for a small intercom system. As in earlier experiments, you should analyze the operation of the amplifier by first computing the dc parameters. After analyzing the dc conditions, the ac parameters for the amplifier are evaluated and power input, power output, and power gain are calculated. The analysis steps are reviewed in the experiment.

Materials Needed:

Resistors: one 22 Ω (2 W), one 100 Ω, one 560 Ω, one 4.7 kΩ, two 10 kΩ, one 22 kΩ, one 56 kΩ
Capacitors: one 0.22 µF, one 1.0 µF, one 10 µF, two 100 µF
Transistors: two 2N3904, one SK3024 (or equivalent) with heat sink
One small 8 Ω speaker

For Further Investigation:
  One additional 2N3904 transistor
  One low resistance microphone (a small speaker can be substituted)
  Resistors as specified by student

Procedure:

1. Measure and record the values of the resistors listed in Table 16-1.

Table 16-1

Resistor	Listed Value	Measured Value
R_1	56 kΩ	
R_2	10 kΩ	
R_{E1}	100 Ω	
R_{E2}	560 Ω	
R_C	4.7 kΩ	
R_3	10 kΩ	
R_4	22 kΩ	
R_{E3}	22 Ω	

2. Using the methods described in Experiment 7 and the text, compute the parameters listed in Table 16-2 for the common-emitter stage (Q_1) of the amplifier shown in Figure 16-1. The voltage divider is relatively stiff, so you can use the simplifying assumption that the base voltage for Q_1 is determined directly from the voltage-divider equation. Compute the unloaded and loaded gain. The unloaded gain is found by assuming the coupling capacitor between the CE and CC stages is open. Enter your computed values in Table 16-2.

Table 16-2

Parameters for CE Amp (Q_1)	Computed Value	Measured Value
V_B		
V_E		
I_E		
V_C		
V_{CE}		
r_e'		
$A_{v(NL)}$		
$A_{v(FL)}$		

Table 16-3

Parameters for CC Amp ($Q_{2,3}$)	Computed Value	Measured Value
V_B		
V_E		
I_E		
V_C		
V_{CE}		
r_e'		
$A_{v(NL)}$		
$A_{v(FL)}$		

3. Using the methods described in Experiment 9 and the text, compute the parameters listed in Table 16-3 for the common-collector stage (Q_2 and Q_3) of the amplifier shown in Figure 16-1. The voltage divider is again relatively stiff. Compute both the unloaded and loaded

gain. The unloaded gain is found by assuming the output coupling capacitor, C_4, is open. Enter your computed values in Table 16-3.

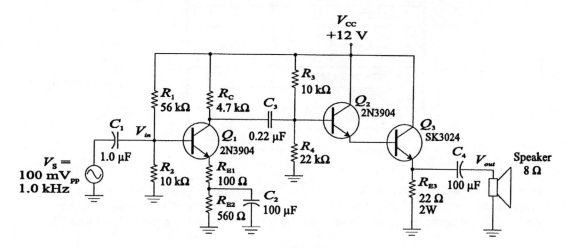

Figure 16-1

4. Construct the circuit shown in Figure 16-1. Q_3 is a power transistor and needs a heat sink. Measure and record the parameters that you computed in steps 2 and 3 in Tables 16-2 and 16-3. When measuring gain, it is important that no distortion or clipping can be observed on the output signal. The unloaded gain of the CE stage is measured by disconnecting the coupling capacitor between the stages, and finding the ratio of the peak-to-peak collector voltage to the peak-to-peak base voltage. To measure the gain of the CC stage, replace the first coupling capacitor and find the ratio of the peak-to-peak output voltage across R_{E3} to the peak-to-peak input base voltage on Q_2. For the unloaded gain, open C_4.

   For the ac parameters, measured and computed values should agree within 10%.

5. In this step, you will determine the power input, load power, and power gain of the amplifier. Enter all values in Table 16-4.

   (a) Enter the speaker's resistance, R_L, in Table 16-4. The value should be marked on the speaker.

   (b) Compute the input resistance of the amplifier, R_{in}.

   (c) While observing the peak-to-peak output voltage on the speaker, increase the input signal to the onset of clipping. Then measure the maximum undistorted output voltage, V_{out}. Convert the reading to rms voltage.

   (d) Without changing the generator, measure the rms input voltage, V_{in}.

   (e) Compute the power to the load, P_L, from the equation, $P_L = \dfrac{V_{out}^2}{R_L}$

   (f) Compute the input power, P_{in}, from the equation, $P_{in} = \dfrac{V_{in}^2}{R_{in}}$

   (g) Compute the power gain, A_p, for the circuit from the ratio of the load to input power.

Table 16-4

Quantity	Value
Load resistance, R_L	
Input resistance, R_{in}	
Output rms voltage, V_{out}	
Input rms voltage, V_{in}	
Load power, P_L	
Input power, P_{in}	
Power gain, A_p	

6. Predict the effects of each trouble listed in Table 16-5 on the amplifier's performance. After predicting the effect of the trouble on the amplifier, then insert the trouble into the circuit and test your prediction. Summarize the results in the space provided in Table 16-5.

Table 16-5

Trouble	Effect on Circuit
R_{E1} switched with R_{E2}	
R_C open	
$C_3 = 10\ \mu F$	
$V_{CC} = 6\ V$	
R_4 open	
$C_4 = 10\ \mu F$	
Q_2 has open collector	

Conclusion:

Evaluation and Review Questions:

1. What is the advantage of the darlington arrangement for the CC amplifier in this experiment?

2. Explain why the loaded and unloaded gain is different for the CE amplifier.

3. A disadvantage of a class-A power amplifier is that it dissipates power from the supply even when no signal is present. From the measurements taken in this experiment, estimate:

   (a) the power supplied by the dc source with no ac input.

   (b) power dissipated in Q_3 when no ac input.

4. From the measurements taken in this experiment, compute the Q-point for Q_3.

   (a) $V_{CEQ} =$

   (b) $I_{CQ} =$

5. Assume you needed to modify the circuit so that you could use a *pnp* transistor for Q_1. The power supply cannot be changed. What changes would you make to the circuit?

For Further Investigation:

A common-base amplifier (such as the one shown in Figure 3-43 of the text) can be driven with a *low* resistance microphone forming the input stage for the circuit used in this experiment to complete an intercom system. (High resistance microphones will be loaded too much by a CB preamp.) You will also need gain adjustment. This can be accomplished by adding a potentiometer that has no effect on the dc conditions but changes the ac resistance of the CE amplifier (how?). Draw a new schematic showing the addition of the CB amplifier and the gain control. Then construct and test the circuit. Note: a small speaker can be used as a low resistance microphone.

Class B Push-Pull Amplifiers

Objectives:
After performing this experiment, you will be able to:
1. Construct a push-pull amplifier driven by a common-emitter voltage amplifier.
2. Predict and measure performance characteristics of the circuit constructed in objective 1.

Summary of Theory:
The efficiency of a power amplifier is the ratio of the average signal power delivered to the load to the power drawn from the supply. Amplifiers that conduct continuously are called *class A* amplifiers and are not particularly efficient (typically less than 25%) as you observed in Experiment 16. For small signals, this isn't important, but when a larger amount of power must be delivered, *class B* amplifiers are much more efficient. In class B operation, a transistor is on during 50% of the cycle (half-wave operation). By combining two transistors that alternately conduct on positive and negative half-cycles of the input waveform, a very efficient amplifier can be made. This type of amplifier is called a *push-pull* amplifier. An example, using common collector amplifiers, is shown in Figure 17-1(a). The key to its high efficiency is the fact that the circuit dissipates very little quiescent (standby) power because both transistors are off when no signal is present.

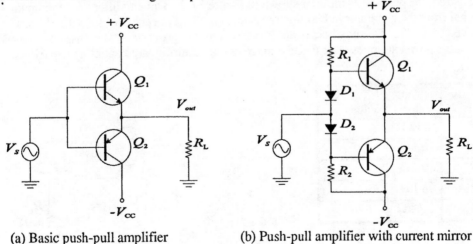

(a) Basic push-pull amplifier   (b) Push-pull amplifier with current mirror

Figure 17-1

The push-pull circuit shown uses complementary (*npn* and *pnp*) transistors. One transistor is active for the positive part of the signal (*pushing*), while the other is active for the negative portion of the signal (*pulling*).

A problem with this basic circuit is that the output signal is one diode drop behind the input. This is because the signal must overcome the base-emitter diode drop for each transistor before it will conduct. The output signal follows the input except for the 0.7 V diode drop on both the positive and negative excursion. This causes distortion on the output called *crossover* distortion. Crossover distortion can be eliminated by using diodes to bias the transistors into slight conduction as illustrated in Figure 17-1(b). This type of bias is called *diode current mirror bias*. The forward-biased diodes will each have approximately the same 0.7 V drop as the base-emitter junction. If the diode is matched to the transistor's base-emitter diode, the current in the collector circuit is equal ("mirrors") the current in the diode.

In addition to eliminating cross-over distortion, the current mirror offers another advantage. If the temperature increases, the output current will tend to increase. If the diodes are identical to the base-emitter junction, and in the same thermal environment, any thermal change will tend to be compensated by the diodes, thus maintaining stable bias.

Materials Needed:
Resistors: one 330 Ω, one 2.7 kΩ, two 10 kΩ, one 68 kΩ
One 1.0 μF capacitor
Transistors: one 2N3906 *pnp*, two 2N3904 *npn* (or equivalent)
Two 1N914 diodes (or equivalent)
One 5 kΩ potentiometer

For Further Investigation:
One 15 kΩ resistor, one additional resistor to be determined by student

Procedure:
1. Measure and record the resistance of the resistors listed in Table 17-1.

2. Construct the push-pull amplifier shown in Figure 17-2. The amplifier uses the input signal from the generator to bias the transistors on. Set the generator for a 10 V$_{pp}$ sine wave at 1.0 kHz. Be sure there is <u>no</u> dc offset from the generator. The dual positive and negative power supplies offer the advantage of not requiring large coupling capacitors.

Table 17-1

Resistor	Listed Value	Measured Value
R_L	330 Ω	
R_1	10 kΩ	
R_2	10 kΩ	
R_3	68 kΩ	
R_4	2.7 kΩ	

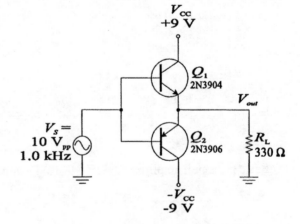

Figure 17-2

298

3. Sketch the input and output waveforms you observe on Plot 17-1. Show the amplitude difference between the peak input waveform and the output waveform and note the crossover distortion on your plot. Label the plot for voltage and time.

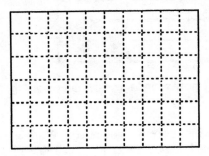

Plot 17-1

4. Add the diode current mirror bias shown in Figure 17-3. Compute the dc parameters listed in Table 17-2. The dc emitter voltage will be 0 V if each half of the circuit is identical and there is no dc offset from the generator. The current in R_1 can be found by applying Ohm's law to R_1. This current is nearly identical to I_{CQ} because of current mirror action.

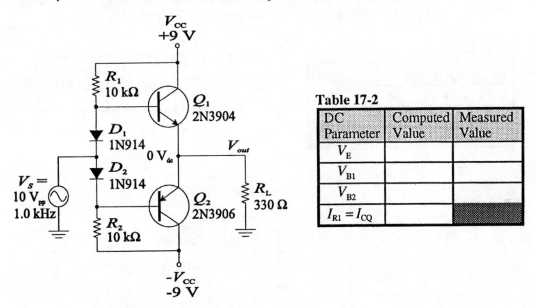

DC Parameter	Computed Value	Measured Value
V_E		
V_{B1}		
V_{B2}		
$I_{R1} = I_{CQ}$		

Table 17-2

Figure 17-3

5. Compute the ac parameters listed in Table 17-3. Compute the maximum undistorted output voltage (V_p) and current (I_p). With dual power supplies, the output can swing nearly to positive and negative V_{CC}. Then compute the peak output current based on the load resistance. The ac power is found by $P_{out} = 0.5 I_{p(out)} V_{p(out)}$. By substituting for I_p, the ac power out can also be expressed as:

$$P_{out} = \frac{V^2_{p(out)}}{2R_L}$$

Table 17-3

AC Parameter	Computed Value	Measured Value
$V_{p(out)}$		
$I_{p(out)}$		
$P_{(out)}$		

6. With the signal generator off, apply power, and measure and record the dc parameters listed in Table 17-2.

7. Turn on the signal generator and ensure there is no dc offset. While viewing V_{out} adjust the generator for the maximum unclipped output. Enter $V_{p(out)}$ in Table 17-3.

8. One method for applying a signal to a push-pull amplifier is shown in Figure 17-4. The signal is first amplified by Q_3, a common-emitter amplifier. The quiescent current in the collector circuit produces the same dc conditions as in the circuit of Figure 17-3. The bias adjust allows the dc output voltage to be set to zero to compensate for tolerance variations in the components. Compute the dc parameters listed in Table 17-4. Assume the bias potentiometer is set to 3 kΩ and apply the voltage-divider rule to find $V_{B(Q3)}$. Note that the voltage across the divider string is the difference between $+V_{CC}$ and $-V_{CC}$.

Table 17-4

DC Parameter	Computed Value	Measured Value
$V_{B(Q3)}$		
V_{E3}		
$I_{C(Q3)}$		

Table 17-5

AC Parameter	Computed Value	Measured Value
A_v'		

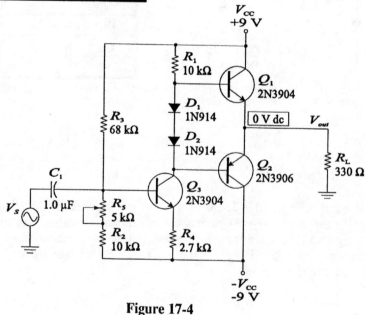

Figure 17-4

300

9. Compute the voltage gain of Q_3 by taking into account the load presented to the collector circuit of Q_3 by the push-pull amplifier and by dividing by the resistance of the Q_3 emitter circuit. The voltage gain of the push-pull amplifier is nearly 1.0, so the total voltage gain of the amplifier, A_v', is approximately equal to the gain of Q_3. That is,

$$A_v' \cong A_{v(Q3)} \cong \frac{R_1 \| \{\beta_{Q1}(R_L + r_{e(Q1)}')\}}{r_{e(Q3)}' + R_4}$$

10. Connect the circuit shown in Figure 17-4. Measure the dc voltage across the load resistor and adjust the bias potentiometer (R_5) for 0 V. Measure and record the voltages listed in Table 17-4. Set the signal generator for the maximum unclipped voltage across the load resistor and measure the total voltage gain. Enter the computed and measured gains in Table 17-5.

Conclusion:

Evaluation and Review Questions:
1. With no signal applied, what power is provided by the power supplies in Figure 17-3? (Remember the current in the diodes is equal to the current in the transistors.)

2. Assume the circuit in Figure 17-3 has a positive half-wave rectified output. What failure(s) could account for this?

3. (a) If one of the diodes in Figure 17-3 shorts, what symptoms will it produce?

   (b) If one of the diodes in Figure 17-3 opens, what symptoms will it produce?

4. In step 10, you found that the total voltage gain was fairly low for the circuit of Figure 17-4. What change to the circuit would you suggest to increase the voltage gain?

5. The bias adjust resistor in Figure 17-4 was chosen to allow a range of bias voltage to Q_3 in order to compensate for variations in components. Compute the minimum and maximum bias voltage based on setting R_s to its smallest and largest value.

$$V_{(bias)min} = \underline{\hspace{2cm}} \qquad V_{(bias)max} = \underline{\hspace{2cm}}$$

For Further Investigation:

As you observed in the experiment, a diode current mirror can cause a specific current in a transistor. The technique is used in integrated circuits and in push-pull amplifiers. Another current mirror is illustrated in Figure 17-5(a). Notice that Q_2 is connected as a diode. The current in Q_2 is determined by the drop across R_B which is one diode drop less than the supply voltage. The current in Q_1 is virtually identical to the current in Q_2 because of the identical base-emitter characteristics.

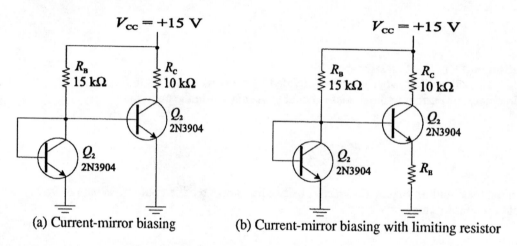

(a) Current-mirror biasing   (b) Current-mirror biasing with limiting resistor

Figure 17-5

Current mirrors can be designed to mirror a *smaller* current into a circuit by adding a resistor in the emitter circuit as shown in Figure 17-5(b). The resistor needs to drop a portion of the original base-emitter voltage. A drop of 60 mV in the emitter resistor will cause the collector current of Q_1 to drop by a factor of ten.

Construct the current-mirror circuit shown in Figure 17-5(a). Measure the voltage drop across R_B and determine the collector current in Q_2. Then, using the 60 mV rule, determine the size of the emitter resistor needed to cut the collector current of Q_2 to 10% of its original value. Modify the original circuit by adding the resistor, R_E, that you calculated. Measure the new collector current and compare it with your expected value. Summarize your findings.

Comparators and the Schmitt Trigger

Objectives:
After performing this experiment, you will be able to:
1. Compare the input and output waveforms for comparator and Schmitt trigger circuits.
2. Use an oscilloscope to plot the transfer curve for a comparator circuit, including one with hysteresis.
3. Construct and test a relaxation oscillator using a Schmitt trigger.

Summary of Theory:
A comparator is a switching device that produces a high or low output, depending on which of the two inputs is larger. The comparator is run with the very high open-loop gain. When the noninverting input is very slightly larger than the inverting input, the output goes to positive saturation; otherwise it goes to negative saturation. Although general-purpose op-amps can be used as comparators, specially designed op-amps can switch faster and have additional features not found on general-purpose op-amps. For noncritical applications, general-purpose op-amps are satisfactory and will be used in this experiment.

A comparator circuit is characterized by its transfer characteristic. The transfer characteristic (curve) is a plot of the output voltage (plotted along the y-axis) as a function of the input voltage (plotted along the x-axis). Consider the comparator shown in Figure 22-1(a). The reference voltage is +6 V. When the input is greater than +6.0 V, the output will go to positive saturation (approximately +13 V); when the input is less than +6.0 V, the output will be in negative saturation. A glance at the transfer curve will show the output for any given input voltage.

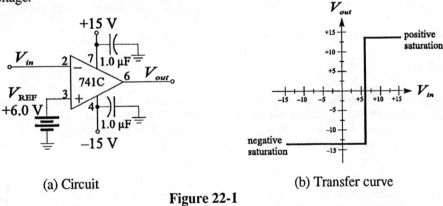

(a) Circuit   (b) Transfer curve

Figure 22-1

Because of the sensitivity to a small input change, the output of a comparator may change due to noise on the input or when the input changes very slowly. To avoid this, hysteresis is added to the comparator circuit by introducing positive feedback. The circuit, called a *Schmitt trigger*, has two switching thresholds - one for a rising input voltage, the other for a falling input. By separating the two thresholds, noise effects can be eliminated. In this experiment, you will investigate two comparators and an inverting Schmitt trigger circuit.

Materials Needed:
Resistors: one 100 kΩ
Two 1.0 μF capacitors
One 10 kΩ potentiometer
One 741C op-amp

For Further Investigation:
  One additional 100 kΩ resistor
  One 0.1 μF capacitor

Procedure:
Comparator and Comparator Transfer Curve
1. Figure 22-2 shows an inverting comparator circuit with a variable threshold determined by the potentiometer setting. Construct the circuit and set V_{REF} to near 0 V. Set the function generator for a 3.0 V_{pp} triangle waveform at 50 Hz and observe the input and output waveforms on a two-channel oscilloscope. Sketch the waveforms on Plot 22-1. Note the point where switching takes place. Be sure to label all plots in this experiment.

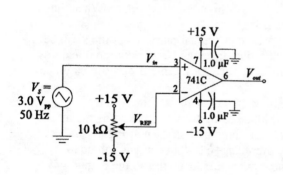

Figure 22-2

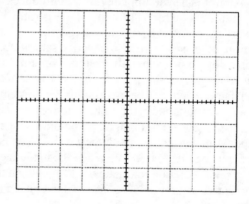

Plot 22-1 Comparator waveform.

2. Observe the output as you vary the potentiometer. Then reset V_{REF} to 0 V.

   Observations:_____

3. In this step, you will plot the transfer curve for the comparator on the oscilloscope. Place V_{in} on the X-channel and V_{out} on the Y-channel. Set the VOLTS/DIV control so that both signals are on the screen. Neither channel should be inverted. Then switch the oscilloscope to the X-Y mode. Sketch (and label) the transfer curve you see in Plot 22-2.[1]

---

[1] You may observe a slight difference in the switching point, depending on whether the input rises or falls, due to the slew rate limitation of the op-amp. Slowing the generator will reduce the effect.

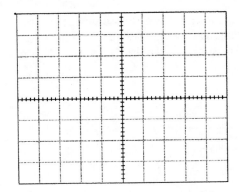

Plot 22-2 Comparator transfer curve.

Plot 22-3 Comparator transfer curve (inputs reversed).

4. Vary the potentiometer as you observe the transfer curve.

   Observations:_____

5. While observing the transfer curve, reverse the inputs to the comparator. Sketch the new transfer curve in Plot 22-3.

Schmitt Trigger and Schmitt Trigger Transfer Curve

6. Construct the Schmitt trigger circuit shown in Figure 22-3. Set the potentiometer to the maximum resistance and put the oscilloscope in normal time base mode (not X-Y mode). Slowly reduce the resistance of the potentiometer and observe the input and output waveforms. Note that when the output changes states, the input voltage is different for a rising and a falling signal. Sketch the observed input and output waveforms in Plot 22-4.

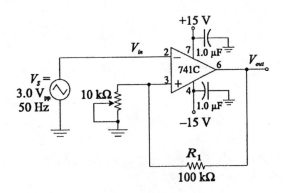

Figure 22-3

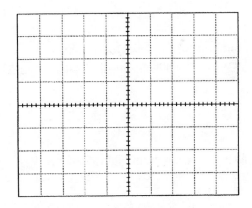

Plot 22-4 Schmitt trigger waveform.

7. In this step, you will plot the transfer curve for the Schmitt trigger on the oscilloscope. The input signal is again on the X-channel and the output signal is on the Y-channel. Select the X-Y mode and adjust the controls to view the transfer curve. Notice the hysteresis. Sketch (and label) the transfer curve you see in Plot 22-5.

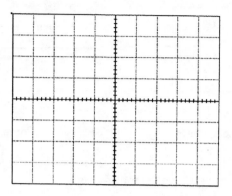

Plot 22-5 Schmitt trigger transfer curve.

8. While observing the transfer curve, vary the potentiometer.

Observations:_____

Conclusion:

Evaluation and Review Questions:
1. Describe how the threshold voltage changes the transfer curve for a comparator.

2. Assume the circuit in Figure 22-2 had V_{REF} set to zero volts. How would you expect the output to be affected by varying the dc offset control on the generator?

3. Would a sinusoidal input to the comparators produce the same transfer curve as a triangle waveform? Explain.

4. Summarize the important differences between a comparator and a Schmitt trigger.

5. Assume the input signal in Figure 22-3 could have as much as 100 mV_{pp} noise. In order to avoid multiple tripping due to noise, you need to set the trip points at least 100 mV apart. What is the minimum value of resistance that the potentiometer can be set? Assume the output saturates at ± 13 V.

For Further Investigation:

The Schmitt trigger you investigated in the experiment can be modified slightly to form a relaxation oscillator. Investigate the relaxation oscillator shown in Figure 22-4. (For simplicity, power supply connections are not shown.) Look at the waveform across the capacitor and at the output. Test the effect of the potentiometer on the frequency and waveform on the capacitor. Normally, a triangle waveform is observed. Under what conditions can you obtain a sine wave? Then observe the transfer curve by observing the signal on pin 2 and pin 6 in the X-Y mode – can you explain the shape? Summarize your findings in a short report.

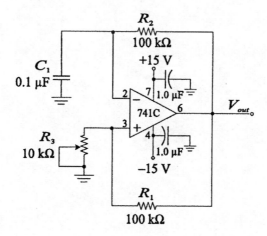

Figure 22-4

IF Amplifiers

Objectives:

After performing this experiment, you will be able to:

1. Construct an intermediate frequency amplifier and measure its dc and ac parameters including gain, bandwidth, and Q.

2. *For Further Investigation:* Determine the effect of different loads on the Q of the circuit.

Summary of Theory:

An IF (intermediate frequency) amplifier is an example of a tuned amplifier that is specially designed for a narrow band of frequencies. Tuned amplifiers are commonly used in high-frequency communication systems and in instruments such as the spectrum analyzer. They usually account for most of the required gain in a communication system. As explained in the text, a radio frequency (RF) is converted to a lower frequency by mixing the RF with a local oscillator. The oscillator frequency is variable, and "tracks" the incoming signal at a fixed difference frequency producing the IF which is fixed.

Both IF and RF amplifiers use similar principles of operation. Although an IF amplifier is nearly identical in principle to an RF amplifier, it differs from most RF amplifiers because it is designed to amplify only a *fixed* narrow frequency band that is not adjustable (by the operator). In this experiment, you will test an IF amplifier and observe the response of the amplifier at and near its resonant frequency.

The IF amplifier for this experiment is shown in Figure 34-1. The IF transformer in the collector circuit is a standard IF transformer that is used in many radios; it is tuned to 455 kHz, forming a narrow band, high Q circuit. The transformer has a small capacitor (about 180 pF) in parallel with the primary, forming a parallel resonant circuit. The entire assembly is mounted inside a shielded metal enclosure that in normal operation is grounded. The exact IF frequency is adjusted by using a nonmetallic screwdriver to adjust a tuning slug in the core. In communication applications, the IF gain is usually quite high for small input signals but is reduced automatically (with automatic gain control) when the input signal is large. To avoid noise problems in this experiment, the gain of this circuit has been reduced by the inclusion of a relatively large swamping resistor in the emitter circuit.

Circuit construction in high-frequency circuits should be done carefully, keeping lead lengths to a minimum and ensuring that all grounds return to a single point. To avoid noise, a bypass capacitor may be needed across the power supply.

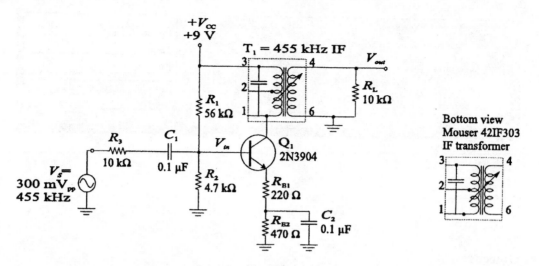

Figure 34-1 An IF amplifier.

Materials Needed:

3rd stage IF transformer (20 kΩ primary to 5 kΩ secondary) Mouser 42IF303 (or equivalent)
Resistors: one 220 Ω, one 470 Ω, one 4.7 kΩ, two 10 kΩ, one 56 kΩ
Capacitors: two 0.1 µF
Transistors: two 2N3904 npn (or equivalent)
Frequency counter (if available) (An oscilloscope can substitute.)
For Further Investigation:
 Resistors: one 100 Ω, one 270 Ω, one 1.0 kΩ, one 2.0 kΩ

Procedure:

1. Measure and record the values of the resistors listed in Table 34-1.

Table 34-1

Resistor	Listed Value	Measured Value
R_1	56 kΩ	
R_2	4.7 kΩ	
R_3	10 kΩ	
R_{E1}	220 Ω	
R_{E2}	470 Ω	
R_L	10 kΩ	

Table 34-2

DC Parameter	Computed Value	Measured Value
V_B		
V_E		
I_E		
V_C		
V_{CE}		

2. Compute the dc parameters listed in Table 34-2 for the IF amplifier shown in Figure 34-1. (Review Experiment 7 for the method.) V_B, V_E, and V_C are referenced to ground. Because of the low dc resistance of the transformer primary (about 5 Ω), assume that $V_C = V_{CC}$. Enter your computed values in Table 34-2.

3. Construct the amplifier shown in Figure 34-1. The signal generator should be turned off. Measure and record the dc voltages listed in Table 34-2.

4. The input signal, V_{in}, is measured at the transistor's base. This input voltage will *increase* at resonance due to the reduced loading on the generator and will depend to some extent on the exact frequency of the resonant circuit. Set the function generator for a 300 mV$_{pp}$ sinusoidal wave at 455 kHz. A low capacitance probe should be used for measurements to avoid probe loading effects. While observing the generator, adjust the frequency (slightly) for maximum amplitude (or tune the transformer for maximum amplitude). You will need to readjust the level for the 300 mV$_{pp}$ value at the point where the frequency peaks. This is both V_{in} and the ac base voltage, V_b. Record the measured value as V_b in Table 34-3.

5. The collector voltage and the gain depend on the exact Q of the primary resonant circuit, the amount of coupling between the primary and secondary coils, the load on the secondary, and the ac resistance of the emitter circuit. In addition, loading effects from the measuring instrument can affect the results and this is why a low-capacitance probe was suggested. Measuring the primary side of the transformer will produce a greater loading effect than the secondary; however, it is necessary to view the primary to measure the gain. Measure the remaining ac parameters listed in Table 34-3. The gain, A_v, is the ratio of the ac collector voltage to the ac base voltage, V_b. The output voltage is measured at the secondary of the transformer (across the load resistor).

Table 34-3

AC Parameter	Measured Value
V_b	
V_c	
A_v	
$V_{out\ (tot)}$	

Table 34-4

AC Parameter	Measured Value
f_c	
f_{cu}	
f_{cl}	
BW	
Q	

6. In this step, you will measure the center frequency of the IF amplifier. It is much easier to measure it accurately if you have access to a frequency counter. Like the scope, the frequency counter can load the circuit; it will have the smallest effect if used on the secondary side.

   While observing the output voltage on an oscilloscope, adjust the frequency for the maximum output. Then adjust the oscilloscope so that the peak-to-peak output voltage covers exactly 5 vertical divisions. You will probably have to take the oscilloscope out of vertical calibration to set this level exactly. Measure and record the frequency of the maximum output using a frequency counter (or the oscilloscope if a frequency counter is unavailable). Record this as the center frequency, f_c, in Table 34-4.

7. In this step, you will measure the bandwidth (BW) of the IF amplifier. Again, a frequency counter is the best way to measure the frequency accurately. Raise the generator frequency slowly while observing the output on an oscilloscope. Adjust the frequency until the peak-to-peak output voltage indicates 3.5 divisions (70%). The frequency above the center frequency at which the output is 70% of the maximum is the upper cutoff frequency (f_{cu}). Record it in Table 34-4.

8. Adjust the generator frequency for the lower cutoff frequency by watching for the 70% point below the center frequency. Record this as the lower cutoff frequency, f_{cl}, in Table 34-4.

9. Compute the BW of the circuit by subtracting the lower cutoff frequency from the upper cutoff frequency. Compute the Q of the circuit by dividing the center frequency by the BW. Enter the BW and Q in Table 34-4.

Conclusion:

Evaluation and Review Questions:

1. If you wanted to determine if the oscilloscope probe had a loading effect on the circuit, you could connect a second identical probe to the same point in the circuit. Explain how this would allow you to see if probe loading was a factor.

2. In Experiment 8, the value of the emitter bypass capacitor was 47 µF, yet in this experiment, it was only 0.1 µF. Explain the reason for this difference.

3. Explain why the voltage gain of the CE amplifier in this experiment was highest at the resonant frequency.

4. Assume a student determined that the voltage from the generator was 400 mV$_{pp}$ and the drop across R_3 was 100 mV$_{pp}$. For this amplifier, what is the input resistance?

5. If you measured 0 Vdc on the collector, which of the following could account for the problem?
   (a) open primary
   (b) open secondary
   (c) open R_1
   (d) open R_{E1}
   (e) power supply off

For Further Investigation:
Among other things, the bandwidth of the circuit depends on the loading effects from the secondary. Does the load also affect the peak center frequency? Investigate these effects by placing a series of different loads on the secondary (in place of R_L). Suggested resistors to be used for loads are 2.0 kΩ. 1.0 kΩ, 270 Ω, and 100 Ω.

The Phase-Locked Loop

Name _____

Date _____

Class _____

Objectives:

After performing this experiment, you will be able to:

1. Test a phase-locked loop to determine the free-running frequency, the capture and lock range, and the voltage as a function of frequency on the FM output pin.
2. Insert a frequency counter in the feedback loop to change the phase-locked loop to a frequency multiplier. Measure the ratio of the output to input frequency.

Summary of Theory:

The basic phase-locked loop (PLL), illustrated in Figure 35-1, is composed of a phase comparator, a low-pass filter and amplifier, and a voltage-controlled oscillator (VCO). The frequency of the input signal is compared with the VCO frequency and the sum and difference frequencies are generated by the phase comparator. The higher (sum) frequency is filtered out and the difference frequency is converted to a control voltage for the VCO. This control voltage causes the oscillator to change in the direction of the input frequency. As a result, the VCO can "track" any change in the input frequency. This condition is called "lock" for the PLL. The internally generated VCO is a "clean" signal that can track a noisy input or even generate a different shaped waveform from the input.

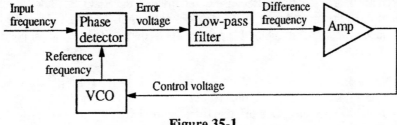

Figure 35-1

In this experiment, you will test an integrated circuit PLL, the 565, and construct a frequency multiplier. For reference, the pin out of a 565 PLL is shown in Figure 35-2. When no signal is present, the VCO oscillates at a frequency determined by the external resistance and capacitance. (See Procedure, step 2, for the equation.)

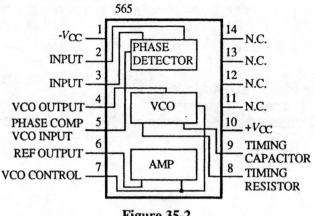

Figure 35-2

The 565 "captures" a signal when the VCO is synchronized to the input frequency. The capture range is defined as the range of frequencies over which the VCO can establish this synchronization. After a signal is captured, the VCO can track it over a wider range of frequencies known as the lock range. For the 565 PLL, the lock and capture range are computed from the equations:

$$f_{\text{lock}} = \pm \frac{8f_0}{V_{\text{CC}}} \qquad\qquad f_{\text{cap}} = \pm \frac{1}{2\pi}\sqrt{\frac{2\pi f_{\text{lock}}}{3.6\ \text{k}\Omega \times C_2}}$$

where:

f_{lock} = range of frequencies the PLL can track
f_0 = free running frequency
V_{CC} = *total* power supply voltage (measured between pins 10 and 1)
f_{cap} = range of frequencies over which the PLL can acquire a lock.

PLLs are used in frequency multiplier applications for use in frequency synthesizers. To form a multiplier, the path between the VCO and the phase detector is broken and a frequency divider is inserted in the path. The phase detector compares the frequencies on both inputs, which are nearly identical. Because of the divider, the VCO oscillates at a frequency that is a multiple of the input frequency. One interesting application is to lock the higher frequency video sync signal to the 60 Hz power line frequency to prevent 60 Hz pickup from affecting a video display.

Materials Needed:
Resistors: three 1.0 kΩ, one 2.0 kΩ, one 10 kΩ
Capacitors: one 1000 pF, one 2200 pF, one 0.1 μF, one 1.0 μF
One 10 kΩ potentiometer
One 2N3904 *npn* transistor (or equivalent)
One LM565 phase-locked loop
One 7490A decade counter
Optional: frequency counter

Procedure:

1. Measure and record the values of the components listed in Table 35-1. If you cannot measure the capacitors, enter the listed values.

Table 35-1

Component	Listed Value	Measured Value
R_1*	2.0 kΩ	
R_2	1.0 kΩ	
R_3	1.0 kΩ	
C_1	2200 pF	
C_2	0.1 μF	
C_3	1000 pF	

* plus 10 kΩ potentiometer in circuit

2. The circuit in Figure 35-3 is a 565 phase-locked loop in which the VCO output is returned to the phase detector by the jumper from pin 4 to 5. The VCO has a free-running frequency determined from the equation:

$$f_0 = \frac{0.3}{R_1 C_1}$$

Compute the free-running frequency range by assuming R_1 is set to the minimum and to the maximum value. Enter the computed free-running frequencies in Table 35-2.

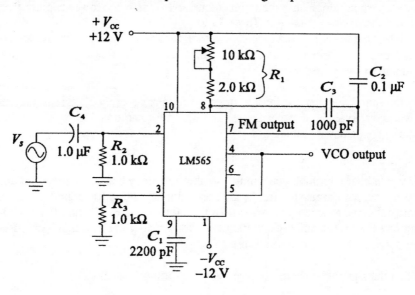

Figure 35-3

3. Construct the circuit, but leave the signal generator turned off or disconnected. Connect a scope (or frequency counter) to pin 4 and measure the free-running frequency, f_0, of the VCO with R_1 set to the minimum and maximum value. Enter the measured frequencies in Table 35-2.

Table 35-2

Step	Quantity	Computed Value	Measured Value
2 and 3	free-running frequency, $f_{0(min)}$		
	free-running frequency, $f_{0(max)}$		
4	lower capture frequency	Range =	
5	upper capture frequency	± 1.9 kHz	
6	lower lock frequency	Range =	
	upper lock frequency	± 8.3 kHz	
8	frequency in (multiplier)	2.5 kHz	
	frequency out (multiplier)		

Capture Range

4. With the generator off, adjust R_1 for a free-running frequency of 25 kHz. Then turn on the generator and view it on Ch-1 of your oscilloscope. Trigger the scope from Ch-1. Adjust the generator for a 1.0 V$_{pp}$ signal at 20 kHz. Connect the Ch-2 probe to the VCO output (pin 4). You should see that the signal on Channel 2 appears to free run. *Slowly* increase the frequency of the generator while observing the two signals. As you approach 25 kHz, the VCO should lock onto the input frequency. This is the lower capture frequency. Record the measured value in Table 35-2.

    Note that the computed capture and lock ranges have already been entered into the table based on the equations in the Summary of Theory. The free-running frequency will not be centered in these ranges.

5. Set the function generator for a frequency of approximately 30 kHz. This time *slowly* lower the frequency of the generator and watch for capture. Record the measured upper capture frequency in Table 35-2.

Lock Range

6. Note that once captured, you can reduce the frequency below the lower capture frequency and retain lock or raise the frequency above upper capture frequency and retain lock. Notice that the lock range is wider than the capture range. Capture the input signal and measure the lowest and highest frequency for which you can retain lock. Record the measured lock frequencies in Table 35-2.

7. When the signal is locked, observe the waveform on pin 7.

    Observations:_____

Frequency Multiplier
8. The circuit in Figure 35-4 is a multiplier that uses a 7490A decade counter in the feedback circuit of the phase-locked loop. Add the 7490A and transistor to the circuit as shown. The 7490A operates only between +5.0 V and ground. The transistor prevents the input signal from exceeding this range. Set the input frequency for 2.5 kHz and observe the output on pin 4 of the LM565. The output should be locked to the input. The computed output frequency is the input frequency times the decade count ratio provided by the 7490A. Record this as the computed value of frequency out in Table 35-2. Then measure the input and output frequencies and record them in Table 35-2.

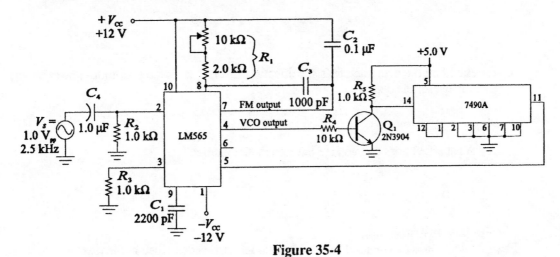

Figure 35-4

Conclusion:

Evaluation and Review Questions:
1. What change would you make to the circuit in Figure 35-3 to increase the free-running frequency by a factor of ten?

2. What is the purpose of the *npn* transistor in the multiplier circuit of Figure 35-4?

3. Explain the difference between the capture range and the lock range. Which is normally larger?

4. Assume you want to set up a phase-locked loop to multiply a frequency by 3.5. A divide by seven divider is used in the feedback loop. What must be done to the output frequency?

5. (a) Based on the manufacturer's specification sheet, what is the maximum power supply voltage for the 565?

   (b) What effect does this voltage have on the lock range?

For Further Investigation:
Phase-locked loops can be used to as FM demodulators as described in the text. A demodulator extracts information from an FM signal. Observe the dc voltage on the FM output (pin 7) of the PLL while you change the frequency within the lock range. Using a DMM, measure the voltage on the FM output at 20 kHz, 22.5 kHz, 25 kHz, 27.5 kHz and 30 kHz (retaining lock). It is much easier to set these frequencies if you use a frequency counter. Tabulate the data and plot the output voltage as a function of frequency. Is it linear?

Interpreting Manufacturer's Data Sheets

Objectives

After completing this experiment, you will be able to

- Measure the static electrical specifications for TTL and CMOS logic.
- Interpret manufacturer's data sheets including voltage and current requirements and limits.
- Measure the transfer curve for a TTL inverter.

Materials Needed

7404 hex inverter
4081 quad AND gate
One 10 kΩ variable resistor
Resistors (one of each): 300 Ω, 1.0 kΩ, 15 kΩ, 1.0 MΩ, load resistor (to be calculated)

Summary of Theory

In this experiment, you will start by testing a TTL (transistor-transistor logic) 7404 hex inverter, a single package containing six inverters. As you know, an inverter performs the NOT or complement function. Ideally, the output is in either of two defined states. As long as the manufacturer's specifications are not exceeded, these conditions will hold and the logic will not be damaged.

TTL logic is designed to have conventional current (plus to minus) flowing into the output terminal of the gate when the output is LOW. This current, called *sink* current, is shown on a data sheet as a *positive* current, indicating that it is flowing into the gate. Conventional current leaves the gate when the output is HIGH. This current is indicated on the data sheet as a *negative* current and is said to be *source* current. TTL logic can sink much larger current than it can source.

In the last part of this experiment, you will test CMOS (complementary metal-oxide semiconductor) logic. An important advantage to CMOS logic is its low power consumption. When it is not switching from one logic level to another, the power dissipation in the IC approaches zero; however, at high frequencies the power dissipation increases. Other advantages include high fanout, high noise immunity, temperature stability, and ability to operate from power supplies from 3 V to 15 V.

CMOS logic uses field-effect transistors, whereas TTL uses bipolar transistors. This results in significantly different characteristics. Consequently, CMOS and TTL logic cannot be connected directly to each other without due consideration of their specifications, since voltage levels and current sourcing and sinking capabilities differ. Interfacing between various types of logic is determined by these specifications. In addition, all MOS families of logic are more sensitive to static electricity, and special precautions to avoid static damage should be

From *Experiments in Digital Fundamentals*, Sixth Edition, David Buchla. Copyright © 2003 by Pearson Education, Inc. All rights reserved.

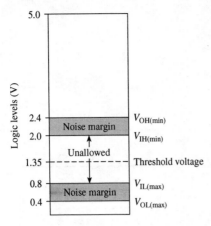

(a) TTL levels and noise margin

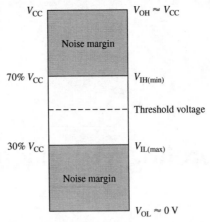

(b) CMOS levels and noise margin.

FIGURE 1

observed when handling MOS devices. In addition to static handling precautions, you should use the following operating precautions:

1. Unused inputs must NOT be left open even on gates that are not being used. They should be tied to V_{CC}, ground, or an input signal.
2. Power supply voltages must always be on when signal voltages are present at the inputs. Signal voltage must never exceed the power supply.
3. CMOS devices must never be inserted into or removed from circuits with the power on.

One important specification for any logic family is *noise margin*. Noise margin is the voltage difference that can exist between the output of one gate and the input of the next gate and still maintain guaranteed logic levels. For TTL, this difference is 0.4 V, as illustrated in Figure 1(a). For CMOS, the voltage thresholds are approximately 30% and 70% of V_{CC}. The noise margin is 30% of the supply voltage, as illustrated in Figure 1(b). A technique that is used to avoid noise problems in logic circuits is to place a small bypass capacitor (about 0.1 μF) between the supply and ground near every IC in a circuit.

A graphic tool to help visualize the characteristics of a circuit is called the *transfer curve*. The transfer curve is a graph of the input voltage plotted along the x-axis against the corresponding output voltage plotted along the y-axis. A linear circuit should have a straight-line transfer curve. On the other hand, a digital circuit has a transfer curve with a sharp transition between a HIGH and a LOW value. In the Further Investigation section, you will investigate the transfer curve for a 7404 inverter.

Procedure

1. The data table in the Report section is from the manufacturer's specified characteristics for the 7404 inverter. You will be measuring many of these characteristics in this experiment and entering your measured value next to the specified value. Begin by connecting the circuit shown in Figure 2(a). Inputs that are connected HIGH are normally connected through a resistor to protect the input from voltage surges and the possibility of shorting the power supply directly to ground in case the input is grounded.

2. Measure the voltage at the input of the inverter, with respect to ground, as shown in Figure

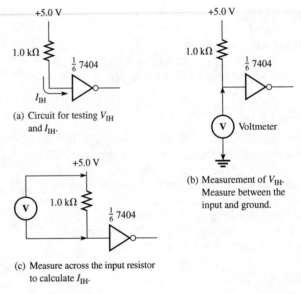

(a) Circuit for testing V_{IH} and I_{IH}.

(b) Measurement of V_{IH}. Measure between the input and ground.

(c) Measure across the input resistor to calculate I_{IH}.

FIGURE 2

2(b). Since the input is pulled HIGH, this voltage will be labeled V_{IH}. Enter your measured voltage in Table 1, line a. (Note that the specified V_{IH} is a *minimum* level; your measured value is probably much higher.)

3. Measure the voltage *across* the 1.0 kΩ resistor, as shown in Figure 2(c). TTL logic requires a very small input current to pull it HIGH. Using your measured voltage and Ohm's law, calculate the current in the resistor. This current is the input HIGH current, abbreviated I_{IH}. Enter your measured current in Table 1, line g. Compare your measured value with the specified maximum I_{IH}. Since conventional current is into the IC, the sign of this current is positive.

4. Measure the output voltage with respect to ground. Since the input is HIGH, the output is LOW. This voltage is called V_{OL}. Do not record this voltage; you will record V_{OL} in Step 5. Notice that without a load, the V_{OL} is much lower than the maximum specified level.

5. In order to determine the effect of a load on V_{OL}, look up the maximum LOW output current I_{OL} for the 7404. Then connect a resistor, R_{LOAD}, between the output and +5.0 V that allows $I_{OL(max)}$ to flow. Assume 4.8 V is dropped *across* the load resistor. Using Ohm's law, determine the appropriate load resistor, measure it, and place it in the circuit of Figure 3. Then measure V_{OL} and record it in Table 1, line f.

6. Measure the voltage drop across R_{LOAD}, and apply Ohm's law to determine the actual load current. Record the measured load current as I_{OL} in Table 1, line d.

7. Change the previous circuit to the one shown in Figure 4. Measure V_{IL} and V_{OH}, and record the measured voltages in Table 1, lines b and e.

8. Calculate I_{IL} by applying Ohm's law to the 300 Ω input resistor in Figure 4. (Note the sign.) Record the measured I_{IL} in Table 1, line h.

9. Measure the output load current by applying Ohm's law to the 15 kΩ load resistor. Record this current, I_{OH}, in Table 1, line c. Note the units and the sign. The minus sign indicates that the

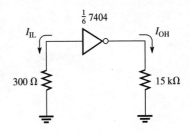

FIGURE 4

current is leaving the IC. This current, called *source* current, is significantly lower than the maximum LOW current, I_{OL}, which is positive current, or *sink* current.

10. In this and remaining steps, you will test a CMOS IC for several important characteristics. CMOS is static sensitive and it should be handled with special care. Avoid touching the pins. Always remove power before installing or removing a CMOS IC.[*] Disconnect power from your protoboard and replace the 7404 with a 4081 quad AND gate. Although in practice you could test any CMOS gate, this gate will be used because it is needed in the next experiment and you have already tested an inverter. Check the manufacturer's specification sheet.[**] Enter the specified values for $V_{OL(max)}$, $V_{OH(min)}$, $V_{IL(max)}$, $V_{IH(min)}$, $I_{OL(min)}$, $I_{OH(min)}$ and $I_{IN(typ)}$ for a supply voltage of +5.0 V and a temperature of 25°C in Table 2. Notice on the pinout that the power is supplied to a pin labeled V_{DD} and ground is supplied to a pin labeled V_{SS}. Although this convention is commonly used, both pins are actually connected to transistor drains; V_{DD} is used to indicate the positive supply. (For +5.0 V supplies, the supply is often referred to as V_{CC}.)

11. Connect the circuit shown in Figure 5 and ground the inputs to all other gates except the two gates you are using. Reconnect the power supply and keep it at +5.0 V for these tests. Adjust the input voltage using the potentiometer to the manufac-

---

*More precautions are given in Section 15–2 of the text.
**See Appendix.

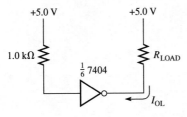

FIGURE 3

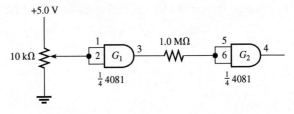

FIGURE 5

FIGURE 6

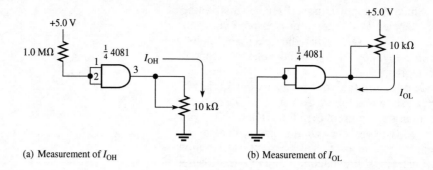

(a) Measurement of I_{OH} (b) Measurement of I_{OL}

turer's specified value of $V_{IH(min)}$ for $V_{DD} = +5.0$ V. Record your measured value of the $V_{IH(min)}$ on line d of Table 2.

12. Read the output voltage of the first AND gate at pin 3. Notice the difference between the CMOS gate and the TTL gate you tested earlier. Since the output is HIGH, record it as $V_{OH(min)}$ in Table 2, line b.

13. Measure the voltage *across* the 1.0 MΩ test resistor. A very high impedance meter is necessary to make an accurate measurement in this step. Determine the current flowing into the input of the second gate by applying Ohm's law to the test resistor. Record this as the input current in Table 2, line g.

14. Adjust the potentiometer until the input voltage on the first AND gate is at the specified value of $V_{IL(max)}$. Record the measured input voltage in Table 2, line c. Measure the output voltage on pin 3 and record this as $V_{OL(max)}$ in Table 2, line a.

15. Turn off the power supply and change the circuit to that of Figure 6(a). The potentiometer is moved to the output and the 1.0 MΩ resistor is used as a pull-up resistor on the input. This circuit will be used to test the HIGH output current of the gate. After connecting the circuit, restore the power and adjust the potentiometer until the output voltage is 4.6 V (see manufacturer's stated conditions for specification of output current). Remove the power, measure the potentiometer's resistance, and apply Ohm's law to determine the output current I_{OH}. Record your measured current in Table 2, line f.

16. Change the circuit to that of Figure 6(b).

Restore the power and adjust the potentiometer until the output voltage is 0.4 V. Remove the power, measure the potentiometer's resistance, and apply Ohm's law to determine the output current I_{OL}. Remember, Ohm's law is applied by substituting the voltage measured *across* the resistor, not the output voltage. Record your measured current in Table 2, line e.

For Further Investigation

1. To investigate further the voltage characteristics of TTL, connect the circuit shown in Figure 7. The variable resistor is used to vary the input voltage.

2. Vary the input voltage through the range of values shown in Table 3. Set each input voltage; then measure the corresponding output voltage and record it in Table 3.

3. Plot the data from Table 3 onto Plot 1. Since V_{out} depends on V_{in}, plot V_{out} on the y-axis and V_{in} on the x-axis. This graph is called the *transfer curve* for the inverter.

4. Label the region on the transfer curve for V_{OH}, V_{OL}, and the threshold. The threshold is the

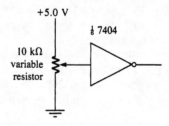

FIGURE 7

region where the transition from HIGH to LOW takes place.

Report for "Interpreting Manufacturers' Data Sheets" Experiment

Name: _____ Date: _____ Class: _____

Objectives:

☐ Measure the static electrical specifications for TTL and CMOS logic.
☐ Interpret manufacturer's data sheets including voltage and current requirements and limits.
☐ Measure the transfer curve for a TTL inverter.

TABLE 1
TTL 7404.

Recommended Operating Conditions									
		DM5404			DM7404				
Symbol	Parameter	Min	Nom	Max	Min	Nom	Max	Units	Measured Value
V_{CC}	Supply voltage	4.5	5	5.5	4.75	5	5.25	V	
V_{IH}	High-level input voltage	2			2			V	a.
V_{IL}	Low-level input voltage			0.8			0.8	V	b.
I_{OH}	High-level output current			−0.4			−0.4	mA	c.
I_{OL}	Low-level output current			16			16	mA	d.
T_A	Free air operating temperature	−55		125	0		70	°C	
Electrical Characteristics Over Recommended Operating Free Air Temperature (unless otherwise noted)									
Symbol	Parameter	Conditions		Min	Typ	Max	Units		
V_I	Input clamp voltage	V_{CC} = Min, I_I = −12 mA				−1.5	V		
V_{OH}	High-level output voltage	V_{CC} = Min, I_{OH} = Max V_{IL} = Max		2.4	3.4		V		e.
V_{OL}	Low-level output voltage	V_{CC} = Min, I_{OL} = Max V_{IH} = Min			0.2	0.4	V		f.
I_I	Input current @ max input voltage	V_{CC} = Max, V_I = 5.5 V				1	mA		

Continued.

TABLE 1
Continued.

Electrical Characteristics Over Recommended Operating Free Air Temperature (unless otherwise noted)

Symbol	Parameter	Conditions		Min	Typ	Max	Units	Measured Value
I_{IH}	High-level input current	V_{CC} = Max, V_I = 2.4 V				40	μA	g.
I_{IL}	Low-level input current	V_{CC} = Max, V_I = 0.4 V				-1.6	mA	h.
I_{OS}	Short circuit output current	V_{CC} = Max	DM54	-20		-55	mA	
			DM74	-18		-55		
I_{CCH}	Supply current with outputs HIGH	V_{CC} = Max			6	12	mA	
I_{CCL}	Supply current with outputs LOW	V_{CC} = Max			18	33	mA	

TABLE 2
CMOS CD4081.

	Quantity	Manufacturer's Specified Value	Measured Value
(a)	$V_{OL(max)}$, low-level output voltage		
(b)	$V_{OH(min)}$, high-level output voltage		
(c)	$V_{IL(max)}$, low-level input voltage		
(d)	$V_{IH(min)}$, high-level input voltage		
(e)	$I_{OL(min)}$, low-level output current		
(f)	$I_{OH(min)}$, high-level output current		
(g)	$I_{IN(typ)}$, input current		

326

Data and Observations:

Results and Conclusion:

TABLE 3

V_{in} (V)	V_{out} (V)
0.4	
0.8	
1.2	
1.3	
1.4	
1.5	
1.6	
2.0	
2.4	
2.8	
3.2	
3.6	
4.0	

PLOT 1

Further Investigation Results:

Evaluation and Review Questions

1. In Step 4, you observed V_{OL} with no load resistor. In Step 5, you measured V_{OL} with a load resistor. What is the effect of a load resistor on V_{OL}?

2. Assume a TTL logic gate has a logic HIGH output voltage of $+2.4$ V. Using the maximum specified I_{OH} from Table 1, determine the *smallest* output resistor that can be connected between the output and ground.

3. A hypothetical logic family has the following characteristics: $V_{IL} = +0.5$ V; $V_{IH} = +3.0$ V; $V_{OL} = +0.2$ V; $V_{OH} = +3.5$ V. Compute the LOW and HIGH noise margin for this family.

   V_{NL} (LOW) = _____; V_{NL} (HIGH) = _____

4. Assume that an LED requires 10 mA of current.

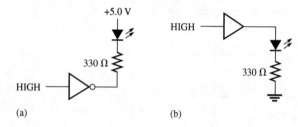

(a)   (b)

FIGURE 8

   a. Which of the two TTL circuits shown in Figure 8 is the better way to drive the LED? (Hint: look at I_{OL} and I_{OH}) _____ . b. Why? _____

5. Explain why it is important for a troubleshooter to be aware of the ground level on an oscilloscope display.

6. Assume you connected the inputs of a TTL AND gate together and plotted the transfer curve. Sketch the shape of the curve and label the threshold.

Name _____
Date _____
Class _____

The 555 Timer

Objectives:
After performing this experiment, you will be able to:
1. Calculate and measure the frequency and duty cycle for a 555 timer in the astable mode.
2. Test an astable circuit with a light sensor.
3. Calculate and measure the pulse width of a 555 timer configured as a one shot.

Summary of Theory:
The 555 timer was the first integrated circuit timer and is still one of the most popular because of its low price, wide range of times available (from microseconds to hours), and its versatility. It can be configured as either an astable (continuous pulses) or as a one-shot depending on the external circuit. In the astable configuration, it is a relaxation oscillator, using an RC timing circuit to control the frequency.

Internally, the 555 timer contains a voltage divider consisting of three series 5 kΩ resistors, two comparators, a control flip-flop, a discharge transistor, and an inverting output buffer, as shown in Figure 29-1. In normal operation (control input not used), the voltage divider sets a reference voltage on comparator A of 2/3 of V_{CC}. If the threshold input exceeds 2/3 of V_{CC}, comparator A output is high and sets the control flip-flop output high. On comparator B, the divider sets a reference voltage of 1/3 V_{CC}. If the trigger input goes below 1/3 of V_{CC}, the output of comparator B resets the control flip-flop output low.

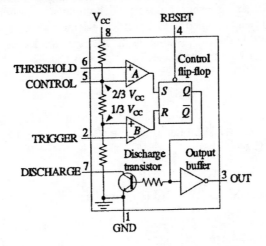

Figure 29-1

Other inputs include the *discharge, reset,* and *control* inputs. When the flip-flop is set, the Q output is high, causing the discharge transistor to be forward-biased, acting as a closed switch to ground through the discharge input. In the astable mode of operation, this provides a path through a resistor for discharging the timing capacitor. The reset input is normally connected to a logic high, but can be used to place the 555 output to a low state. The control input enables the user to change the reference voltage on the voltage divider, but for most applications, the control input is left open or connected through a small capacitor to ground. In this experiment, it will not be used.

An example of a basic astable circuit is shown in Figure 29-2(a). In this mode of operation, the equations for frequency and duty cycle are given in the text (Equations 10-7 and 10-8) and repeated here for reference.

$$f = \frac{1.44}{(R_1 + 2R_2)C_{ext}} \qquad \text{Duty cycle} = \left(\frac{R_1 + R_2}{R_1 + 2R_2}\right)100\%$$

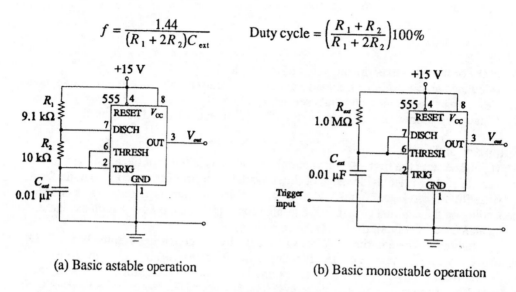

(a) Basic astable operation   (b) Basic monostable operation

Figure 29-2

A basic monostable circuit is shown in Figure 29-2(b). Mechanical switches tend to produce multiple pulses when closed, a problem for many digital circuits. One application of this circuit is to produce a single short pulse for "debouncing" a switch as you will see in step 7. The switch is capacitively coupled with a pull-up resistor on each side to keep the line high when the switch is open. In the monostable mode, the equation for pulse width is as given in the text (Equation 10-10) and repeated here for reference:

$$t_w = 1.1R_{ext}C_{ext}$$

Materials Needed:
Resistors: two 1.0 kΩ, one 9.1 kΩ, one 10 kΩ, one 22 kΩ, one 1.0 MΩ
Capacitors: one 0.01 μF, one 0.1 μF
One 555 timer IC
One 1N914 diode (or equivalent)
One CdS photocell (Radio-Shack 276-116) or equivalent

For Further Investigation:
    One 100 kΩ potentiometer

Procedure:

1. Measure and record the values of the resistors and capacitor listed in Table 29-1.

Table 29-1

Resistor	Listed Value	Measured Value
R_1	9.1 kΩ	
R_2	10 kΩ	
C_{ext}	0.01 μF	

Table 29-2

Quantity	Computed Value	Measured Value
frequency		
duty cycle		

2. Compute the frequency and duty cycle of the astable circuit shown in Figure 29-2(a). Enter the computed values in Table 29-2.

3. Connect the circuit shown in Figure 29-2(a). Measure and record the frequency and duty cycle listed in Table 29-2.

4. With the circuit operating, observe the waveform across the capacitor, C_{ext}. Couple the oscilloscope with dc coupling and note the ground level for the signal. Sketch the waveform on Plot 29-1. Label the voltage and note the ground position on your sketch.

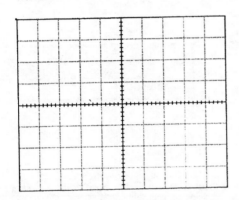

Plot 29-1

Figure 29-3

5. Connect a diode across R_2 as shown in Figure 29-3. The diode represents a path around R_2 for charging the capacitor but has no effect on the discharge path. Because of the diode's forward drop and temperature dependence, this circuit works best with the +15 V supply shown. Observe the effect on the frequency and the duty cycle. Try changing the supply voltage and observe what happens to the output.

Observations: _____

_____

331

6. An interesting variation in this circuit is made by replacing R_1 with a CdS photocell. The CdS photocell changes resistance as light strikes it. For many transducers, converting the output to a variable frequency is a useful first step in processing the data.

Replace R_1 with the photocell and observe the variation in the output frequency as you cover it with your hand.

Observations: _____

_____

7. Figure 29-4 shows a one-shot circuit to debounce a pushbutton switch. The switch is shown for reference only; you will simulate the switch with a pulse generator. The purpose of the input circuit consisting of R_1, R_2, R_3 and C_1 is to assure the trigger conditions are met even if the trigger is smaller. Compute the pulse width and enter it in Table 29-3.

Connect the circuit; then measure the output pulse width. To measure this relatively long pulse, replace the switch with a pulse generator set for a 0 to 5 V pulse at 5 Hz and obtain a stable display on an oscilloscope. It is difficult to obtain a stable display on an oscilloscope with a frequency this low. Try triggering the scope using *normal* triggering, and carefully adjust the trigger level for a stable display. Measure the pulse width and record it in Table 29-3.

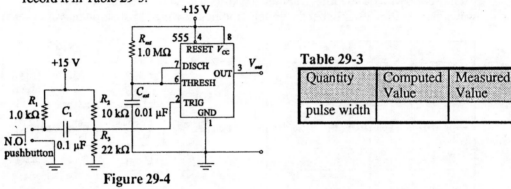

Figure 29-4

Table 29-3

Quantity	Computed Value	Measured Value
pulse width		

8. When you have achieved a stable trace for the circuit in step 7, try connecting the second channel of your oscilloscope across the capacitor. Sketch the waveforms on Plot 29-2.

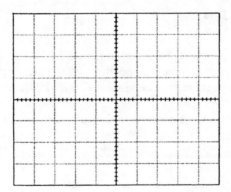

Plot 29-2

Conclusion:

Evaluation and Review Questions:

1. In the basic astable circuit drawn in Figure 29-2(a), it is not possible to obtain a 50% duty cycle. Explain why not.

2. (a) In step 4, you observed the voltage across the capacitor for the basic astable circuit. How would the amplitude of this voltage change if the power supply voltage were reduced to +12 V?

   (b) Would this have an effect on the frequency from the 555 timer? Why or why not?

3. What change to the astable circuit would you suggest to produce output pulses that were on for 1 s and off for 1 s? Draw the circuit and show how you could light an LED with the high output and another LED with the low output.

4. Look up the manufacturer's specification sheet for the 555 timer[1].
   (a) What is the maximum current the output can source or sink?

   (b) What happens to the output voltage when the timer supplies higher current?

5. Why was a frequency of 5 Hz suggested in step 7 for looking at the debounce circuit?

---

[1] The specification sheet is available from Texas Instruments at http://www.ti.com

For Further Investigation:

A simple change to the basic astable circuit will allow a 555 timer to be used as a triangle waveform generator. The circuit is shown in Figure 29-5. Construct the circuit. Vary the potentiometer and observe the results. Summarize your findings in a short report.

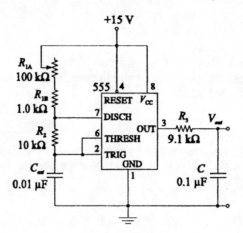

Figure 29-5

System
Application

Number Systems

Objectives

After completing this experiment, you will be able to
- Convert binary or binary coded decimal (BCD) numbers to decimal.
- Construct a portion of a digital system that decodes a BCD number and displays it on a seven-segment display.
- Troubleshoot the circuit for simulated faults.

Materials Needed

Four LEDs
7447A BCD/decimal decoder
MAN72 seven-segment display
Four-position DIP switch
Resistors: eleven 330 Ω, one 1.0 kΩ

For Further Investigation:
Additional LED
One 330 Ω resistor

Summary of Theory

The number of symbols in a number system is called the *base*, or *radix*, of that system. The decimal number system uses ten counting symbols, the digits 0 through 9, to represent quantities. Thus it is a base ten system. In this system, we represent quantities larger than 9 by using positional weighting of the digits. The position, or column, that a

digit occupies indicates the weight of that digit in determining the value of the number. The base 10 number system is a weighted system because each column has a value associated with it.

Digital systems use two states to represent quantities and thus are *binary* in nature. The binary counting system has a radix of two and uses only the numbers 0 and 1. (These are often called *bits,* which is a contraction of BInary digiT). It too is a weighted counting system, with each column value worth twice the value of the column to the immediate right. Because binary numbers have only two digits, large numbers expressed in binary require a long string of 0s and 1s. Other systems, which are related to binary in a simple way, are often used to simplify these numbers. These systems include octal, hexadecimal, and BCD.

The octal number system is a weighted number system using the digits 0 through 7. The column values in octal are worth 8 times that of the column to the immediate right. You convert from binary to octal by arranging the binary number in groups of 3 bits, starting at the binary point, and writing the octal symbol for each binary group. You can reverse the procedure to convert from octal to binary. Simply write an equivalent 3-bit binary number for each octal character.

The hexadecimal system is a weighted number

system using 16 characters. The column values in hexadecimal (or simply hex) are worth 16 times that of the column to the immediate right. The characters are the numbers 0 through 9 and the first six letters of the alphabet, A through F. Letters were chosen because of their sequence, but remember that they are used to indicate numbers, not letters. You convert binary numbers to hexadecimal numbers by arranging the binary number into 4-bit groups, starting at the binary point. Then write the next symbol for each group of 4 bits. You convert hex numbers to binary by reversing the procedure. That is, write an equivalent 4-bit binary number for each hexadecimal character.

The BCD system uses four binary bits to represent each decimal digit. It is a convenient code because it allows ready conversion from base ten to a code that a machine can understand; however, it is wasteful of bits. A 4-bit binary number could represent the numbers 0 to 15, but in BCD it represents only the quantities 0 through 9. The binary representations of the numbers 10 through 15 are not used in BCD and are invalid.

A tablet control digital system from the text is shown in Figure 1. The circuit for this experiment represents the BCD decoder to a seven-segment display and is the upper right portion of the system. You will construct a simplified portion of the display for this system.

Procedure

1. Take a moment to review "Circuit Wiring" in the Introduction before constructing this experiment. The pin numbers for the integrated circuits (ICs) in this and succeeding experiments are not shown; pin numbers may be found in the data sheets in the back of this lab manual or in manufacturer's data books. It is a good idea to write the pin numbers directly on the schematic before you begin

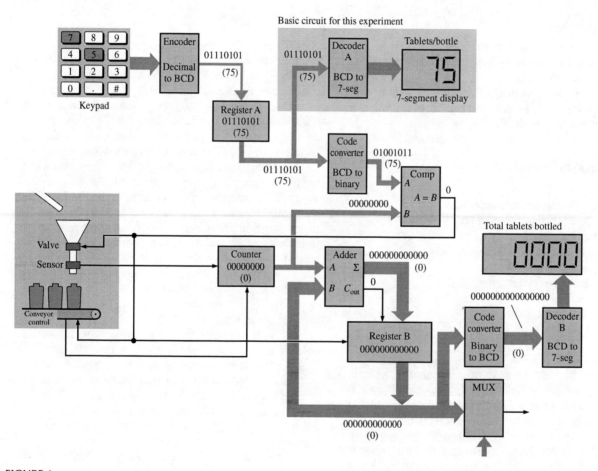

FIGURE 1
Tablet control digital system.

336

FIGURE 2

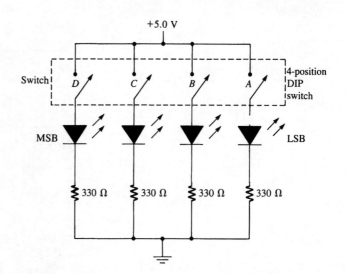

wiring.

2. Begin by constructing the circuit shown in Figure 2. This set of switches represents a portion of register A of the digital system shown in Figure 1. Although it only indicates a 4-bit BCD number, the concept is the same as that shown in the digital system as the input to the decoder. After wiring the circuit, connect power and test each switch to see that it lights an LED.

3. Remove power and add the circuit shown

in Figure 3. An example of the wiring is shown in the photograph in Figure 4. If you have not already done so, write the pin numbers on the schematic. The pin numbers for the MAN72 display are shown in Figure 5.* Note that the 7447A has 16 pins, but the MAN72 has only 14 pins.

Before applying power, check that you have

---

*Pin numbers for the 7447A decoder can be found in the appendix.

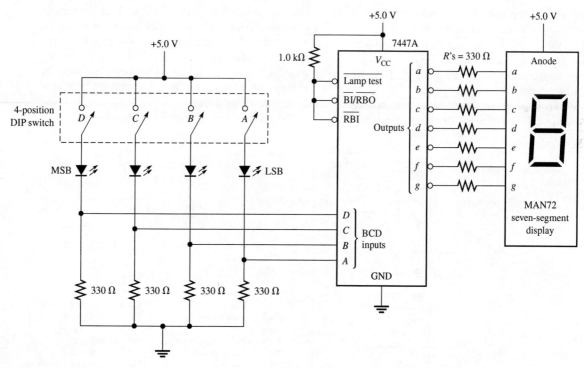

FIGURE 3

FIGURE 4

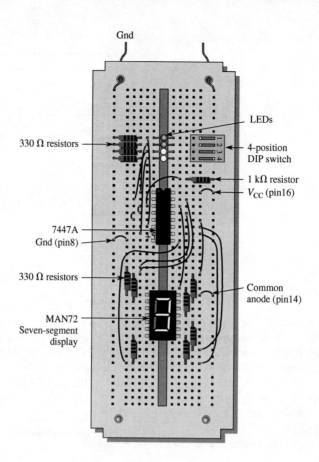

4-position
DIP switch

1 kΩ resistor

V_{CC} (pin16)

LEDs

330 Ω resistors

7447A
Gnd (pin8)

330 Ω resistors

MAN72
Seven-segment
display

Common
anode (pin14)

Gnd

connected a 330 Ω current-limiting resistor between each output of the decoder and the input to the MAN72. Connect the $\overline{\text{Lamp test}}$, $\overline{\text{BI/RBO}}$, and $\overline{\text{RBI}}$ inputs through a 1.0 kΩ resistor to +5.0 V. This is a *pull-up resistor,* used to assure a solid logic HIGH is present at these inputs.

4. When you have completed the wiring, apply power, and test the circuit by setting each

switch combination listed in Table 1 of the report. The last six codes are invalid BCD codes; however, you can set the switch combinations in binary and observe the display. It will show a unique display for each of the invalid codes. Complete the table by showing the appearance of the seven-segment display in the output column.

5. In this step, you will insert some simulated

FIGURE 5
MAN72 seven-segment display.

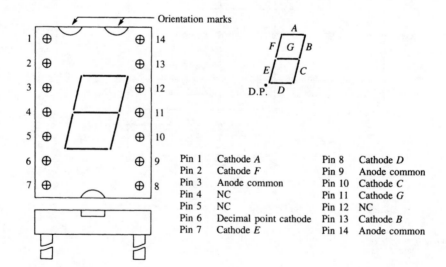

Orientation marks

Pin 1	Cathode *A*	Pin 8	Cathode *D*
Pin 2	Cathode *F*	Pin 9	Anode common
Pin 3	Anode common	Pin 10	Cathode *C*
Pin 4	NC	Pin 11	Cathode *G*
Pin 5	NC	Pin 12	NC
Pin 6	Decimal point cathode	Pin 13	Cathode *B*
Pin 7	Cathode *E*	Pin 14	Anode common

"troubles" in the circuit and observe the effect of these troubles on the output. The troubles are listed in Table 2 of the report. Insert the given trouble, and test its effect. Indicate what effect it has on the output. Assume each trouble is independent of others; that is, restore the circuit to its normal operating condition after each test.

6. The display you have built for this experiment is satisfactory only for showing a single decimal digit at a time. You could show more digits by simply replicating the circuit for as many digits as needed, although this isn't the most efficient way to make larger displays. With a larger number of digits, it is useful to blank (turn off) leading zeros in a number. Look at the function table in the manufacturer's specification sheet for the 7447A and decide what has to be applied to the $\overline{\text{Lamp test}}$, $\overline{\text{BI/RBO}}$, and $\overline{\text{RBI}}$ inputs in order to suppress leading zeros.* Summarize the method in the space provided in the report.

For Further Investigation

As you observed, the 7447A decoder used in this

---

*A complete discussion of these inputs can be found in Section 6–4 of the text. The data sheets are in the appendix.

experiment is designed for BCD-to-decimal decoding; however, a slight modification of the circuit can be made to decode a binary number into octal. The largest number that we can show with a 4-bit binary input is octal 17, which requires two seven-segment displays to show both digits.

Recall that the conversion of a binary number to octal can be accomplished by grouping the binary number by threes, starting at the binary point. To display the octal numbers larger than binary 111 would normally require a second decoder and seven-segment display. For this problem, the most significant digit is either a zero or a one; therefore, we can dispense with the extra decoder and we could even use an ordinary LED to represent the most significant digit. The seven-segment display you have will still show the least significant digit. Modify the circuit in Figure 3 so that it correctly shows the octal numbers from 0 to 17. For example, if the switches are set to binary 1011, your circuit should light the LED representing the most significant digit and the seven-segment display should show a three.

A partial schematic is shown in the report to help you get started. Complete the schematic, showing how to connect the circuit to show octal numbers. Construct the circuit, test it, and summarize how it works.

Report for "Number Systems" Experiment

Name: _____ Date: _____ Class: _____

Objectives:

- ☐ Convert binary or BCD numbers to decimal.
- ☐ Construct a portion of a digital system that decodes a BCD number and displays it on a seven-segment display.
- ☐ Troubleshoot the circuit for simulated faults.

TABLE 1

Inputs		Output
Binary Number	BCD Number	Seven-Segment Display
0 0 0 0		
0 0 0 1		
0 0 1 0		
0 0 1 1		
0 1 0 0		
0 1 0 1		
0 1 1 0		
0 1 1 1		
1 0 0 0		
1 0 0 1		
1 0 1 0	INVALID	
1 0 1 1	INVALID	
1 1 0 0	INVALID	
1 1 0 1	INVALID	
1 1 1 0	INVALID	
1 1 1 1	INVALID	

TABLE 2

Trouble Number	Trouble	Observations
1	LED for the C input is open.	
2	A input to 7447A is open.	
3	$\overline{\text{LAMP TEST}}$ is shorted to ground.	
4	Resistor connected to pin 15 of the 7447A is open.	

Data and Observations:

Step 6. Method for causing leading zero suppression:

Results and Conclusion:

Further Investigation Results:

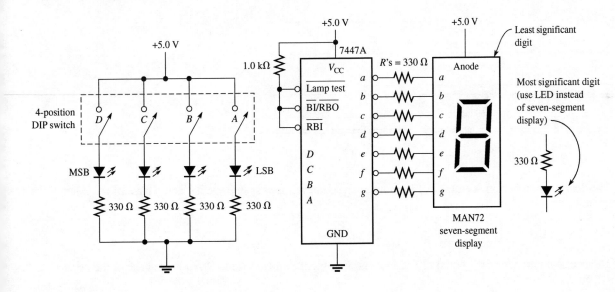

Evaluation and Review Questions

1. Assume the switches in Figure 3 are set for a binary 1000, but the display shows a zero. What are three possible causes for this error?

2. Looking at the possible causes for an error from Question 1, how would you go about troubleshooting the problem?

3. Suppose that the $\overline{\text{BI}/\text{RBO}}$ input line was shorted to ground on the 7447A decoder and all other input lines were okay. Looking at the function table for the 7447A in the appendix for Manufacturers' Data Sheets, determine the effect this would have on the display.

4. Explain the difference between binary and BCD.

5. Convert each number shown into the other bases:

Binary	Octal	Hexadecimal	Decimal	BCD
01001100				
	304			
		E6		
			57	
				0100 1001

6. a. The decimal number 85 is equal to 125 in a certain other number system. What is the base of the other system?

   b. The decimal number 341 is equal to 155 in a certain other number system. What is the base of the other system?

Boolean Laws and DeMorgan's Theorem

Objectives

After completing this experiment, you will be able to

☐ Experimentally verify several of the rules for Boolean algebra.

☐ Design circuits to prove Rules 10 and 11.

☐ Experimentally determine the truth tables for circuits with three input variables, and use DeMorgan's theorem to prove algebraically whether they are equivalent.

Materials Needed

4071 quad 2-input OR gate
4069 hex inverter
4081 quad 2-input AND gate
One LED
Four-position DIP switch
Four 1.0 kΩ resistors
Three 0.1 µF capacitors

Summary of Theory

Boolean algebra consists of a set of laws that govern logical relationships. Unlike ordinary algebra, where an unknown can take any value, the elements of Boolean algebra are binary variables and can have only one of two values: 1 or 0.

Symbols used in Boolean algebra include the overbar, which is the NOT or complement; the connective $+$, which implies logical addition and is read "OR"; and the connective $\cdot$, which implies logical multiplication and is read "AND." The dot is frequently eliminated when logical multiplication is shown. Thus $A \cdot B$ is written AB. The basic rules of Boolean algebra are listed in Table 1 for convenience.

The Boolean rules shown in Table 1 can be applied to actual circuits, as this experiment demonstrates. For example, Rule 1 states $A + 0 = A$ (remember to read $+$ as "OR"). This rule can be demonstrated with an OR gate and a pulse generator, as shown in Figure 1. The signal from the pulse generator is labeled A and the ground represents the logic 0. The output, which is a replica of the pulse generator, represents the ORing of the two inputs—hence, the rule is proved. Figure 1 illustrates this rule.

In addition to the basic rules of Boolean algebra, there are two additional rules called DeMorgan's theorems that allow simplification of logic expressions that have an overbar covering more than one quantity. DeMorgan wrote two theorems for reducing these expressions. His first theorem is

The complement of two or more variables ANDed is equivalent to the OR of the complements of the individual variables.

Algebraically, this can be written as

$$\overline{X \cdot Y} = \overline{X} + \overline{Y}$$

His second theorem is

The complement of two or more variables ORed is equivalent to the AND of the complements of the individual variables.

Algebraically, this can be written as

$$\overline{X + Y} = \overline{X} \cdot \overline{Y}$$

As a memory aid for DeMorgan's theorems, some people like to use the rule "Break the bar and change the sign." The dot between ANDed quantities is implied if it is not shown, but it is given here to emphasize this idea.

The circuits constructed in this experiment use CMOS logic. You should use static protection to prevent damage to your ICs.

Procedure

1. Construct the circuit shown in Figure 1. Set the power supply to +5.0 V and use a 0.1 μF capacitor between V_{CC} and ground for each IC throughout this experiment.* If your pulse generator has a variable output, set it to a frequency of 10 kHz with a 0 to +4 V level on the output. Observe the signals from the pulse generator and the output at the same time on your oscilloscope. If you are using an analog scope, you need to be sure to trigger the scope on one channel only; otherwise a timing error can occur with some signals. The timing diagram and Boolean rule for this circuit has been completed in Table 2 in the report as an example.

2. Change the circuit from Step 1 to that of Figure 2. Complete the second line in Table 2.

3. Connect the circuit shown in Figure 3. Complete the third line in Table 2.

4. Change the circuit in Step 3 to that of Figure 4. Complete the last line in Table 2.

5. Design a circuit that will illustrate Rule 10. The pulse generator is used to represent the A input and a switch is used for the B input. Switch B is open for $B = 1$ and closed for $B = 0$. Complete the schematic, build your circuit, and draw two timing diagrams in the space provided in Table 3. The first timing diagram is for the condition $B = 0$ and the second is for the condition $B = 1$.

*In keeping with standard practice, capacitors are specified, particularly with CMOS devices, to return switching current "spikes" to the source through the shortest possible path.

TABLE 1
Basic rules of Boolean algebra.

1. $A + 0 = A$
2. $A + 1 = 1$
3. $A \cdot 0 = 0$
4. $A \cdot 1 = A$
5. $A + A = A$
6. $A + \overline{A} = 1$
7. $A \cdot A = A$
8. $A \cdot \overline{A} = 0$
9. $\overline{\overline{A}} = A$
10. $\overline{A} + AB = A$
11. $A + \overline{A}B = A + B$
12. $(A + B)(A + C) = A + BC$

NOTE: A, B, or C can represent a single variable or a combination of variables.

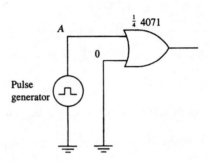

FIGURE 1

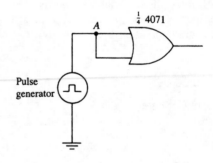

FIGURE 2

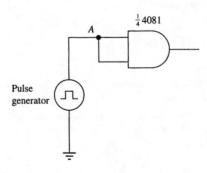

FIGURE 3

344

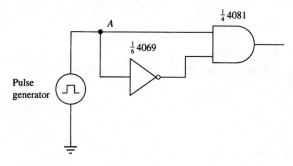

FIGURE 4

6. Design a circuit that illustrates Rule 11. Draw your schematic in the space provided in Table 4. Construct the circuit and draw two timing diagrams for the circuit in Table 4.

For Further Investigation

1. Build the circuit shown in Figure 5. Test each combination of input variables by closing the appropriate switches as listed in truth Table 5 in the report. Using the LED as a logic monitor, read the output logic, and complete Table 5.

2. Construct the circuit of Figure 6. Again, test each combination of inputs and complete truth Table 6 in the report. Observe the two truth tables. Can you prove (or disprove) that the circuits perform equivalent logic?

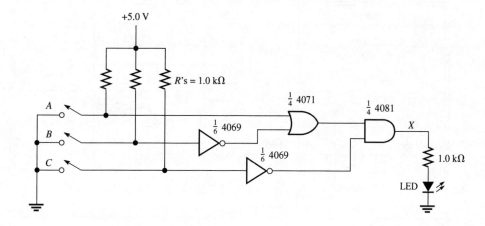

FIGURE 5

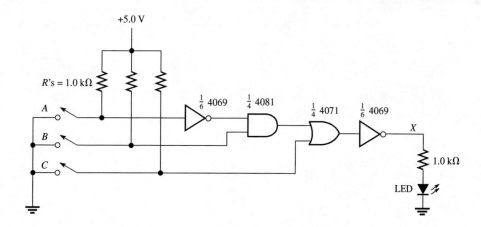

FIGURE 6

Report for "Boolean Laws and DeMorgan's Theorem" Experiment

Name: _____ Date: _____ Class: _____

Objectives:

☐ Experimentally verify several of the rules for Boolean algebra.
☐ Design circuits to prove Rules 10 and 11.
☐ Experimentally determine the truth tables for circuits with three input variables, and use DeMorgan's theorem to prove algebraically whether they are equivalent.

Data and Observations:

TABLE 2

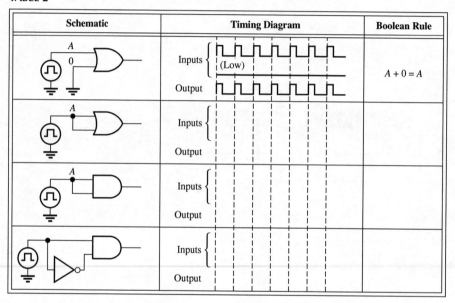

Schematic	Timing Diagram		Boolean Rule
	Inputs { (Low)	Output	$A + 0 = A$
	Inputs {	Output	
	Inputs {	Output	
	Inputs {	Output	

TABLE 3

Schematic	Timing Diagram
Rule 10: 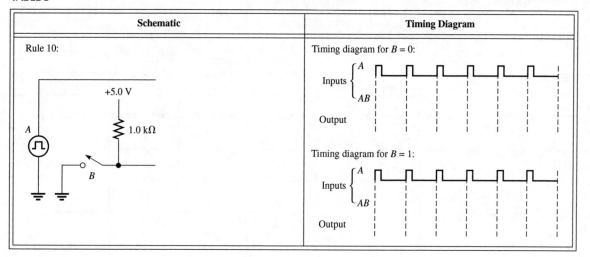	

TABLE 4

Schematic	Timing Diagram
Rule 11: 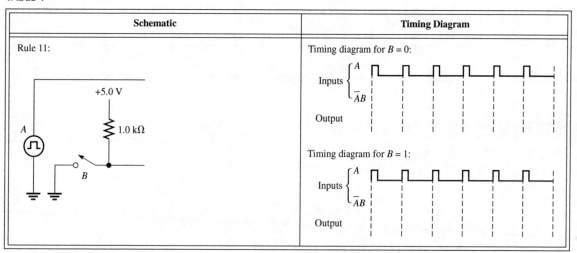	

Results and Conclusion:

Further Investigation Results:

TABLE 5
Truth table for Figure 5.

Inputs			Output
A	B	C	X
0	0	0	
0	0	1	
0	1	0	
0	1	1	
1	0	0	
1	0	1	
1	1	0	
1	1	1	

TABLE 6
Truth table for Figure 6.

Inputs			Output
A	B	C	X
0	0	0	
0	0	1	
0	1	0	
0	1	1	
1	0	0	
1	0	1	
1	1	0	
1	1	1	

Write the Boolean expression for each circuit.

Evaluation and Review Questions

1. The equation $X = A(A + B) + C$ is equivalent to $X = A + C$. Prove this with Boolean algebra.

2. Show how to implement the logic in Problem 1 with NOR gates.

3. Draw two equivalent circuits that could prove Rule 12. Show the left side of the equation as one circuit and the right side as another circuit.

4. Determine whether the circuits in Figures 5 and 6 perform equivalent logic. Then, using DeMorgan's theorem, prove your answer.

5. Write the Boolean expression for the circuit shown in Figure 7. Then, using DeMorgan's theorem, prove that the circuit is equivalent to that shown in Figure 1.

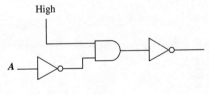

FIGURE 7

6. Assume the LED in Figure 5 is off no matter what the switch positions. List steps you would take to isolate the problem.

Logic Gates

Objectives

After completing this experiment, you will be able to

- □ Determine experimentally the truth tables for the NAND, NOR, and inverter gates.
- □ Use NAND and NOR gates to formulate other basic logic gates.
- □ Use the ANSI/IEEE Std. 91–1984 logic symbols.

Materials Needed

7400 quad 2-input NAND gate
7402 quad 2-input NOR gate
1.0 kΩ resistor

For Further Investigation:
  7486 quad XOR gate

Summary of Theory

Logic deals with only two normal conditions: logic "1" or logic "0." These conditions are like the yes or no answers to a question. Either a switch is closed (1) or it isn't (0); either an event has occurred (1) or it hasn't (0); and so on. In Boolean logic, 1 and 0 represent conditions. In positive logic, 1 is represented by the term *HIGH* and 0 is represented by the term *LOW*. In positive logic, the more positive voltage is 1 and the less positive voltage is 0. Thus, for positive TTL logic, a voltage of $+2.4$ V $= 1$ and a voltage of $+0.4$ V $= 0$.

In some systems, this definition is reversed. With negative logic, the more positive voltage is 0 and the less positive voltage is 1. Thus, for negative TTL logic, a voltage of $+0.4$ V $= 1$ and a voltage of $+2.4$ V $= 0$.

Although negative logic is sometimes useful in simplifying designs, it can easily become confusing. For example, in positive logic a 2-input AND gate has a HIGH output if both input A AND input B are HIGH. But in negative logic it becomes an OR gate because if either input A OR input B is LOW, the output is LOW. Figure 1 illustrates this idea. The electrical signals are identical for both gates, but the logic definitions are not. The AND gate can also be drawn as an OR gate if inversion "bubbles" are added to both the inputs and the output to indicate the active-LOW signals. The operation of the AND gate can be given by two rules.

Rule 1: If A is LOW OR B is LOW OR both are LOW, then X is LOW.

Rule 2: If A is HIGH AND B is HIGH, then X is HIGH.

A = 0 —
B = 0 — ▷o— X = 0

A = 0 —
B = 1 — ▷o— X = 0 } "0 **OR** 0 produces a 0"

A = 1 —o
B = 0 —o ▷— X = 0

(a)

A = 1 —
B = 1 — ⊃— X = 1 } "1 **AND** 1 produces a 1"

(b)

FIGURE 1
Two distinctive shape symbols for an AND gate. The two symbols represent the same gate.

The operation can also be shown by the truth table. The AND truth table is

Inputs		Output
A	B	X
LOW	LOW	LOW
LOW	HIGH	LOW
HIGH	LOW	LOW
HIGH	HIGH	HIGH

Rule 1 brackets rows with LOW output; Rule 2 points to the HIGH HIGH HIGH row.

Notice that the first rule describes the first *three* lines of the truth table and the second rule describes the last line of the truth table. Sometimes, it is useful to draw the gate to emphasize one or another of the rules. For this reason, there are *two* distinctive shape symbols for the AND gate. Although two rules are needed to specify completely the operation of the gate, each symbol best illustrates only one of the rules. If you are reading the symbol for a gate, read a bubble as a logic 0 and the absence of a bubble as a logic 1.

The first three lines of the truth table are illustrated with the negative-logic OR symbol (Figure 1(a)); the last line of the truth table is illustrated with the positive-logic AND symbol (Figure 1(b)). Similar rules and logic diagrams can be written for the other basic gates.

A useful method of dealing with negative logic is to label the signal function with a bar written over the label to indicate that the signal is LOW when the stated condition is true. Figure 2 shows some examples of this logic, called *assertion-level* logic. You should be aware that manufacturers are not always consistent in the way labels are applied to diagrams and function tables. Assertion-level logic is frequently shown to indicate an action. As shown in Figure 2, the action to read (R) is asserted (1) when the input line is HIGH; the opposite action is to write ($\overline{W}$), which is asserted (0) when the line is LOW. Other examples are shown in the figure.

The symbols for the basic logic gates are shown in Figure 3. The newer ANSI/IEEE rectangular symbols are shown along with the older distinctive-shape symbols. The ANSI/IEEE symbols contain a qualifying symbol to indicate the type of logic operation performed. The distinctive-shape symbols for logic gates are still very popular because they enable you to visualize the standard Boolean operations of AND, OR, and INVERT immediately. The distinctive shapes also enable you to analyze logic networks because each gate can be represented with a positive logic symbol or an equivalent negative logic symbol. Both shapes are used in this experiment.

In addition to the AND, OR, and INVERT functions, two other basic gates are very important to logic designers. These are the NAND and NOR gates, in which the output of AND and OR, respectively, have been negated. These gates are important because of their "universal" property; they can be used to synthesize the other Boolean logic functions including AND, OR, and INVERT functions.

Two gates that are sometimes classified with the basic gates are the exclusive-OR (abbreviated

FIGURE 2
Examples of assertion logic.

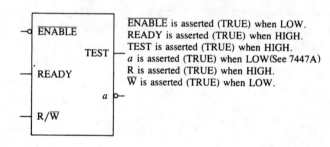

$\overline{ENABLE}$ is asserted (TRUE) when LOW.
READY is asserted (TRUE) when HIGH.
TEST is asserted (TRUE) when HIGH.
a is asserted (TRUE) when LOW(See 7447A)
R is asserted (TRUE) when HIGH.
$\overline{W}$ is asserted (TRUE) when LOW.

FIGURE 3
Basic logic gates.

Distinctive shape symbols   Rectangular outline symbols (ANSI/IEEE symbols)

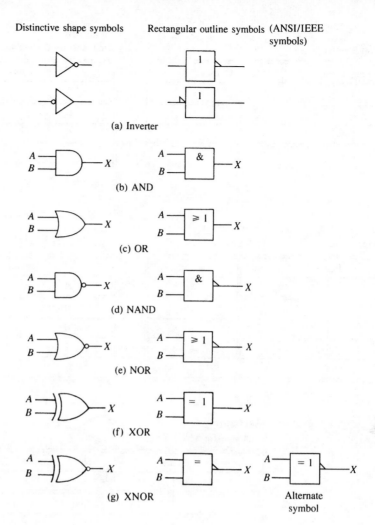

(a) Inverter

(b) AND

(c) OR

(d) NAND

(e) NOR

(f) XOR

(g) XNOR

Alternate symbol

XOR) and the exclusive-NOR (abbreviated XNOR) gates. These gates always have two inputs. The symbols are shown in Figure 3(f) and (g). The output of the XOR gate is HIGH when either A or B is HIGH, but not both (inputs "disagree"). The XNOR is just the opposite; the output is HIGH only when the inputs are the same (agree). For this reason, the XNOR gate is sometimes called a CO-INCIDENCE gate.

The logical operation of any gate can be summarized with a truth table, which shows all the possible inputs and outputs. The truth tables for AND, OR, INVERT, XOR, and XNOR are shown in Table 1 (a) through (e). The tables are shown with 1 and 0 to represent positive logic HIGH and LOW, respectively. Except in Figure 1 (where negative logic is illustrated), only positive logic is used in this lab book and 1 and 0 mean HIGH and LOW, respectively.

In this experiment, you will test the truth tables for NAND and NOR gates as well as those for several combinations of these gates. Keep in mind that if any two truth tables are identical, then the logic circuits that they represent are equivalent.

Procedure

Logic Functions

1. Find the connection diagram for the 7400 quad 2-input NAND gate and the 7402 quad 2-input NOR gate in the manufacturer's specification sheet.* Note that there are four gates on each of these ICs. Apply V_{CC} and ground to the appropriate pins. Then test one of the NAND gates by connect-

---

*See Appendix.

353

TABLE 1(a)
Truth table for inverter.

Input	Output
A	X
0	1
1	0

TABLE 1(b)
Truth table for 2-input AND gate.

Inputs		Output
A	B	X
0	0	0
0	1	0
1	0	0
1	1	1

TABLE 1(c)
Truth table for 2-input OR gate.

Inputs		Output
A	B	X
0	0	0
0	1	1
1	0	1
1	1	1

TABLE 1(d)
Truth table for XOR gate.

Inputs		Output
A	B	X
0	0	0
0	1	1
1	0	1
1	1	0

TABLE 1(e)
Truth table for XNOR gate.

Inputs		Output
A	B	X
0	0	1
0	1	0
1	0	0
1	1	1

ing all possible combinations of inputs, as listed in Table 2 of the report. Apply a logic 1 through a series 1.0 kΩ resistor and a logic 0 by connecting directly to ground. Show the logic output (1 or 0) as well as the measured output voltage in Table 2. Use the DMM to measure the output voltage.

2. Repeat Step 1 for one of the NOR gates; tabulate your results in Table 3 of the report.

3. Connect the circuits of Figures 4 and 5. Connect the input to a 0 and a 1, measure each output voltage, and complete truth Tables 4 and 5 for the circuits.

4. Construct the circuit shown in Figure 6 and complete truth Table 6. This circuit may appear at first to have no application, but in fact can be used as a buffer. Because of amplification within the IC, a buffer provides more drive current.

5. Construct the circuit shown in Figure 7 and complete truth Table 7. Notice that the truth table for this circuit is the same as the truth table for one of the single gates. (What does this imply about the circuit?)

6. Repeat Step 5 for the circuits shown in Figures 8 and 9. Complete truth Tables 8 and 9.

For Further Investigation

The circuit shown in Figure 10 has the same truth table as one of the truth tables shown in Figure 1 (a) through (e). Test all input combinations and complete truth Table 10. What is the equivalent gate?

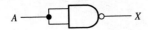

FIGURE 4

FIGURE 5

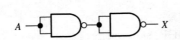

FIGURE 6

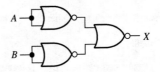

FIGURE 7

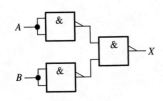

FIGURE 8

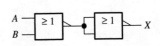

FIGURE 9

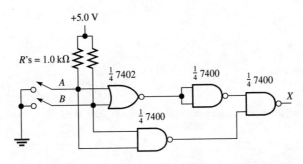

FIGURE 10

355

Report for "Logic Gates" Experiment

Name: _____ Date: _____ Class: _____

Objectives:

☐ Determine experimentally the truth tables for the NAND, NOR, and inverter gates.
☐ Use NAND and NOR gates to formulate other basic logic gates.
☐ Use the ANSI/IEEE Std. 91–1984 logic symbols.

Data and Observations:

TABLE 2
NAND gate.

Inputs		Output	Measured Output Voltage
A	B	X	
0	0		
0	1		
1	0		
1	1		

TABLE 3
NOR gate.

Inputs		Output	Measured Output Voltage
A	B	X	
0	0		
0	1		
1	0		
1	1		

TABLE 4
Truth table for Figure 4.

Input	Output	Measured Output Voltage
A	X	
0		
1		

TABLE 5
Truth table for Figure 5.

Input	Output	Measured Output Voltage
A	X	
0		
1		

356

TABLE 6
Truth table for Figure 6.

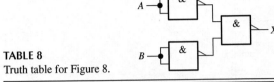

Input	Output	Measured Output Voltage
A	X	
0		
1		

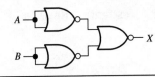

TABLE 7
Truth table for Figure 7.

Inputs		Output	Measured Output Voltage
A	B	X	
0	0		
0	1		
1	0		
1	1		

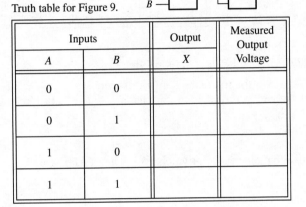

TABLE 8
Truth table for Figure 8.

Inputs		Output	Measured Output Voltage
A	B	X	
0	0		
0	1		
1	0		
1	1		

TABLE 9
Truth table for Figure 9.

Inputs		Output	Measured Output Voltage
A	B	X	
0	0		
0	1		
1	0		
1	1		

Results and Conclusion:

357

Further Investigation Results:

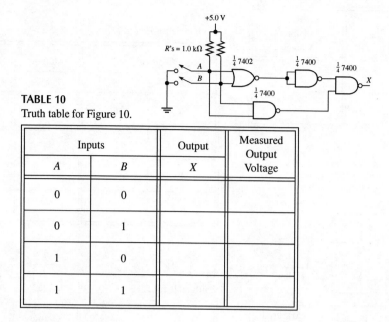

TABLE 10
Truth table for Figure 10.

Inputs		Output	Measured Output Voltage
A	B	X	
0	0		
0	1		
1	0		
1	1		

Evaluation and Review Questions

1. Look over the truth tables in your report.
  a. What circuits did you find that are equivalent to inverters?

  b. What circuit is equivalent to a 2-input AND gate?

  c. What circuit is equivalent to a 2-input OR gate?

2. An alarm circuit is needed to indicate that either the temperature OR the pressure in a batch process is too high. If either of the conditions is true, a microswitch closes to ground, as shown in Figure 11. The required output for an LED is a LOW signal when the alarm condition is true. George thinks that an OR gate is needed, but Betty argues that an AND gate is needed. Who is right and why?

FIGURE 11

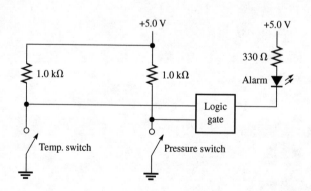

3. A car burglar alarm has a normally LOW switch on each of its four doors when they are closed. If any door is opened, the alarm is set off. The alarm requires an active HIGH output. What type of basic gate is needed to provide this logic?

4. Suppose you needed a 2-input NOR gate for a circuit, but all you have available is a 7400 (quad 2-input NAND gate). Show how you could obtain the required NOR function using the NAND gate. (Remember that equivalent truth tables imply equivalent functions.)

5. A control signal that is used in a computer system is labeled DT/$\overline{\text{R}}$ for data transmit/receive. What action is implied when this signal is HIGH? LOW?

6. Assume you were troubleshooting a circuit containing a 4-input NAND gate and you discover that the output of the NAND gate is always HIGH. Is this an indication of a bad gate? Explain your answer.

Logic Circuit Simplification

Objectives

After completing this experiment, you will be able to

☐ Develop the truth table for a BCD-invalid code detector.

☐ Use a Karnaugh map to simplify the expression.

☐ Build and test a circuit that implements the simplified expression.

☐ Predict the effect of "faults" in the circuit.

Materials Needed

7400 NAND gate
LED
Resistors: one 330 Ω, four 1.0 kΩ
One 4-position DIP switch

Summary of Theory

With combinational logic circuits, the outputs are determined solely by the inputs. For simple combinational circuits, truth tables are used to summarize all possible inputs and outputs; the truth table completely describes the desired operation of the circuit. The circuit may be realized by simplifying the expression for the output function as read from the truth table.

A powerful mapping technique for simplifying combinational logic circuits was developed by M. Karnaugh and was described in a paper he published in 1953. The method involved writing the truth table into a geometric map in which adjacent cells (squares) differ from each other in only one variable. (Adjacent cells share a common border horizontally or vertically.) When you are drawing a Karnaugh map, the variables are written in a Gray code sequence along the sides and tops of the map. Each cell on the map corresponds to one row of the truth table. The output variables appear as 0's and 1's on the map in positions corresponding to those given in the truth table.

As an example, consider the design of a 2-bit comparator. The inputs will be called A_2A_1 and B_2B_1. The desired output is HIGH if A_2A_1 is equal to or greater than B_2B_1. To begin, the desired output is written in the form of a truth table, as given in Table 1. All possible inputs are clearly identified by the truth table and the desired output for every possible input is given.

Next the Karnaugh map is drawn, as shown in Figure 1. In this example, the map is drawn using numbers to represent the inputs. The corresponding values for the output function are entered from the truth table. The map can be read in sum-of-products (SOP) form by grouping adjacent cells containing 1's on the map. The size of the groups must be an integer power of 2 (1, 2, 4, 8, etc.) and should contain only 1's. The largest possible group should

TABLE 1

Truth table for comparator.

Inputs				Output
A_2	A_1	B_2	B_1	X
0	0	0	0	1
0	0	0	1	0
0	0	1	0	0
0	0	1	1	0
0	1	0	0	1
0	1	0	1	1
0	1	1	0	0
0	1	1	1	0
1	0	0	0	1
1	0	0	1	1
1	0	1	0	1
1	0	1	1	0
1	1	0	0	1
1	1	0	1	1
1	1	1	0	1
1	1	1	1	1

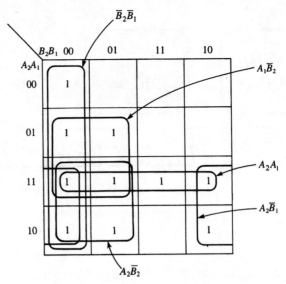

FIGURE 1

Karnaugh map for the truth table shown in Table 1.

be designed for 4 bits, but could easily be expanded to 8 bits for Register A.

Procedure

BCD Invalid Code Detector

Figure 3 illustrates the tablet control system with the invalid code detector. As you know, BCD is a 4-bit binary code that represents the decimal numbers 0 through 9. The binary numbers 1010 through 1111 are invalid in BCD.

1. Complete the truth table shown as Table 2 in the report. Assume the output for the ten valid BCD codes is a 0 and for the six invalid BCD codes is a 1. As usual for representing numbers, the most significant bit is represented by the letter D and the least significant bit by the letter A.

2. Complete the Karnaugh map shown as Figure 4 in the report. Group the 1's according to the rules given in the text and the Summary of Theory. Find the expression of the invalid codes by reading the minimum SOP from the map. Write the Boolean expression in the space provided in the report.

3. If you have correctly written the expression in Step 2, there are two product terms and you will see that the letter D appears in both terms. This expression could be implemented directly as a satisfactory logic circuit. (This is left as a review question!) By factoring D from each term, you will arrive at another expression for invalid codes. Write the new expression in the space provided in the report.

4. Recall that, for TTL logic, a LOW can light an LED without violating the I_{OL} (16 mA) specifi-

be taken; all 1's must be in at least one group and may be taken in more than one group if helpful.

After grouping the 1's on the map, the output function can be determined. Each group is read as one of the product terms in the reduced output function. Within each group larger than one, adjacent boundaries will be crossed, causing the variable that changes to be eliminated from the output expression. A group of two adjacent 1's will have a single adjacent boundary and will eliminate one variable. A group of four 1's will eliminate two variables and a group of eight 1's will eliminate three variables. Figure 1 shows the groupings for the 2-bit comparator. Since each group in this case is a group of four 1's, each product term contains two variables (two were eliminated from each term). The resulting expression is the sum of all of the product terms. The circuit can be drawn directly, as shown in Figure 2.

In this experiment, you will use the Karnaugh mapping method, similar to the one described previously, to design a BCD-Invalid code detector. The detector is an enhancement to the tablet counting and control system described in the text. You will design a circuit to assure that only valid BCD codes are present in Register A and to signal a warning if an invalid BCD code is detected. Your circuit will

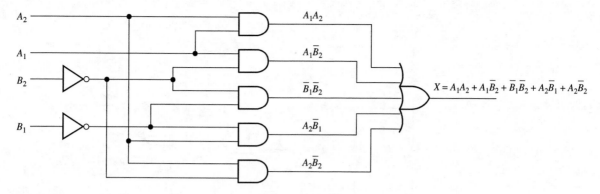

FIGURE 2
Circuit implementation of the comparator given by truth table in Table 1.

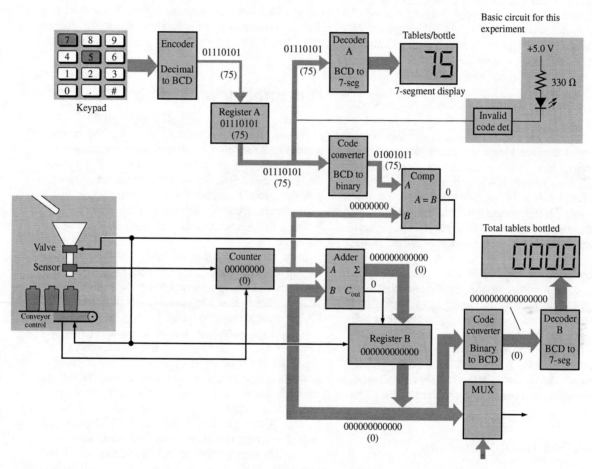

FIGURE 3
Tablet control system.

FIGURE 5

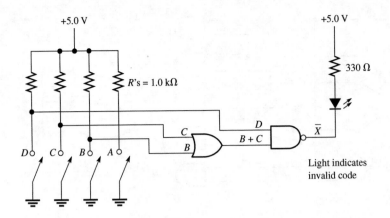

Light indicates
invalid code

cation but a HIGH causes the I_{OH} (400 μA) specification to be exceeded. To avoid this, the output is inverted and $\overline{X}$ is used to light the LED with a LOW logic level. The circuit shown in Figure 5 implements the expression from Step 3 but with the output inverted in order *sink* rather than *source* current.

5. Although the circuit shown in Figure 5 satisfies the design requirements with only two gates, it requires two *different* ICs. In some cases, this might be the best design. However, using the universal properties of the NAND gate, the OR gate could be replaced with three NAND gates. This change allows the circuit to be implemented with only *one* IC—a quad 7400. Change the circuit in Figure 5 by replacing the OR gate with three NAND gates. Draw the new circuit in the space provided in the report.

6. Construct the circuit you drew in Step 5. Test all combinations of the inputs and complete truth Table 3 in the report. If you have constructed and tested the circuit correctly, the truth table will be the same as Table 2.

7. For each problem listed in Table 4, state what effect it will have on your circuit. (Some "problems" may have no effect). If you aren't sure, you may want to simulate the problem and test the result.

EWB/MSM Troubleshooting

The CD packaged with this lab manual contains Electronics Workbench (.ewb) and Multisim (.msm)

files. Open the file named Exp-08. The file has three circuits that are the same as Figure 5. Each of the three circuits has a fault. Analyze the logic indicators and determine the most likely fault in each circuit.

For Further Investigation

Design a circuit that will indicate if a BCD number is evenly divisible by three (3, 6, or 9). The input is a valid BCD number—assume that invalid numbers have already been tested and rejected by your earlier circuit! Since invalid numbers are now impossible, the Karnaugh map will contain "don't care" entries. An "X" on the map means that if the input is *not possible,* then you *don't care* about the outcome.

1. Complete the truth Table 5 in the report for the problem stated above. Enter 0's for BCD numbers that are not divisible by three and 1's for BCD numbers that are divisible by three. Enter an "X" to indicate an invalid BCD code.

2. Complete the Karnaugh map shown as Figure 6. Group the 1's on the map in groups of 2, 4, 8, etc. Do not take any 0's but do take X's if you can obtain a larger group. Read the minimum SOP from the map and show your expression in the space provided in the report.

3. Draw a circuit using only NAND gates that will implement the expression. The LED should be turned ON with a LOW output. Build the circuit and test each of the possible inputs to see that it performs as expected.

Report for "Logic Circuit Simplification" Experiment

Name: _____ Date: _____ Class: _____

Objectives:

☐ Develop the truth table for a BCD-invalid code detector.
☐ Use a Karnaugh map to simplify the expression.
☐ Build and test a circuit that implements the simplified expression.
☐ Predict the effect of "faults" in the circuit.

Data and Observations:

TABLE 2
Truth table for BCD-invalid code detector.

Inputs				Output
D	C	B	A	X
0	0	0	0	
0	0	0	1	
0	0	1	0	
0	0	1	1	
0	1	0	0	
0	1	0	1	
0	1	1	0	
0	1	1	1	
1	0	0	0	
1	0	0	1	
1	0	1	0	
1	0	1	1	
1	1	0	0	
1	1	0	1	
1	1	1	0	
1	1	1	1	

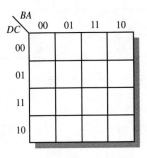

FIGURE 4
Karnaugh map of truth table for invalid BCD code detector.

Minimum sum-of-products read from map:

$X =$ _____

Factoring D from both product terms gives:

$X =$ _____

Step 5. Circuit for BCD-invalid code detector:

TABLE 3

Truth table for BCD-invalid code detector constructed in step 6.

Inputs				Output
D	C	B	A	X
0	0	0	0	
0	0	0	1	
0	0	1	0	
0	0	1	1	
0	1	0	0	
0	1	0	1	
0	1	1	0	
0	1	1	1	
1	0	0	0	
1	0	0	1	
1	0	1	0	
1	0	1	1	
1	1	0	0	
1	1	0	1	
1	1	1	0	
1	1	1	1	

TABLE 4

Problem Number	Problem	Effect
1	The pull-up resistor for the *D* switch is open.	
2	The ground to the NAND gate is open.	
3	A 3.3 kΩ resistor was accidently used in place of the 330 Ω resistor.	
4	The LED was inserted backward.	
5	Switch *A* is shorted to ground.	

Results and Conclusion:

EWB/MSM Troubleshooting:

Circuit 1   Most likely problem: _____

_____

Circuit 2   Most likely problem: _____

_____

Circuit 3   Most likely problem: _____

_____

Further Investigation Results:

TABLE 5

Truth table for BCD numbers divisible by three.

Inputs				Output
D	C	B	A	X
0	0	0	0	
0	0	0	1	
0	0	1	0	
0	0	1	1	
0	1	0	0	
0	1	0	1	
0	1	1	0	
0	1	1	1	
1	0	0	0	
1	0	0	1	
1	0	1	0	
1	0	1	1	
1	1	0	0	
1	1	0	1	
1	1	1	0	
1	1	1	1	

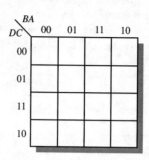

FIGURE 6

Karnaugh map of truth table for BCD numbers divisible by three.

Minimum sum-of-products read from map:

$X =$ _____

Circuit:

Evaluation and Review Questions

1. Assume that the circuit in Figure 5 was constructed but doesn't work correctly. The output is correct for all inputs except *DCBA* = 1000 and 1001. Suggest at least two possible problems that could account for this and explain how you would isolate the exact problem.

2. Draw the equivalent circuit in Figure 5 using only NOR gates.

3. Assume a circuit already had a 7442 BCD decoder in it and you wanted to add a BCD-invalid code detector to the circuit. Design a circuit that uses only one 3-input NAND gate and the 7442 to turn on an LED for invalid codes. (*Hint:* Use two outputs from the 7442 and one input to the 7442.)

4. The circuit shown in Figure 7 has an output labeled $\overline{X}$. Write the expression for $\overline{X}$; then, using DeMorgan's theorem, find the expression for X.

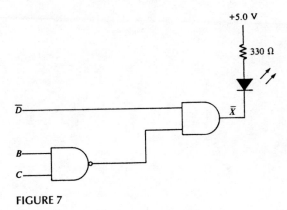

FIGURE 7

5. Convert the SOP form of the expression for the invalid code detector (Step 2) into POS form.

6. Draw a circuit, using NAND gates, that implements the invalid code detector from the expression you found in Step 2.

EWB/
MSM

More Logic Gates

Objectives

After completing this experiment, you will be able to
- Determine experimentally the truth tables for OR and XOR.
- Test OR and XOR logic gates with pulse waveforms.
- Use OR and XOR gates to form a circuit that performs the 1's or 2's complement of a 4-bit binary number.
- Troubleshoot the complement circuit for simulated faults.

Materials Needed

ICs: one 7432 OR gate, one 7486 XOR gate
Four LEDs
Resistors: nine 330 Ω, one 1.0 kΩ
One 4-position DIP switch
One SPST switch (wire may substitute)

For Further Investigation:

Three additional 1.0 kΩ resistors

Summary of Theory

In this experiment, you will test the OR and XOR gates but go one step further and use these gates in an application.

The truth table for an OR gate is shown in Table 1(a) for a two-input OR gate. OR gates are available with more than two inputs. The operation of an n-input OR gate is summarized in the following rule:

The output is HIGH if any input is HIGH, otherwise it is LOW.

The XOR gate is a 2-input gate. Recall that the truth table is similar to the OR gate except for when both inputs are HIGH; in this case, the output is LOW. The truth table for a 2-input XOR gate can be summarized with the statement

The output is HIGH only if one input is HIGH; otherwise it is LOW.

The truth table for XOR is shown in Table 1(b).

Procedure

Logic Functions for the OR and XOR Gates

1. Find the connection diagram for the 7432 quad 2-input OR gate and the 7486 quad 2-input XOR gate in the manufacturer's specification sheet.[*] Note that there are four gates on each of

---

[*]See Appendix.

TABLE 1(a)
Truth table for 2-input OR gate.

Inputs		Output
A	B	X
0	0	0
0	1	1
1	0	1
1	1	1

TABLE 1(b)
Truth table for XOR gate.

Inputs		Output
A	B	X
0	0	0
0	1	1
1	0	1
1	1	0

these ICs. Apply V_{CC} and ground to the appropriate pins. Then test one of the OR gates in the 7432 by connecting all possible combinations of inputs, as listed in Table 2 of the report. Apply a logic 1 through a series 1.0 kΩ resistor and a logic 0 by connecting directly to ground. Show the logic output (1 or 0) as well as the measured output voltage in Table 2. Use the DMM to measure the output voltage.

2. Repeat Step 1 for one of the XOR gates in the 7486; tabulate your results in Table 3 of the report.

3. The XOR gate has a very useful feature enabling selective inversion of a waveform. Construct the circuit shown in Figure 1. The input on pin 2 is from your pulse generator, which should be set to a TTL compatible pulse. Set the frequency for 1 kHz and observe the input and the output simultaneously with S_1 open. Then close S_1 and observe the input and the output. Sketch the observed waveforms in Plot 1 of the report.

4. In this step, you will test a circuit that uses combinations of OR and XOR gates and complete the truth table for the circuit. The purpose of the circuit is to use the selective inversion property of the XOR gate to produce either the 1's complement or the 2's complement of a 4-bit number. Both the input and output number are read from the LEDs; the LEDs are on when the bit shown is LOW in keeping with TTL current specifications. Construct the circuit shown in Figure 2. You will need to assign pin numbers to the various pins.

5. Open the complement switch, and test the data switches. If the circuit is working properly, each output LED should be the exact opposite of the corresponding input LED. If this isn't what you observe, stop and troubleshoot your circuit.

6. Now test the circuit with the complement switch closed. Complete the truth table in the report (Table 4) for all possible inputs. Keep in mind that a 0 is indicated with an LED that is ON.

7. Table 5 (in the report) gives several possible problems that could occur in the complement circuit. For each problem given, list one or two likely causes that would produce the problem. As a check on your idea, you may want to test your idea on the circuit.

EWB/MSM Troubleshooting

The CD packaged with this lab manual contains Electronics Workbench (.ewb) and Multisim (.msm) files. Open the file named Exp-05. The file contains two circuits. The first one has no fault and is the 1's and 2's complement circuit you tested in this experiment (Figure 2). The second has a fault. Analyze the fault by changing the input switches and observing the outputs. From your observations, deduce the most likely fault and state how you would isolate it.

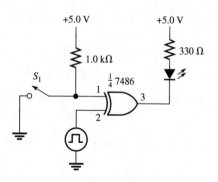

FIGURE 1

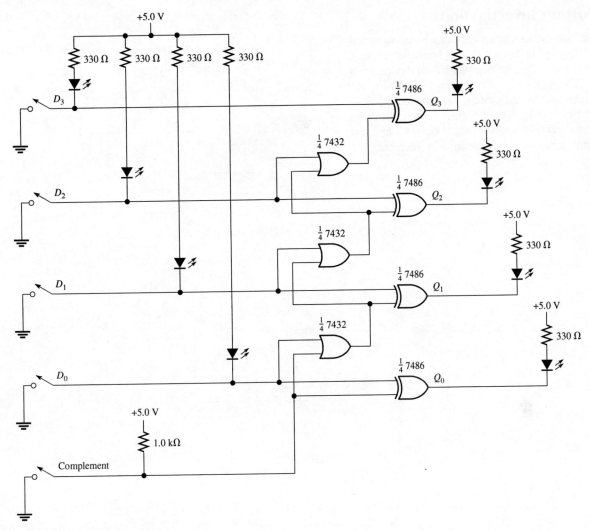

FIGURE 2

For Further Investigation

Another interesting circuit that can be constructed with XOR gates is the solution to the logic problem of controlling a light or other electrical device from several different locations. For two locations, the problem is simple and switches are made to do just that. The circuit shown in Figure 3 can control an LED from any of four locations. Construct and test the circuit; summarize your results in the report.

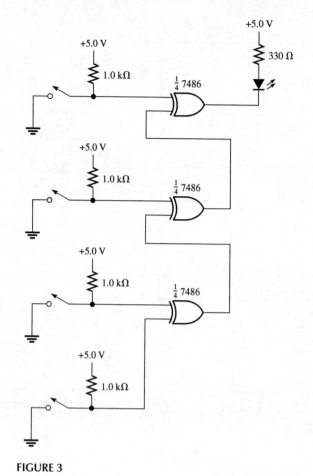

FIGURE 3

Report for "More Logic Gates" Experiment

Name: _____ Date: _____ Class: _____

Objectives:

☐ Determine experimentally the truth tables for OR and XOR.
☐ Test OR and XOR logic gates with pulse waveforms.
☐ Use OR and XOR gates to form a circuit that performs the 1's or 2's complement of a 4-bit binary number.
☐ Troubleshoot the complement circuit for simulated faults.

Data and Observations:

TABLE 2
OR gate.

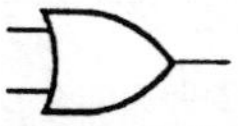

Inputs		Output	Measured Output Voltage
A	B	X	
0	0		
0	1		
1	0		
1	1		

TABLE 3
XOR gate.

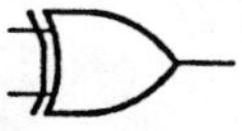

Inputs		Output	Measured Output Voltage
A	B	X	
0	0		
0	1		
1	0		
1	1		

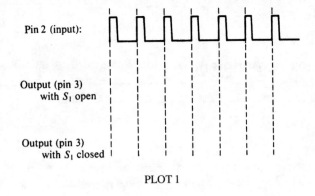

Pin 2 (input):

Output (pin 3)
with S_1 open

Output (pin 3)
with S_1 closed

PLOT 1

TABLE 4

Inputs	Outputs
$D_3\ D_2\ D_1\ D_0$	$Q_3\ Q_2\ Q_1\ Q_0$
0 0 0 0	
0 0 0 1	
0 0 1 0	
0 0 1 1	
0 1 0 0	
0 1 0 1	
0 1 1 0	
0 1 1 1	
1 0 0 0	
1 0 0 1	
1 0 1 0	
1 0 1 1	
1 1 0 0	
1 1 0 1	
1 1 1 0	
1 1 1 1	

TABLE 5

Symptom Number	Symptom	Possible Cause
1	None of the LEDs operate; the switches have no effect.	
2	LEDs on the output side do not work; those on the input side do work.	
3	The LED representing Q_3 is sometimes on when it should be off.	
4	The complement switch has no effect on the outputs.	

Results and Conclusion:

EWB/MSM Troubleshooting:

Most likely problem: _____

_____

Further Investigation Results:

Evaluation and Review Questions

1. Step 3 mentions the selective inversion feature of an XOR gate. Explain how you can choose to invert or not invert a given signal.

2. The circuit in Figure 2 is limited to a 4-bit input. Show how you could expand the circuit to 8 bits by adding two more ICs.

3. The comparator in Figure 4 gives an output that depends on switches S_A, S_B, S_C, and S_D and inputs A, B, C, and D. Explain how the comparator works. (When is the output HIGH and when is it LOW?)

4. Redraw Figure 4 using the ANSI/IEEE Std. 91-1984 logic symbols.

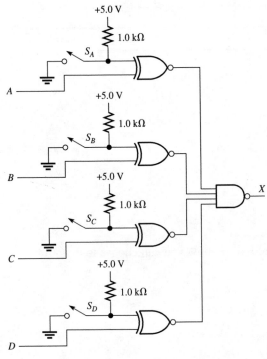

FIGURE 4

5. Assume you have two inputs, A and B, and their complements, $\overline{A}$ and $\overline{B}$, available. Show how you could use 2-input NAND gates to implement the XOR function.

6. Assume you have 2-input OR gates but needed to implement a 4-input OR function. Show how to connect the gates to implement the 4-input requirement.

Combinational Logic Using Multiplexers

Objectives

After completing this experiment, you will be able to
- Use a multiplexer to construct a comparator and a parity generator and test the circuit.
- Use an N-input multiplexer to implement a truth table containing $2N$ inputs.
- Troubleshoot a simulated failure in a test circuit.

Materials Needed

74151A data selector/multiplexer
7404 hex inverter
One LED
Resistors: one 330 Ω, four 1.0 kΩ

Summary of Theory

The *multiplexer* or *data selector* connects any one of several inputs to a single output. The opposite function, in which a single input is directed to one of several outputs, is called a *demultiplexer* or a *decoder.* These definitions are illustrated in Figure 1. Control is determined by additional logic signals called the *select* (or *address*) inputs.

Multiplexers (MUXs) and demultiplexers (DMUXs) have many applications in digital logic.

One useful application for MUXs is implementation of combinational logic functions directly from the truth table. For example, an overflow error detection circuit is described by the truth table shown in Figure 2(a). Each output row containing a "1" represents a minterm. (*Minterm* is a Boolean term in which all input variables appear either in "NOTed" or "true" form. For example, if there are 4 inputs labeled A, B, C, and D, then $A\overline{B}C\overline{D}$ and $\overline{A}BCD$ are both minterms but $A\overline{B}C$ is not.) If the logic for that minterm is connected to the data inputs of a MUX, and if the data selected are controlled by the input variables, the truth table has been implemented directly. Figure 2(b) illustrates this idea conceptually for the overflow detector.

Actually, an 8-input MUX is not required to implement the overflow detection logic. Any N-input MUX can generate the output function for $2N$ inputs. To illustrate, we reorganize the truth table in pairs, as shown in Figure 3(a). The inputs labeled A_4 and B_4 are used to select a data line. Connected to that line can be a logic 0, 1, Σ_4, or $\overline{\Sigma}_4$. For example, from the truth table, if $A_4 = 0$ and $B_4 = 1$, the D_1 input is selected. Since both outputs are the same (in this case a logic 0), then D_1 is connected to a logic 0. If the outputs were different, such as in the first and fourth rows, then the third input variable, Σ_4, would be compared with the output. Either the true (or NOT) form of that variable then would be selected. The results are shown conceptually in Figure 3(b), which is equivalent to but simpler than the circuit in Figure 2(b). This circuit is also on the EWB CD packaged with the text.

FIGURE 1

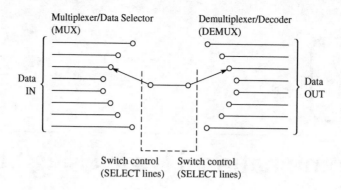

In this experiment you will use an 8:1 MUX to implement a 4-input truth table (with 16 combinations). First you will develop the circuit to implement a special comparator. In the For Further Investigation section the circuit is modified to make a parity generator for a 4-bit code. *Parity* is an extra bit attached to a code to check that the code has been received correctly. *Odd parity* means that the number of 1's in the code, including the parity bit, is an odd number. Odd or even parity can be generated with exclusive-OR gates, and parity generators are available in IC form. However, the implementing of an arbitrary truth table using MUXs is the important concept.

Procedure

Special 2-Bit Comparator

1. Assume you needed to compare two 2-bit numbers called A and B to find whether A is equal to or greater than B. You could use a comparator and OR the $A > B$ and $A = B$ outputs. Another technique is to use an 8:1 MUX with the method shown in the Summary of Theory section. The partially completed truth table for the comparator is shown as Table 1 in the report. The inputs are A_2, A_1 and B_2, B_1, representing the two numbers to be compared. Notice that the A_2, A_1, and B_2 bits are connected to the SELECT

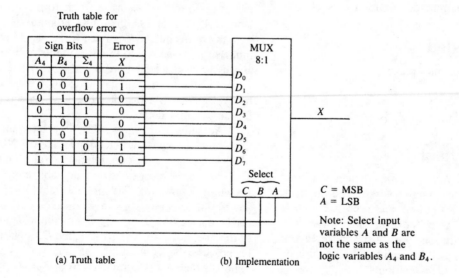

Truth table for overflow error

Sign Bits			Error
A_4	B_4	Σ_4	X
0	0	0	0
0	0	1	1
0	1	0	0
0	1	1	0
1	0	0	0
1	0	1	0
1	1	0	1
1	1	1	0

C = MSB
A = LSB

Note: Select input variables A and B are not the same as the logic variables A_4 and B_4.

(a) Truth table   (b) Implementation

FIGURE 2

Truth table for overflow error

Inputs (Multiplexer)			Output	Connect Data to:
Select Inputs		Data Input		
A_4	B_4	Σ_4	X	
0	0	0	0	Σ_4
0	0	1	1	
0	1	0	0	0
0	1	1	0	
1	0	0	0	0
1	0	1	0	
1	1	0	1	$\overline{\Sigma}_4$
1	1	1	0	

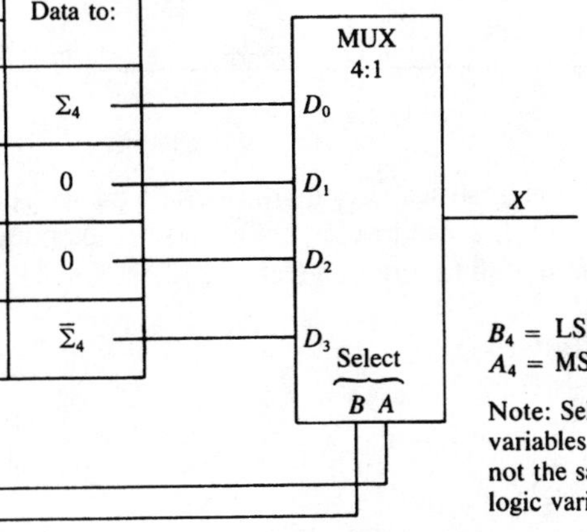

B_4 = LSB
A_4 = MSB

Note: Select input variables A and B are not the same as logic variables A_4 and B_4.

(a) Truth table (b) Implementation

FIGURE 3

inputs of the MUX. The B_1 bit is available to be connected as needed. It is therefore listed in a separate column of the truth table. Determine the logic in which the output represents $A > B$ and complete the X column of truth Table 1. The first two entries are completed as an example.

2. Look at the output X, in groups of two. The first pair of entries in X is the complement of the corresponding entries in B_1; therefore, the data should be connected to $\overline{B}_1$, as shown in the first line. Complete Table 1 by filling in the last column with either 0, 1, B_1, or $\overline{B}_1$.

3. Using the data from Table 1, complete the circuit drawing shown as Figure 4 in the report. From the manufacturer's specification sheet, determine how to connect the STROBE input (labeled $\overline{G}$). Construct the circuit and test its operation by checking every possible input. Demonstrate your working circuit to your instructor.

EWB/MSM Troubleshooting

The CD packaged with this lab manual contains Electronics Workbench (.ewb) and Multisim (.msm) files. The overflow error circuit discussed in the Summary of Theory and shown in Figure 3 is given as Exp-12. Two versions are given; the first has no fault and can be used as a reference. The second circuit has a fault. Analyze the circuit. In the space provided in the report, indicate the most likely problem.

For Further Investigation

Parity Generator Using a Multiplexer

1. The technique to implement an arbitrary function can also generate either odd or even parity. The MUX can generate *both* odd and even parity at the same time because there are two complementary outputs. One interesting aspect of the parity generator circuit is that any of the four inputs can turn the LED on or off in a manner similar to the way in which 3-way switches can turn a light on or off from more than one location. The truth table is shown in the report as Table 2. Four of the bits (A_3 through A_0) represent the information, and the fifth bit (X), which is the output, represents the parity bit. The requirement is for a circuit that generates both odd and even parity; however, the truth table will be set up for even parity. Even parity means that the sum of the 5 bits, *including the output parity bit*, must be equal to an even number. Complete truth Table 2 to reflect this requirement. The first line has been completed as an example.

2. Using the truth table completed in Step 1, complete the schematic for the even parity generator that is started in Figure 5 of the report. Change your original circuit into the parity circuit and test its operation.

Report for "Combinational Logic Using Multiplexers" Experiment

Name: _____ Date: _____ Class: _____

Objectives:

☐ Use a multiplexer to construct a comparator and a parity generator and test the circuit.
☐ Use an N-input multiplexer to implement a truth table containing $2N$ inputs.
☐ Troubleshoot a simulated failure in a test circuit.

Data and Observations:

TABLE 1
Truth table for 2-bit comparator, $A \geq B$.

Inputs				Output	Connect
A_2	A_1	B_2	B_1	X	Data to:
0	0	0	0	1	$\overline{B_1}$
0	0	0	1	0	
0	0	1	0		
0	0	1	1		
0	1	0	0		
0	1	0	1		
0	1	1	0		
0	1	1	1		
1	0	0	0		
1	0	0	1		
1	0	1	0		
1	0	1	1		
1	1	0	0		
1	1	0	1		
1	1	1	0		
1	1	1	1		

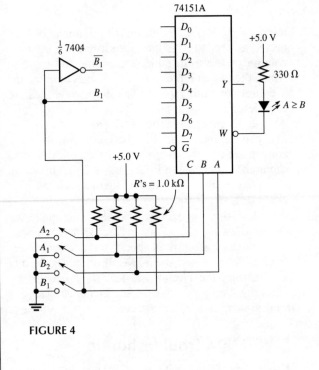

FIGURE 4

Results and Conclusion:

EWB/MSM Troubleshooting:
Most likely problem: _____

Further Investigation Results:

TABLE 2

Truth table for even parity generator.

Inputs				Output	Connect
A_3	A_2	A_1	A_0	X	Data to:
0	0	0	0	0	A_0
0	0	0	1	1	
0	0	1	0		
0	0	1	1		
0	1	0	0		
0	1	0	1		
0	1	1	0		
0	1	1	1		
1	0	0	0		
1	0	0	1		
1	0	1	0		
1	0	1	1		
1	1	0	0		
1	1	0	1		
1	1	1	0		
1	1	1	1		

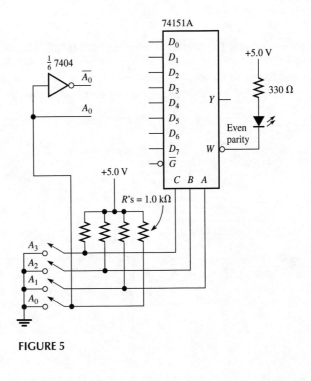

FIGURE 5

Evaluation and Review Questions

1. Design an invalid BCD code detector using a 74151A. Show the connections for your design on Figure 6.

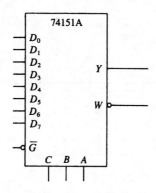

FIGURE 6

2. Can you reverse the procedure of this experiment? That is, given the circuit, can you find the Boolean expression? The circuit shown in Figure 7 uses a 4:1 MUX. The inputs are called A_2, A_1, and A_0. The first term is obtained by observing that when both select lines are LOW, A_2 is routed to the output; therefore the first minterm is written $A_2\overline{A_1}\overline{A_0}$. Using this as an example, find the remaining minterms.

$$X = A_2\overline{A_1}\overline{A_0} + \underline{\hspace{9cm}}$$

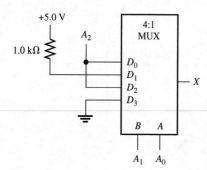

FIGURE 7

3. Assume the circuit shown in Figure 4 had the correct output for the first half of the truth table but had some incorrect outputs for the second half of the truth table. You decide to change ICs (not necessarily the best choice!) but the problem persists. What is the most likely cause of the problem? How would you test the circuit for your suspected problem?

4. Assume the circuit in Figure 4 had a short to ground on the output of the inverter. What effect would this have on the output logic? What procedure would you use to find the problem?

5. Assume that the input to the 7404 in Figure 4 was open, making the output, $\overline{B_1}$, a constant LOW. Which lines on the truth table would give incorrect readings on the output?

6. How can both odd and even parity be obtained from the circuit in Figure 5?

System
Application

Combinational Logic Using Demultiplexers

Objectives

After completing this experiment, you will be able to

☐ Complete the design of a multiple output combinational logic circuit using a demultiplexer.

☐ Use an oscilloscope to develop a timing diagram for a counter-decoder circuit.

Materials Needed

7408 or 74LS08 quad AND gate
7474 dual D flip-flop
74LS139A decoder/demultiplexer
One 4-position DIP switch
LEDs: two red, two yellow, two green
Resistors: six 330 Ω, two 1.0 kΩ

For Further Investigation:
7400 quad NAND gate

Summary of Theory

The demultiplexer (DMUX) can serve as a decoder or a data router. In this experiment, we will focus on the decoding function. A decoder takes binary information from one or more input lines and generates a unique output for each input combination. You are already familiar with the 7447A IC, which performs the decoding function. It converts a 4-bit binary input number to a unique code that is used to drive a

7-segment display. A DMUX can serve as a decoder by providing a unique output for every combination of input variables. The input variables are applied to the decoder's SELECT lines.

For most DMUXs, the selected output is LOW, whereas all others are HIGH. To implement a truth table that has a *single* output variable with a decoder is not very efficient and is rarely done; however, a method for doing this is shown conceptually in Figure 1. In this case, each line on the output represents one row on the truth table. If the decoder has active HIGH outputs, the output lines on the truth table with a 1 are ORed together, as illustrated in Figure 1. The output of the OR gate represents the output function. If the outputs of the decoder are active LOW, the output lines with a 1 on the truth table are connected with a NAND gate. This is shown in Figure 2.

A DMUX is superior for implementing combinational logic when there are several outputs for the same set of input variables. As you saw, each output line of the demultiplexer represents a line on the truth table. For active HIGH decoder outputs, OR gates are used, but a separate OR gate is required for each output function. Each OR gate output represents a different output function. In the case of active LOW decoder outputs, the OR gates are replaced by NAND gates.

FIGURE 1

Implementing a combinational logic
function with an active HIGH DMUX.

Truth table for overflow error

Inputs			Output
A_4	B_4	Σ_4	X
0	0	0	0
0	0	1	1
0	1	0	0
0	1	1	0
1	0	0	0
1	0	1	0
1	1	0	1
1	1	1	0

(a) Truth table

(b) Implementation

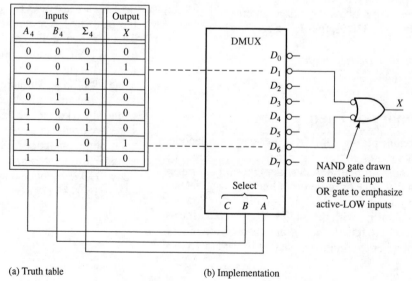

The problem presented in this experiment is the output logic for a traffic light controller.* A brief synopsis of the problem is as follows:

A digital controller is required to control traffic at a busy intersection and an occasionally used side street. The main street is to have a green light for a minimum of 25 seconds or as long as there is no vehicle on the side street. The side street is to have a green light until there is no vehicle on the side street or for a maximum of 25 seconds. There is to be a 4-second caution light (yellow) between changes from green to red on both the main

* This is described in Floyd's text.

street and the side street. These requirements are illustrated in the pictorial diagram in Figure 3. A block diagram of the system, showing the essential details, is given in Figure 4.

We will focus on state decoding and output logic. The block in Figure 4 can be separated into a state decoder, an output logic block, and trigger logic as shown in Figure 5. The state decoder has two inputs (2-bit Gray code) and must have an output for each of the four states. The 74LS139A is a dual 2-line to 4-line decoder and will do the job nicely, so it is selected.

The output logic takes the four active-LOW states from the decoder and must produce six

FIGURE 2

Truth table for overflow error

Inputs			Output
A_4	B_4	Σ_4	X
0	0	0	0
0	0	1	1
0	1	0	0
0	1	1	0
1	0	0	0
1	0	1	0
1	1	0	1
1	1	1	0

NAND gate drawn
as negative input
OR gate to emphasize
active-LOW inputs

(a) Truth table

(b) Implementation

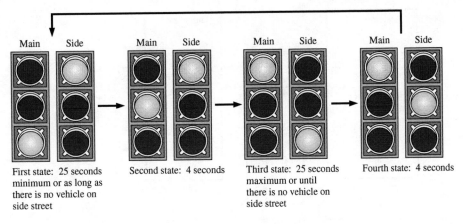

First state: 25 seconds minimum or as long as there is no vehicle on side street

Second state: 4 seconds

Third state: 25 seconds maximum or until there is no vehicle on side street

Fourth state: 4 seconds

FIGURE 3
Requirements for the traffic light sequence.

outputs for activating the traffic lights. A truth table for the decoding and output logic is given in Table 1. The truth table is organized in Gray code, which is used by the sequential logic to step through the states. The state outputs ($\overline{SO_1}$ to $\overline{SO_4}$) are active-LOW (0) and the output logic must be active-LOW (0) to drive LEDs that simulate the traffic lights. Later, you will see how to design this circuit for a programmable logic device (PLD).

Procedure

Traffic Light Decoder

The circuit represents the state decoder for four states and the output logic of a traffic light controller

system as described in the Summary of Theory section. There are six outputs representing a red, yellow, and green traffic light on a main and side street. The outputs are shown in the desired sequence for the lights on the truth Table 1. A logic "0" is used to turn on an LED. For example, state 00 (the first row of the truth table) will have a green light ON for the main street and a red light ON for the side street.

1. A partially completed schematic is shown in Figure 6 in the report. The 74LS139A is the state decoder and the AND gates, drawn as negative NOR gates, form the output logic. Refer to the truth table and complete the schematic. You need to decide what to do with the $1\overline{G}$ input and you should draw switches with pull-up resistors to each of the

FIGURE 4
System block diagram showing essential elements.

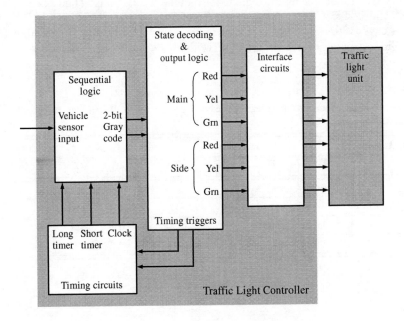

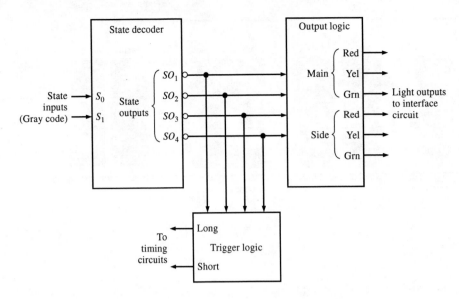

FIGURE 5
Block diagram of the state decoding and output logic.

decoder's select inputs. The $1Y_0$ output of the decoder (state 00) has been connected to the green LED on the main street and the red LED on the side street as an example.

2. Construct the circuit and test every combination according to the truth table. You should be able to observe the correct traffic light sequence if you open and close the switches in the same sequence as listed in truth Table 1.

3. Although you have not studied counters yet, the Gray-code counter shown in Figure 7 is simple to build and will illustrate the important role counters have in state machine design. Construct the counter, and connect the outputs to the SELECT inputs of the 74139A (switches should be removed). Set the pulse generator for 1 Hz and observe the se-

quence. This counter provides the correct sequence, but it is not controlled by the inputs (vehicle sensor and timers). These improvements will be covered later.

4. In this step, you will determine the relative timing of the various signals in the system. Speed up the pulse generator to 10 kHz. Connect channel 1 of your oscilloscope to the $1B_1$ select input. Trigger the scope using channel 1; do not move channel 1 as this will serve as the reference for the various timing measurements. Connect channel 2 to the $1A_1$ input and observe the time relationship of the SELECT signals. Then observe each of the decoder outputs ($1Y_0$, $1Y_1$, $1Y_2$, and $1Y_3$) moving the channel 2 probe only. Plot the timing diagram in Figure 8 in the report.

TABLE 1
Truth table for the decoding and output logic. State outputs are active-LOW and light outputs are active-LOW. $\overline{MR}$ = main red; $\overline{MY}$ = main yellow; etc.

State Code		State Outputs				Light Outputs					
S_1	S_0	$\overline{SO_1}$	$\overline{SO_2}$	$\overline{SO_3}$	$\overline{SO_4}$	$\overline{MR}$	$\overline{MY}$	$\overline{MG}$	$\overline{SR}$	$\overline{SY}$	$\overline{SG}$
0	0	0	1	1	1	1	1	0	0	1	1
0	1	1	0	1	1	1	0	1	0	1	1
1	1	1	1	0	1	0	1	1	1	1	0
1	0	1	1	1	0	0	1	1	1	0	1

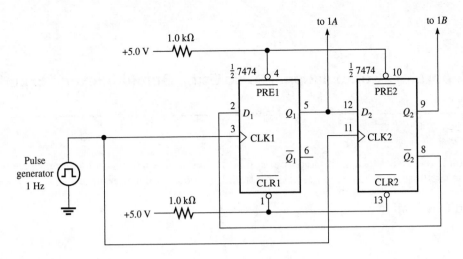

FIGURE 7
Gray-code counter for sequencing the traffic light decoder.

For Further Investigation

An interesting application of both multiplexer (MUX) and DMUX is in time division multiplexing. Time division multiplexing is often done with displays. In this case, the DMUX is used to turn on only one 7-segment display at a time.

Time-division multiplexing is also applied to some data transmission systems. In this application, data is sent to the enable input of the DMUX and routed to the appropriate location by the DMUX. Naturally, the data and SELECT inputs have to be carefully synchronized.

A few changes to the circuit for this experiment will produce a similar idea. The simulated data is applied to the enable ($\overline{G}$) input. The particular output is addressed by the SELECT inputs, and synchronization is achieved by using the counter from Step 3 of the experiment to provide both the data and the address. The modified circuit, including the counter, is shown in Figure 9 in the report. The inputs to the NAND gate are not shown. Start by connecting them to the Q outputs of the counter.

Connect the circuit and observe the results. Notice the visual appearance of the LEDs. Compare the visual appearance with the waveform viewed on the oscilloscope. Try moving the inputs of the NAND gate to the $\overline{Q}$ outputs of the counter. What happens? Connect the NAND input to other combinations of the counter output. Summarize your findings in the report.

Report for "Combinational Logic Using Demultiplexers" Experiment

Name: _____ Date: _____ Class: _____

Objectives:

☐ Complete the design of a multiple output combinational logic circuit using a demultiplexer.
☐ Use an oscilloscope to develop a timing diagram for a counter-decoder circuit.

Data and Observations:

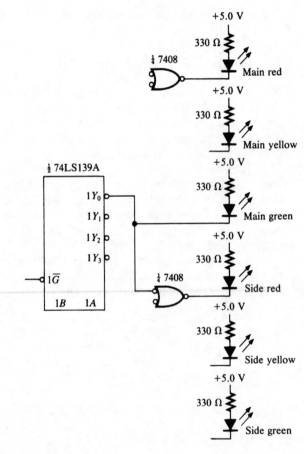

FIGURE 6
Traffic light output logic.

FIGURE 8
Timing diagram for Step 4.

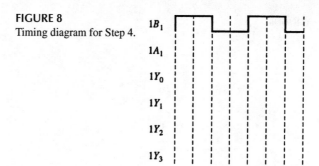

Results and Conclusion:

Further Investigation Results:

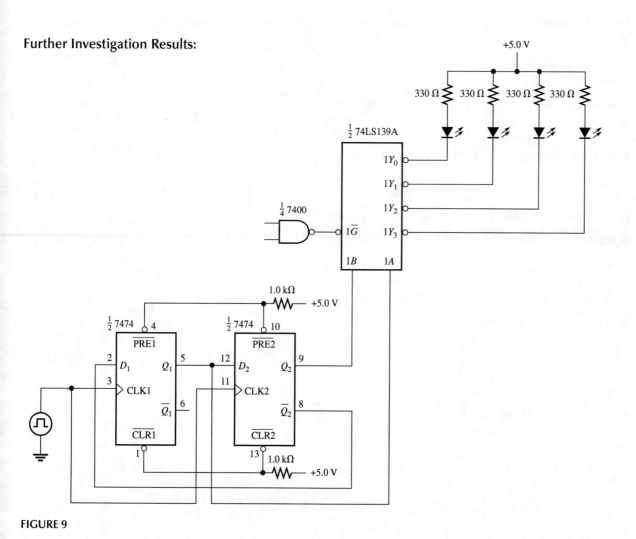

FIGURE 9

Evaluation and Review Questions

1. Assume you needed an 8-bit decoder, but all that is available is a dual 74LS139A. Show how you could use it, along with an inverter, to form an 8-bit decoder. (*Hint:* Consider using the enable inputs.)

2. Why were the AND gates in Figure 6 drawn as negative-NOR gates?

3. What is the advantage of Gray code for the state sequence?

4. For the circuit in Figure 6, what symptom would you observe if:
   a. The 1*B* select input were open?

   b. The 1*B* select input were shorted to ground?

   c. The enable ($\overline{G}$) input were open?

5. In Step 3, you added a Gray-code counter to the circuit. How would the circuit be affected if instead of a Gray-code counter, you had used a binary counter with the sequence 00-01-10-11?

6. The circuit in Figure 6 could be modified by adding a state 4 (binary 100) to the truth table. Assume you want to turn on both yellow lights at the same time in state 4 (for New York drivers). Set up the new state by adding a switch labeled C. When switch C is opened (HIGH), the decoder is disabled and at the same time the yellow lights turn on. Show the circuit. (*Hint:* Draw a truth table showing the decoder output [$1Y_1$] and switch C as the inputs and the main yellow as the output. You can accomplish this change with two 2-input gates.)

CODE CONVERTERS

OBJECTIVES:

[ ]   Design and construct a BCD to Decimal decoder from truth table data
[ ]   Examine operating characteristics of a 4-line to 16-line decoder/demultiplexer
[ ]   Examine operating characteristics of a 10-line to 4-line decimal-to-BCD encoder
[ ]   Examine characteristics of a BCD to Seven-Segment decoder

MATERIALS:

[ ]   + 5V Power Supply
[ ]   Logic Probe
[1]   74LS47 BCD-to-Seven Segment Decoder
[1]   74LS147 Decimal-to-BCD Encoder
[2]   74LS00 Quad NAND
[2]   74LS08 Quad AND
[1]   74LS11 3-Input AND
[2]   74LS04 Hex Inverter
[1]   Seven Segment Display
[9]   1K Ohm Resistors
[7]   220 Ohm Resistors
[7]   330 Ohm Resistors
[1]   8-Input DIP Switch

INFORMATION:

When working in a digital system, it is necessary to convert our normal arithmetic and communication systems into a binary code with which the circuits can function, and then back again. For instance, if doing simple arithmetic, we want to enter the numbers in decimal, the circuits need binary to perform the calculations, and we want the answer in decimal, or some understandable form. This experiment will familiarize us with a few of the "encoder" and "decoder" circuits that are common in digital systems.

From *Laboratory Manual (A Troubleshooting Approach) to accompany Digital Electronics: A Practical Approach,* Sixth Edition, Michael Wiesner and Vance Venable. Copyright © 2002 by Pearson Education, Inc. All rights reserved.

An encoder changes some number system into binary. One of the most common encoders is the BCD to Binary, since it allows us to enter numbers using our normal counting system and encode them into binary. This experiment will examine the 74LS147 Encoder which converts from a 0–9 count, representing a decimal keyboard, to a 4-bit BCD system. The four bits of BCD could then be used to perform addition, subtraction, etc. The answer would then be output to some decimal display through a decoder.

The BCD decoder is examined in detail in this experiment. To better understand a decoder, a circuit will be designed from a truth table using the sum-of-products method. The designed circuit will then be constructed and tested using one LED to represent each decimal digit, 0–9! This circuit is a BCD to Decimal decoder. The 74LS47 BCD to 7-Segment decoder will also be used. This system supplies the decoding for the easily readable 7-segment display.

The 7-segment display is a set of seven LED's that are either common-anode or common-cathode. The 74LS47 supplies an active low output, so it uses the common-anode type display. Each display input (a through g) requires a separate input, exactly as seven LED's would. Each input also must have a current limiting resistor, normally about 330 Ohms. The 74LS47 then decodes the 4-bit BCD input into the combinations necessary to display digits 0 through 9 on the display.

A circuit encoding decimal to BCD and BCD to 7-segment is presented. This circuit should familiarize us with the 7-segment display and driver, which will be used in many later experiments. In addition to the decimal-BCD, BCD-decimal, and BCD-7-segment encoders/decoders, a 4-to-16 line decoder chip will be examined.

PROCEDURE:

1.   Examine the data in the BCD-to-Decimal truth table of Figure 1. From the truth table, design a circuit to implement the decoding logic. Use a four input DC switch for the input logic, and LED's for the output logic. Whenever possible, use term sharing to simplify the circuit. In order to cut down the number of chips necessary, you may want to use NAND- or NOR-only logic. Construct the circuit and check out all ten possible inputs.

TRUTH TABLE-BCD to DECIMAL

A	B	C	D	0	1	2	3	4	5	6	7	8	9
0	0	0	0	1	0	0	0	0	0	0	0	0	0
0	0	0	1	0	1	0	0	0	0	0	0	0	0
0	0	1	0	0	0	1	0	0	0	0	0	0	0
0	0	1	1	0	0	0	1	0	0	0	0	0	0
0	1	0	0	0	0	0	0	1	0	0	0	0	0
0	1	0	1	0	0	0	0	0	1	0	0	0	0
0	1	1	0	0	0	0	0	0	0	1	0	0	0
0	1	1	1	0	0	0	0	0	0	0	1	0	0
1	0	0	0	0	0	0	0	0	0	0	0	1	0
1	0	0	1	0	0	0	0	0	0	0	0	0	1

Figure 1

2.   Fill in the functions for the pin diagrams for the 74LS147 and 74LS47 chips in Figure 2.

PIN CONFIGURATION DIAGRAM   DESCRIPTION

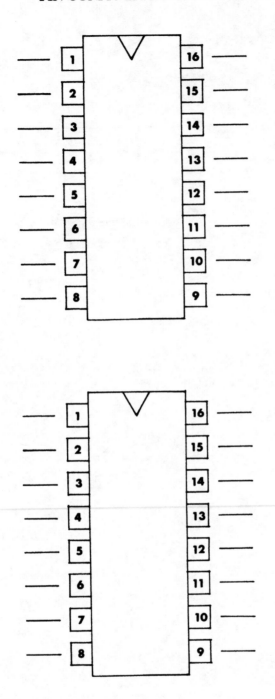

Figure 2

7-SEGMENT DISPLAY PINOUT

This exercise will demonstrate how to find the correct pin-out for a 7-segment display. This example shows a common-anode display which doesn't have pins 4, 5, and 12. However, using this same method it is possible to determine the pin configuration of any 7-segment display.

Install the 7-segment display and connect pin 14 through a resistor to + 5V Vcc. Each pin will be tested to determine which LED lights with each pin. As the pin-out is determined, mark the spaces provided on the 7-segment and keep it for future experiments.

Beginning at pin 1, ground each pin in sequence.

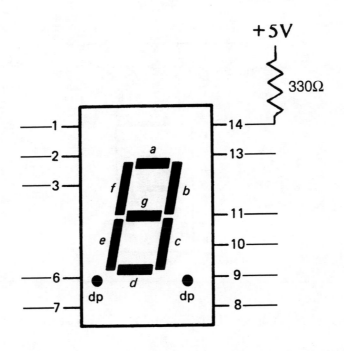

Figure 3

QUESTION: The 7-segment display can be set up with one resistor to Vcc or with seven resistors, one to each diode, pins a–g! What is the difference in the operation of the 7-segment with the two setups?

3.   The following circuit demonstrates the operation of the 7-segment display with the 74LS47 Decoder/driver. Build the circuit and then follow the steps below. Note: The common anode pin is connected directly to +5V.

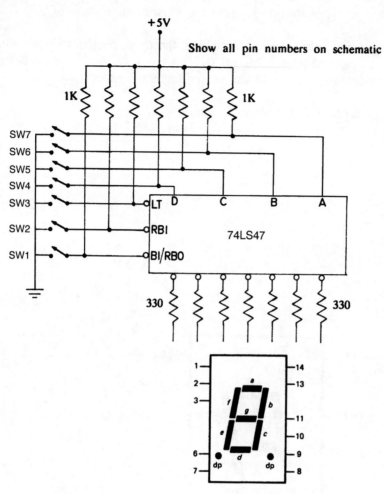

Figure 4

A.   OPEN all switches (Logic 1). Is the display on or off? ----- Why?

B.   CLOSE switch 1 (BI/RBO). Now what does the display show?

C.   OPEN switches 1, 2, and 3, and CLOSE switches 4, 5, 6, and 7. What does the 7-segment display show?

D.   Leave the switches in their present position, except CLOSE switch 3. Now what does the display show?

E.   With switch 3 still closed, OPEN switch 5. Now what is on the display?

F.   OPEN switch 3 and CLOSE switch 2. What shows? ----- Why?

4.   Construct the circuit of Figure 5. Use the lamp test function of the 74LS47 decoder to check that the 7-segment display is connected properly. Run the decimal input count 0 through 9 through the circuit and observe the 7-segment display. Have your instructor check the circuit.

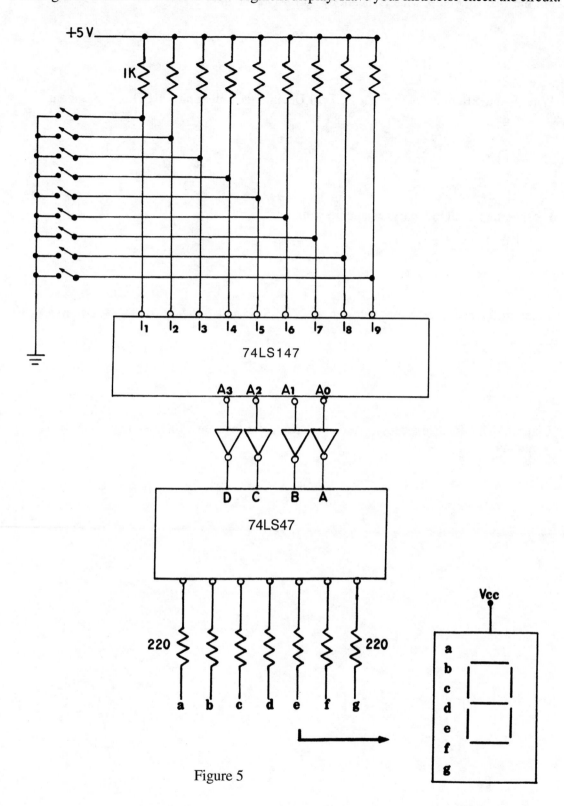

Figure 5

QUESTIONS:

1.   For the 74LS147 chip, what is meant by "priority encoding"?

2.   What is the difference between a BCD to Decimal decoder and a BCD to 7-Segment decoder?

3.   If converting octal to binary, what chip would be used?

4.   What differences are there between the 74LS42 and 74LS45 BCD to Decimal decoders?

5.   Using AND, OR, Inverter logic, draw the schematic for converting decimal count 0–3 to binary outputs.

The J-K Flip-Flop

Objectives

After completing this experiment, you will be able to

- Test various configurations for a J-K flip-flop, including the asynchronous and synchronous inputs.
- Observe frequency division characteristics in the toggle mode.
- Measure the propagation delay of a J-K flip-flop.

Materials Needed

74LS76 dual J-K flip-flop
LEDs: one red, one green, one yellow
Resistors: three 390 Ω, four 1.0 kΩ
One 4-position DIP switch

Summary of Theory

The D flip-flop is an edge-triggered device that allows the output to change only during the active clock edge. The D flip-flop can only be set and reset, a limitation for some applications. Furthermore, it cannot be latched unless the clock pulses are removed—a condition that limits applications for

this device. The S-R flip-flop could be latched but one combination of inputs is disallowed ($S = 1$, $R = 1$). A solution to these problems is the J-K flip-flop, which is basically a clocked S-R flip-flop with additional logic to replace the S-R invalid output states with a new mode called *toggle*. Toggle causes the flip-flop to change to the state opposite to its present state. It is similar to the operation of an automatic garage door opener. If the button is pressed when the door is open, the door will close; otherwise, it will open.

The J-K flip-flop is the most versatile of the three basic flip-flops. All applications for flip-flops can be accomplished with either the D or the J-K flip-flop. The clocked S-R flip-flop is seldom used; it is used mostly as an internal component of integrated circuits. (See the 74165 shift register, for example.) The truth tables for all three flip-flops are compared in Figure 1. The inputs are labeled J (the set mode) and K (the reset mode) to avoid confusion with the S-R flip-flop.

A certain amount of time is required for the input of a logic gate to affect the output. This time, called the *propagation delay time,* depends on the logic family. In the For Further Investigation section, you will investigate the propagation delay for a J-K flip-flop.

The need to assure that input data do not affect the output until they are at the correct level led to the concept of edge-triggering, which is the preferred method to assure synchronous transitions. An older method that is sometimes used is *pulse-triggered* or *master-slave* flip-flops. In these flip-flops,

FIGURE 1
Comparison of basic flip-flops.

S-R flip-flop

Inputs		Output
S	R	Q
0	0	Latched
0	1	0
1	0	1
1	1	Invalid

D flip-flop

Input	Output
D	Q
No equivalent	
0	0
1	1
No equivalent	

J-K flip-flop

Inputs		Output
J	K	Q
0	0	Latched
0	1	0
1	0	1
1	1	Toggle

the data are clocked into the master on the leading edge of the clock and into the slave on the trailing edge of the clock. It is imperative that the input data not change during the time the clock pulse is HIGH or the data in the master may be changed. J-K flip-flops are available as either edge- or pulse-triggered devices. The older 7476 is a dual pulse-triggered device; the 74LS76 is edge-triggered on the HIGH to LOW transition of the clock. Either type will work for this experiment.*

Procedure

The J-K Edge-Triggered Flip-Flop

1. Construct the circuit of Figure 2(a). The LEDs are logic monitors and are ON when their output is LOW. Select the inactive level (HIGH) for $\overline{PRE}$ and $\overline{CLR}$. Select the "set" mode by connecting J to a logic 1 and K to a logic 0. With the clock LOW (not active), test the effect of $\overline{PRE}$ and $\overline{CLR}$ by putting a logic 0 on each, one at a time. Are preset and clear inputs synchronous or asynchronous?

Put $\overline{CLR}$ on LOW; then pulse the clock by putting a HIGH, then a LOW, on the clock. Observe that the $\overline{CLR}$ input overrides the J input.

Determine what happens if both $\overline{PRE}$ and $\overline{CLR}$ are connected to a 0 at the same time. Summarize your observations from this step in the report.

2. Put both $\overline{PRE}$ and $\overline{CLR}$ on a logic 1. Connect a TTL level pulse generator set to 1 Hz on the clock input. Add an LED clock indicator to the pulse generator, as shown in Figure 2(b), so that you can observe the clock pulse and the outputs at the same time. Test all four combinations of J and K inputs while observing the LEDs.

Are data transferred to the output on the leading or the trailing edge of the clock?

Observe that the output frequency is not the same as the clock frequency in the toggle mode. Also note that the output duty cycle in the toggle mode is not the same as the clock duty cycle. This is

a good way to obtain a 50% duty cycle pulse. Summarize your observations in the report. Include a discussion of the truth table for the J-K flip-flop.

3. Look at the circuit shown in Figure 3. From your knowledge of the truth table, predict what it will do; then test your prediction by building it. Summarize your observations.

4. An application of the toggle mode is found in certain counters. Cascaded flip-flops can be used to perform frequency division in a circuit called a *ripple counter.* Figure 4 illustrates a ripple counter using the two flip-flops in the 74LS76. Connect the circuit and sketch the Q_A and Q_B outputs on Plot 1 in the report.

Notice that when an LED is ON, the Q output is HIGH. The red and green LEDs indicate that the pulse generator frequency has been changed by the flip-flops.

For Further Investigation

Measurement of t_{PLH}

Note: The measurement of a parameter such as t_{PLH} is done differently for analog and digital scopes. Set up the experiment as in step 1; then if you are using an analog scope, do step 2a. If you are using a digital scope, do step 2b. If both scopes are available, do both steps 2a and 2b.

1. Set up the J-K flip-flop for toggle operation. Set the clock frequency for 100 kHz and view the clock on channel 1 and the Q output on channel 2 of your oscilloscope. Set the scope sweep time for 5 μs/div to observe the complete waveforms of both the clock and the Q output. Set the VOLTS/DIV control on each channel to 2 V/div and center the two waves across the center graticule of the display.

2a. With an analog scope, you will need to trigger the scope on the earlier signal (the clock). Trigger the scope using CH1 and select falling-edge triggering from the trigger controls. Then increase the sweep speed to 5 ns/div (or use the fastest available sweep time if 5 ns/div is not possible). You

---

*The data sheet in the appendix shows both types.

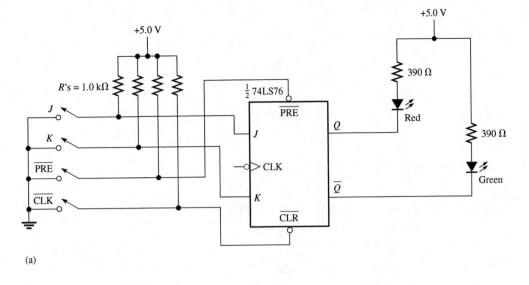

(a)

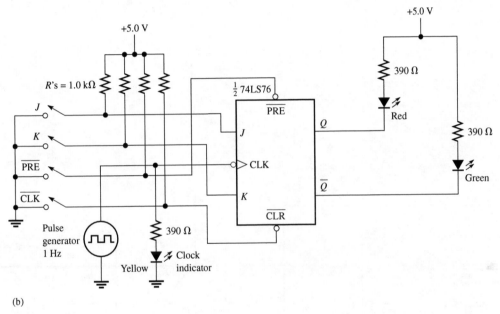

(b)

FIGURE 2

may need to adjust the trigger LEVEL control to see the entire clock waveform. You should see a falling edge of the clock and either a rising or falling edge of the Q output. You can observe the LOW-to-HIGH transition of the output by adjusting the HOLDOFF control. When you have a stable trace, go to step 3.

2b. With a digital scope such as the Tektronix TDS220, you can trigger on the slower waveform (the output) which is on channel 2. This is because the DSO can show signals before the trigger event. From the trigger menu, select CH2 triggering and

select SET LEVEL TO 50%. Then increase the sweep speed to 5 ns/div. In the trigger menu, you can choose between RISING SLOPE or FALLING SLOPE to observe t_{PLH} or t_{PHL}, respectively.

3. Measure the time from the 50% level of the falling clock signal to the 50% level on the output signal for both a rising and falling output signal. Record your time in the report and compare it to the manufacturer's specified maximum values from the data sheet.

Report for "The J-K Flip-Flop"

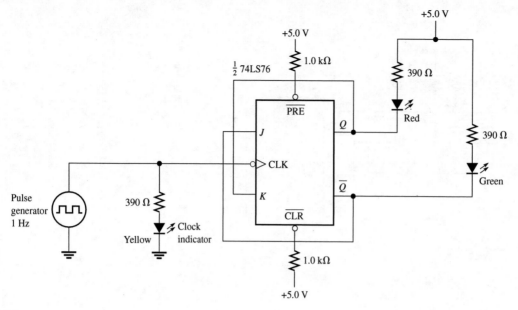

FIGURE 3

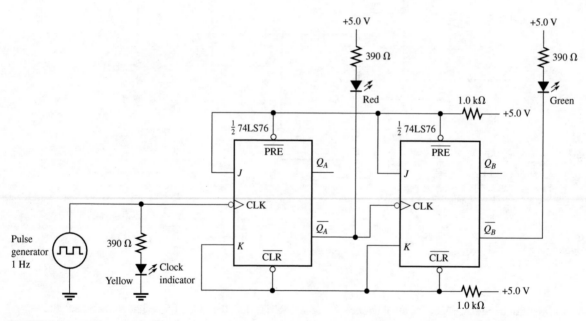

FIGURE 4

Experiment

Name: _____ Date: _____ Class: _____

Objectives:

□ Test various configurations for a J-K flip-flop.
□ Observe frequency division characteristics in the toggle mode.
□ Measure the propagation delay of a J-K flip-flop.

Data and Observations:

Step 1. Observations for $\overline{PRE}$ and $\overline{CLR}$ inputs:

Step 2. Observations of clocking the J-K flip-flop:

Step 3. Observations of test circuit:

Step 4. Ripple counter:

Clock: ⎍⎍⎍⎍⎍⎍⎍⎍⎍⎍⎍⎍⎍⎍⎍

Q_A

Q_B

PLOT 1

Results and Conclusion:

Further Investigation Results:

Evaluation and Review Questions

1. a. What is the difference between an asynchronous and a synchronous input?

b. What is the difference between edge-triggering and pulse-triggering?

2. a. Describe how you would set a J-K flip-flop asynchronously.

b. How would you set it synchronously?

3. If both J and K inputs are LOW and $\overline{PRE}$ and $\overline{CLR}$ are HIGH, what effect does the clock have on the output of a J-K flip-flop?

4. Assume a student accidentally reversed the J and K inputs on the circuit in Figure 3. What effect would be observed?

5. Assume the red LED in Figure 3 is on steady and the green LED is off. The yellow LED is blinking. What are three possible troubles with the circuit?

6. Assume the green LED in Figure 4 is off but the red LED is blinking. A check at the CLK input of the second flip-flop indicates clock pulses are present. What are possible troubles with the circuit?

The D Latch and D Flip-Flop

Objectives

After completing this experiment, you will be able to

☐ Demonstrate how a latch can debounce an SPDT switch.

☐ Construct and test a gated D latch from four NAND gates and an inverter.

☐ Test a D flip-flop and investigate several application circuits for both the latch and the flip-flop.

Materials Needed

Red LED
Green LED
7486 quad XOR gate
7400 quad NAND gate
7404 hex inverter
7474 dual D flip-flop
Resistors: two 330 Ω, two 1.0 kΩ

Summary of Theory

As you have seen, *combinational* logic circuits are circuits in which the outputs are determined fully by the inputs. *Sequential* logic circuits contain information about previous conditions. The difference is that sequential circuits contain *memory* and combinational circuits do not.

The basic memory unit is the *latch,* which uses feedback to lock onto and hold data. It can be constructed from two inverters, two NAND gates, or two NOR gates. The ability to remember previous conditions is easy to demonstrate with Boolean algebra. For example, Figure 1 shows an $\overline{S}$-$\overline{R}$ latch made from NAND gates. This circuit is widely used for switch debouncing and is available as an integrated circuit containing four latches (the 74LS279).

A simple modification of the basic latch is the addition of steering gates and an inverter, as shown in Figure 2. This circuit is called a gated D (for Data) latch. An enable input allows data present on the D input to be transferred to the output when Enable is asserted. When the enable input is not asserted, the last level—Q and $\overline{Q}$—is latched. This circuit is available in integrated circuit form as the 7475A quad D latch. Although there are four latches in this IC, there are only two shared enable signals.

Design problems are often simplified by having all transitions in a system occur synchronously (at the same time) by using a common source of pulses to cause the change. This common pulse is called a *clock.* The output changes occur only on either the leading or the trailing edge of the clock pulse. Some ICs have inputs that directly set or reset the output any time they are asserted. These inputs are labeled *asynchronous* inputs because no clock pulse is required. The D-type flip-flop with positive

FIGURE 1
$\overline{S}$-$\overline{R}$ latch.

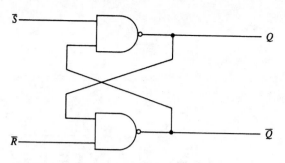

Equation for top NAND gate:

$$Q = \overline{\overline{S} \cdot \overline{Q}}$$

Applying DeMorgan's theorem:

$$Q = S + Q$$

Thus, Q appears on both sides of the equation.
If $\overline{S} = 1$, then $S = 0$ and $Q = 0 + Q$ (Q is previous state)
output is latched.

edge-triggering and asynchronous inputs is the 7474. In this experiment, you will also test this IC.

It is useful to review oscilloscope timing. If you are using an analog dual-trace oscilloscope, you should trigger the scope from the channel with the *slowest* of two waveforms that are being compared to be sure to see the correct time relationship. A digital scope will show it correctly for either trigger channel.

Procedure

$\overline{S}$-$\overline{R}$ Latch

1. Build the $\overline{S}$-$\overline{R}$ latch shown in Figure 3. You can use a wire to simulate the single-pole, double-throw (SPDT) switch. The LEDs will be used in this section as logic monitors. Because TTL logic is much better at sinking current than at sourcing current, the LEDs are arranged to be ON when the output is LOW. To make the LEDs read the HIGH output when they are ON, we read them from the opposite output! This simple trick avoids the use of an inverter.

2. Leave the wire on the A terminal and note the logic shown on the LEDs. Now simulate a bouncing switch by removing the A end of the wire. Do NOT touch B yet! Instead, reconnect the wire to A several times.

3. After touching A several times, touch B. Simulate the switch bouncing several times by removing and reconnecting B. (Switches never bounce back to the opposite terminal, so you should not touch A). Summarize your observations of the $\overline{S}$-$\overline{R}$ latch used as a switch debounce circuit in the report.

D Latch

4. Modify the basic $\overline{S}$-$\overline{R}$ latch into a D latch by adding the steering gates and the inverter shown in Figure 4. Connect the D input to a TTL level pulse generator set for 1 Hz. Connect the enable input to a HIGH (through a 1.0 kΩ resistor). Observe the output; then change the enable to a LOW.

5. Leave the enable LOW and place a momentary short to ground first on one output and then on the other. Summarize your observations of the gated D latch in the report.

FIGURE 2
Gated D latch.

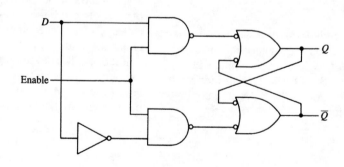

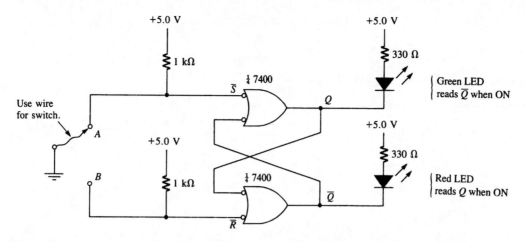

FIGURE 3
SPDT switch debounce. The NAND gates are drawn as negative-input OR gates to emphasize the active-LOW.

6. Now make the simple burglar alarm shown in Figure 5. The data input represents switches connected to windows and doors. The enable input is pulled HIGH when the system is activated or LOW for standby. To reset the system, put a momentary ground on the Q output as shown. Summarize your observations in the report.

The D Flip-Flop

7. The 7474 is a dual, positive edge–triggered D flip-flop containing two asynchronous inputs labeled $\overline{PRE}$ (preset) and $\overline{CLR}$ (clear). Construct the test circuit shown in Figure 6. Connect the clock through the delay circuit. The purpose of the delay is to allow setup time for the D input. Let's look at this

effect first. Observe both the delayed clock signal and the Q output signal on a two-channel oscilloscope. View the delayed clock signal on channel 1, and trigger the scope from channel 1. You should observe a dc level on the output (channel 2).

8. Now remove the clock delay by connecting the clock input directly to the pulse generator. The output dc level should have changed because there is insufficient setup time. Explain your observations in the report.

9. Reinstall the clock delay circuit and move the $\overline{PRE}$ input to a LOW and then a HIGH. Then put a LOW on the $\overline{CLR}$ input followed by a HIGH. Next repeat the process with the clock pulse disconnected. Determine if $\overline{PRE}$ and $\overline{CLR}$ are synchronous or asynchronous inputs.

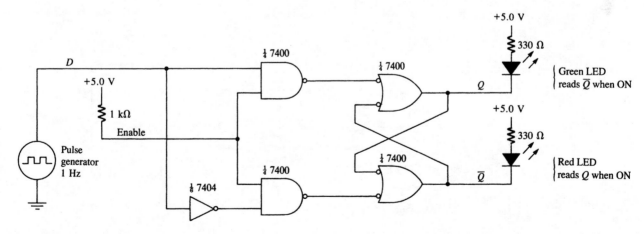

FIGURE 4
Gated D latch.

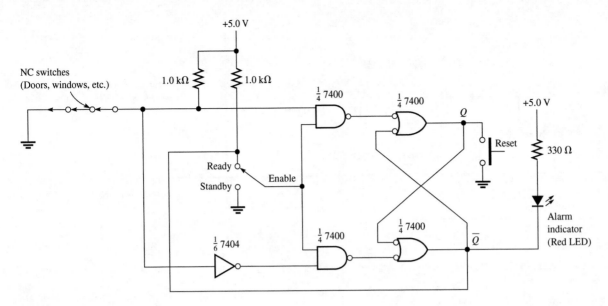

FIGURE 5
Simple burglar alarm.

10. Leave the clock delay circuit in place, but disconnect the *D* input. Attach a wire from $\overline{Q}$ to the *D* input. Observe the waveforms on a scope. Normally, for relative timing measurements, you should trigger the scope using the channel that has the *slowest* waveform as the trigger channel, as discussed in the Summary of Theory. Summarize, in the report, your observations of the D flip-flop. Discuss setup time, $\overline{PRE}$ and $\overline{CLR}$ inputs, and your timing observation from this step.

For Further Investigation

The circuit shown in Figure 7 is a practical application of a D flip-flop. It is a parity test circuit that takes serial data (bits arriving one at a time) and performs an exclusive-OR on the previous result (like a running total). The data are synchronous with the clock; that is, for every clock pulse a new data bit is tested. Construct the circuit and set the clock for 1 Hz. Move the data switch to either a HIGH or a

FIGURE 6

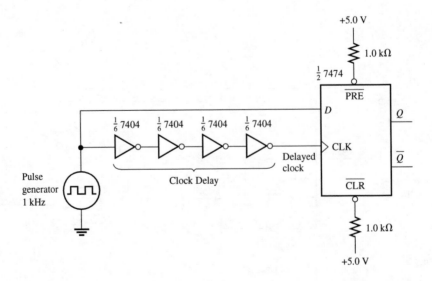

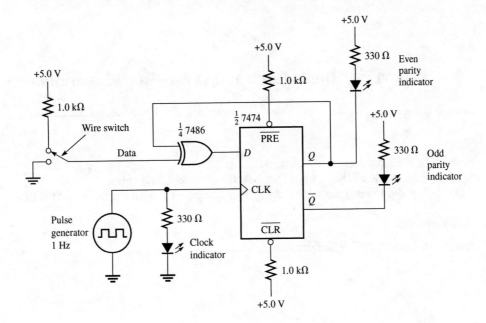

FIGURE 7

LOW prior to the clock pulse, and observe the result. Describe your observations in the report. If a logic 1 is received, what happens to the parity? What happens when a logic 0 is received? Does the circuit have any advantage over the 74LS280 9-bit parity generator/checker?*

---

*See Figure 6–55 of Floyd's text.

Report for "The D Latch and D Flip-Flop" Experiment

Name: _____ Date: _____ Class: _____

Objectives:

☐ Demonstrate how a latch can debounce an SPDT switch.
☐ Construct and test a gated D latch from four NAND gates and an inverter.
☐ Test a D flip-flop and investigate several application circuits for both the latch and the flip-flop.

Data and Observations:

Step 3. Observations for SPDT switch debounce circuit:

Step 5. Observations for D latch circuit:

Step 6. Observations for the simple burgler alarm:

Steps 7 and 8. Observations for setup time:

Step 10. Observations for the D flip-flop:

Results and Conclusion:

Further Investigation Results:

Evaluation and Review Questions

1. a. Explain why the switch debounce circuit in Figure 3 is used only for double-throw switches.

   b. Could NOR gates be used for debouncing a switch? Explain.

2. What advantage does the gated D latch have compared to the $\overline{S}$-$\overline{R}$ latch?

3. Show how the burglar alarm of Step 6 could be constructed with one fourth of a 7475A D latch.

4. The burglar alarm could be constructed with two cross-coupled NOR gates. Complete the circuit so that it has the same functions as the alarm in Step 6 (normally closed switches, alarm, and reset).

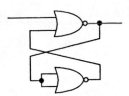

5. Assume that the burglar alarm in Figure 5 does not function correctly. The Enable switch is in the Ready position but the LED does not come on when one of the switches is open. Suggest at least 3 causes for this failure. Circle the reason you think is most likely.

6. The serial parity test circuit in Figure 7 uses a D flip-flop. Why wouldn't a D latch work just as well?

BCD IC COUNTERS

OBJECTIVES

1. To investigate the operation of the 7490 IC counter.
2. To demonstrate that BCD counters may be displayed directly with seven-segment display units.
3. To investigate the cascading of 7490 IC counters.

EQUIPMENT NEEDED

Components

7446 IC (2);

7490 IC (2);

FND507 seven-segment display units (2);

130 ohm resistors (14);

normally HIGH pushbutton switch (debounced).

Instruments

0–5 volt DC power supply;

pulse or square wave generator;

dual trace oscilloscope.

From *Lab Manual: A Troubleshooting Approach to accompany Digital Systems: Principles and Applications*, Ninth Edition, Jim C. DeLoach and Frank J. Ambrosio. Copyright © 2004 by Pearson Education, Inc. All rights reserved.

DISCUSSION

A special IC asynchronous counter is the 7490 BCD counter. There are many applications in digital systems for MOD-10 counters, and since many of these systems use BCD interfaces, counters like the 7490 are often included in the design. An example where BCD is employed is the output indicator of a frequency counter (see Experiment 24).

7490 IC Counter

The 7490 is similar to the 7493. It contains a single toggle flip-flop, a MOD-5 counter, and a gated reset circuit, which can be wired together externally to configure the counter as a BCD counter, which counts from 0 to 9. It may also be configured as a divide-by-10 counter, which does not count sequentially, and therefore is not a BCD counter.

Also, like the 7493, the counter can be wired to produce a counter that has a MOD-number less than 10, although this is not done often in practice. You should be aware that the MOD-5 counter internal to the 7490 is a three-bit counter with a MOD-number that has been reduced from 8 to 5 by internal wiring. The 7490 is often cascaded with other counters whenever the desired MOD-number has the numbers ten and/or five as factors. For example, cascading a 7493 wired as a four-bit counter with a 7490 wired as a BCD counter will result in a counter with a MOD-number of $16 \times 10 = 160$.

In the current experiment, you will investigate the 7490 operating in both of its primary modes, the symmetrical MOD-10 and BCD MOD-10 modes. You will also investigate cascading two BCD counters to form a MOD-100 counter.

BCD Displays

It is often desirable to display the count of a BCD counter. In many applications, a seven-segment LED display is used. The outputs of BCD counters must be converted from BCD into seven-segment codes and then applied to the seven-segment devices through current booster circuits called *drivers*. Both of these functions are found in the 7446 IC BCD-to-seven-segment decoder/driver. In this experiment, you will learn how to connect a 7446 and a seven-segment LED device to function as a BCD display unit.

PROCEDURE

a) Refer to the data sheet for the 7490 IC. This IC contains four flip-flops, which may be arranged as a BCD counter. To do this, the output of flip-flop A must be tied externally to the input of flip-flop B. The MSB of this counter is Q_3, and the LSB is Q_0. The counter's MOD-number may be changed by making the appropriate external connections. The operation of this counter is similar to that of the 7493, which was investigated in Experiment 21.

Draw the pin layout diagram for this IC:

b) *7490 IC operation—symmetrical MOD-10 configuration:* There are two ways to configure the 7490 as a MOD-10 counter. In this step you will investigate the symmetrical MOD-10 configuration. Install a 7490 IC on the circuit board, and wire the counter so that it is like that of Figure 22-1. Connect a normally HIGH pushbutton switch to $\overline{CP}_1$. Connect LED monitors to Q_0, Q_1, Q_2, and Q_3 (Q_0 = MSB; Q_1 = LSB).

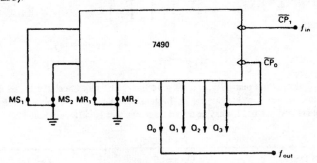

Figure 22-1

c) Pulse $\overline{CP}_1$ repeatedly, and observe the count sequence displayed on the LEDs. Record your observations in Table 22-1. Note that the counter does have ten different states, but the order in which they occur is not the normal binary sequence.

Table 22-1

Input Pulse Applied	Output States				Decimal Number
	Q_3	Q_2	Q_1	Q_0	
None	0	0	0	0	0
1					
2					
3					
4					
5					
6					
7					
8					
9					
10					

d) Disconnect the pushbutton switch, and apply a 10 kHz square wave to $\overline{CP}_1$. Observe the output at Q_0 on the oscilloscope. You should observe that the waveform is a 1 kHz square wave. The square wave signal was obtained by altering the counting sequence while maintaining 10 states.

e) *BCD MOD-10 configuration:* The second way the 7490 can be configured as a MOD-10 counter is the BCD configuration. Rearrange the wiring of the 7490 so that the circuit is like that of Figure 22-2. Connect a normally HIGH pushbutton switch to $\overline{CP}_0$. Connect LED monitors to outputs Q_0, Q_1, Q_2, and Q_3. This time Q_0 = LSB and Q_3 = MSB.

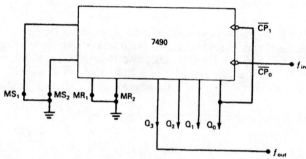

Figure 22-2

f) Pulse $\overline{CP}_0$ repeatedly and observe the count sequence displayed on the LEDs. Record your observations in Table 22-2. You should observe that the sequence is now normal binary and that there are still 10 different states.

Table 22-2

Input Pulse Applied	Output States Q_3 Q_2 Q_1 Q_0				Decimal Number
None	0	0	0	0	0
1					
2					
3					
4					
5					
6					
7					
8					
9					
10					

g) Now disconnect the pushbutton switch from the counter input, and apply a 10 kHz square wave in its place. Observe the signal at Q_3, and draw it in Timing Diagram 22-1. Note that the signal is 1 kHz but not a square wave.

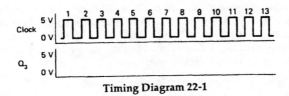

Timing Diagram 22-1

h) *Displaying BCD counters:* The count of the BCD counter can be more conveniently displayed in decimal. One of the most common devices used to display BCD counters is the seven-segment LED driven by a BCD-to-seven-segment decoder/driver, such as a 7446 IC. The seven segments that make up the display device each consist of one or two LEDs, and all are connected in a common cathode or common anode arrangement. The decimal digits are formed by turning on the appropriate segments (see Figure 22-3). The decoder/driver unit decodes a BCD number and supplies the correct levels at its outputs that will cause a seven-segment display unit to display the correct decimal digit.

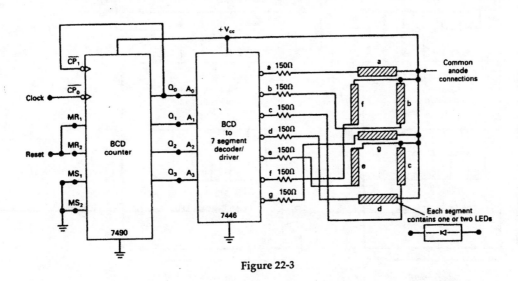

Figure 22-3

Refer to the data sheet for a 7446 IC, and draw its pin layout diagram:

Now examine the circuit of Figure 22-3, and then construct it. Connect a normally LOW pushbutton switch to the reset-to-zero pins. Connect a square wave generator set to a low frequency, and observe that the seven-segment unit is counting in decimal. Pulse the reset pushbutton switch, and note that the counter resets to 0, then continues counting.

Demonstrate the counter for your instructor.

i) *Cascading BCD counters:* BCD counters may be cascaded to count in decimal fashion. For example, two BCD counters may be cascaded to count from 00 to 99. The input counter of such an arrangement will count units, while the output counter will count tens. Refer to Figure 22-4, and cascade two 7490 ICs together to perform this function. Use seven-segment display units to display the counters' outputs. Demonstrate the counter to your instructor when it is operating correctly.

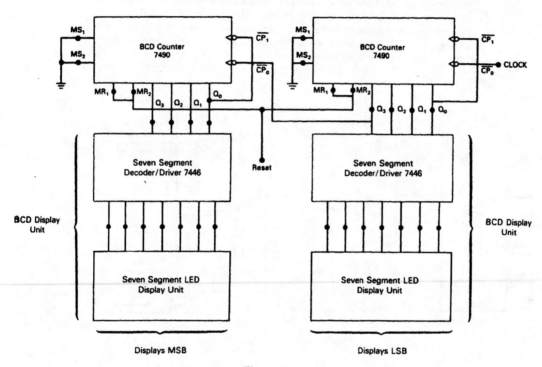

Figure 22-4

424

j) *Review:* This completes the exercises on BCD counters. To test your understanding of the principles covered in this experiment, answer the following questions:

1. Based on your observations, does the count sequence of a counter determine the MOD-number of a counter? _____.

2. Four 7490 IC counters are all configured to count BCD and are cascaded together. What is the MOD-number of the resulting counter? _____. What is the highest decimal number that can be displayed by the counter? _____.

3. Draw a diagram showing how you would convert a 7490 BCD counter into a MOD-6 counter. HINT: use the reset-to-zero inputs.

Shift Register Counters

Objectives

After completing this experiment, you will be able to
- Test two recirculating shift register counters.
- From oscilloscope measurements, draw the timing diagram for the two shift register counters.

Materials Needed

74195 4-bit shift register
7400 quad NAND gate
7493A counter
7474 D flip-flop
7486 quad exclusive OR
Four-position DIP switch
Four LEDs
Resistors: four 330 Ω, six 1.0 kΩ
Two N.O. pushbuttons (optional)

Summary of Theory

A *shift register* is a series of flip-flops connected so that data can be transferred to a neighbor each time the clock pulse is active. An example is the display on your calculator. As numbers are entered on the keypad, the previously entered numbers are shifted to the left. Shift registers can be made to shift data to the left, to the right, or in either direction (bidirectional), using a control signal. They can be made from either D or J-K flip-flops. An example of a simple shift register made from D flip-flops is shown in Figure 1(a). The data are entered serially at the left and may be removed in either parallel or serial fashion. With some additional logic, the data may also be entered in parallel, as shown in Figure 1(b).

Shift registers are available in IC form with various bit lengths, loading methods, and shift directions. They are widely used to change data from serial form to parallel form, and vice versa. Other applications for shift registers include arithmetic operations in computers. To multiply any number by its base, you simply move the radix point one position to the left. To multiply a binary number by 2, the number is shifted to the left. For example, $7 \times 2 = 14$ in binary is $0111 \times 10 = 1110$. Note that the original number 0111 is shifted by one position to the left. Conversely, division by 2 is represented by a right shift.

Another application of the shift register is as a digital waveform generator. Generally, a waveform generator requires feedback—that is, the output of the register is returned to the input and recirculated. Two important waveform generators are the Johnson (or "twisted-ring") counter and the ring counter. The names can be easily associated with the correct circuit if the circuits are drawn in the manner shown in Figure 2. In this experiment, you

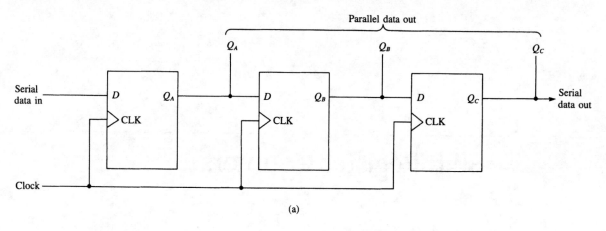

(a)

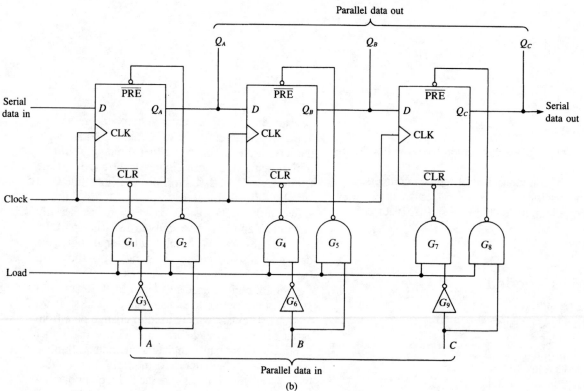

(b)

FIGURE 1
Shift registers made from D flip-flops.

will construct both of these counters using a 74195 4-bit shift register. The ring counter will then be used to generate a bit stream that can be used for various applications.

The 74195 function table is in the manufacturer's data sheet* and is reproduced in Table 1 for convenience. The first input listed on the table is an asynchronous $\overline{\text{CLEAR}}$. Next is a parallel SHIFT/$\overline{\text{LOAD}}$ function on one pin. Assertion level

*See Appendix.

logic is shown to define that a HIGH causes the register to SHIFT from Q_A toward Q_D at the next clock edge, and a LOW causes the register to $\overline{\text{LOAD}}$ at the next clock edge. The inputs A through D are used only when the register is loaded in parallel (also called a *broadside load*). Notice that the internal register portion of the 74195 is shown with S-R flip-flops, but the serial inputs to the leftmost flip-flop are labeled as J and $\overline{K}$. These inputs function the same as the inputs to an ordinary J-K flip-flop, except the K input is inverted.

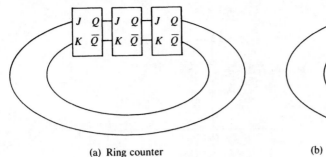

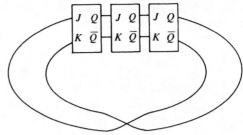

(a) Ring counter   (b) Twisted-ring counter (Johnson counter)

FIGURE 2

Shift register counters drawn to emphasize their names. These circuits were drawn with J-K flip-flops but can be constructed from other flip-flops as well. The CLK, $\overline{\text{PRE}}$, and $\overline{\text{CLR}}$ inputs are not shown.

TABLE 1

Function table for 74195 4-bit shift register.*

Inputs									Outputs				
			SERIAL		PARALLEL								
$\overline{\text{CLEAR}}$	SHIFT/ $\overline{\text{LOAD}}$	CLOCK	J	$\overline{K}$	A	B	C	D	Q_A	Q_B	Q_C	Q_D	$\overline{Q}_D$
L	X	X	X	X	X	X	X	X	L	L	L	L	H
H	L	↑	X	X	a	b	c	d	a	b	c	d	$\overline{d}$
H	H	L	X	X	X	X	X	X	Q_{A0}	Q_{B0}	Q_{C0}	Q_{D0}	$\overline{Q}_{D0}$
H	H	↑	L	H	X	X	X	X	Q_{A0}	Q_{A0}	Q_{Bn}	Q_{Cn}	$\overline{Q}_{Cn}$
H	H	↑	L	L	X	X	X	X	L	Q_{An}	Q_{Bn}	Q_{Cn}	$\overline{Q}_{Cn}$
H	H	↑	H	H	X	X	X	X	H	Q_{An}	Q_{Bn}	Q_{Cn}	$\overline{Q}_{Cn}$
H	H	↑	H	L	X	X	X	X	$\overline{Q}_{An}$	Q_{An}	Q_{Bn}	Q_{Cn}	$\overline{Q}_{Cn}$

H = high level (steady state)

L = low level (steady state)

X = irrelevant (any input, including transitions)

↑ = transition from low to high level

a, b, c, d = the level of steady state input at A, B, C, or D, respectively

Q_{A0}, Q_{B0}, Q_{C0}, Q_{D0} = the level of Q_A, Q_B, Q_C, or Q_D, respectively, before the indicated steady-state input conditions were established

Q_{An}, Q_{Bn}, Q_{Cn} = the level of Q_A, Q_B, or Q_C, respectively, before the most recent transition of the clock

*See Appendix for complete description.

Procedure

Johnson and Ring Counters

1. The circuit shown in Figure 3 is a partially completed schematic for a shift register counter. It could be connected as either a Johnson (twisted-ring) or as a ring counter. Refer to Figure 2 and the function table for the 74195 (Table 1) and determine how to complete the feedback loop for a twisted-ring counter. Show the completed schematic in your report.

2. Connect your circuit. (The $\overline{\text{CLEAR}}$ and SHIFT/$\overline{\text{LOAD}}$ pushbuttons can be made with

pieces of hook-up wire.) Set the pulse generator for a TTL pulse at 1 Hz. Momentarily close the $\overline{\text{CLEAR}}$ switch. One useful feature of the counter is that when the sequence begins in state 0, it forms a Gray code sequence. Although you could load a pattern other than all zeros, this is a typical starting point for a Johnson counter.

3. Observe the pattern in the LEDs. (The LEDs are ON for a zero.) Then speed up the pulse generator to 1 kHz and develop a timing diagram for the Johnson counter outputs. Draw your timing diagram in the space provided in the report.

4. Referring to Figure 2 and the function table for the 74195, change the schematic to that of a ring

FIGURE 3
Partially completed schematic for
twisted-ring or ring counter.

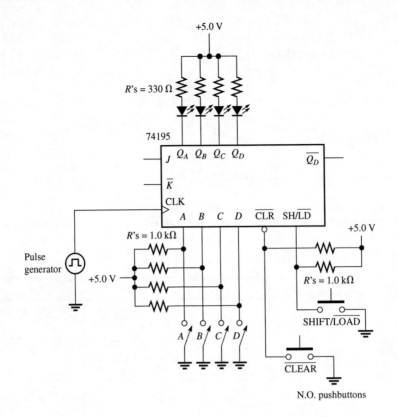

counter. The partially completed schematic is shown in the report. A ring counter does not invert the bits that are fed back, so the desired bit pattern must be preset through the parallel load feature of the shift register. A common pattern is to have either a single 1 or a single 0 recirculate. Set the load switches for 1110_2 and press the SHIFT/$\overline{LOAD}$ pushbutton. From the function table, note that this is a synchronous load, so loading will take place only if a clock is present.

5. Reset the pulse generator for 1 Hz and observe the pattern in the LEDs.* After observing the pattern in the LEDs, speed up the pulse generator to 1 kHz and develop a timing diagram for the ring counter outputs. Draw your timing diagram in the space provided in the report.

For Further Investigation

This investigation is a bit different than previous ones. In this investigation, it is not necessary to

*This pattern is essentially the same pattern used in the ring counter for the keyboard encoder shown in Figure 10–38 of Floyd's text.

build the circuit; rather you should try to figure out timing details (of course you could build it if you choose). The circuit is an automated IC tester for 2-input gates shown in Figure 4. It uses a 74195 shift register to generate a serial data train that represents the predicted data for a device under test (D.U.T.). The way it works is that a 2-input gate receives four states from the 7493A counter and produces a logical one or zero depending on the type of gate that is tested. If the data from the D.U.T. matches the shift register data, the test continues; otherwise the *Device failed LED* will come on. Timing for this simple system is not trivial but by carefully drawing the waveforms for each stage, you can figure out how it works. Start by drawing the waveforms for the 7493A. Assume a 2-input NAND gate is the D.U.T. and the predict data is set for $A = 0$, and $B = C = D = 1$. Show the time relationship between the counter and the Strobe, Input test data, and the Serial predict data. Summarize in a short report how the circuit works and what happens if the Input test data doesn't match the Serial predict data.

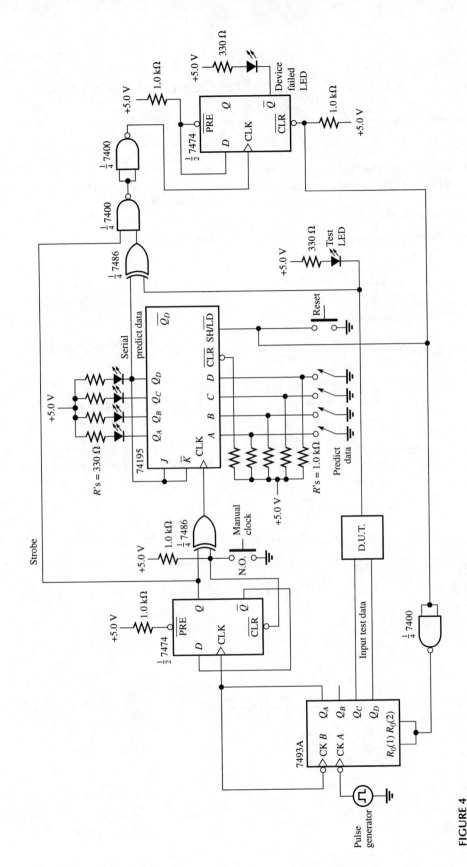

FIGURE 4
Automated IC tester.

Report for "Shift Register Counters" Experiment

Name: _____ Date: _____ Class: _____

Objectives:

- ☐ Test two recirculating shift register counters.
- ☐ From oscilloscope measurements, draw the timing diagram for the two shift register counters.

Data and Observations:

Schematic for Johnson counter: Schematic for ring counter:

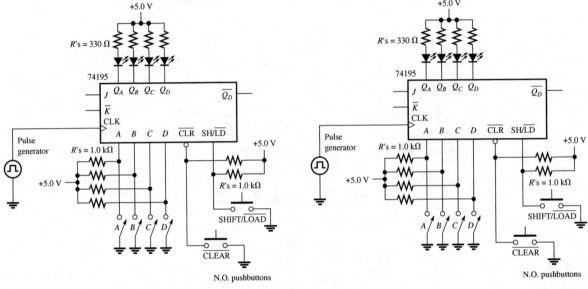

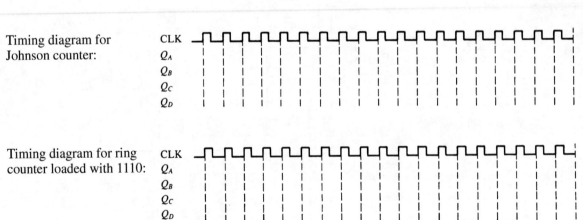

Timing diagram for Johnson counter: CLK Q_A Q_B Q_C Q_D

Timing diagram for ring counter loaded with 1110:   CLK Q_A Q_B Q_C Q_D

Results and Conclusion:

Further Investigation Results:

Evaluation and Review Questions

1. How would you connect a second 74195 to extend the Johnson counter to 8 bits?

2. Explain why it is necessary to use an edge-triggered device for a shift register.

3. a. A 3-stage ring counter is loaded with the binary number 101. What are the next three states of the counter?

   b. Repeat (a) for a Johnson counter.

4. Ring counters and Johnson counters both have a feedback path from the output to the input. If the feedback path opens for either counter, what happens to all outputs?

5. Assume the outputs of the Johnson counter that you drew in the report were decoded to show a series of unique codes. Draw the expected waveforms you would observe on a logic analyzer.

6. Assume your boss asks you to build a decoder for a ring counter. What do you say to him? (be polite!).

Asynchronous Counters - Part I

Objectives:

1. Create a 3-bit (Modulus 8) asynchronous binary counter using J-K flip-flops
2. Create a 3-bit (Modulus 5) asynchronous binary counter using J-K flip-flops
3. Use the Timing Analyzer to determine propagation delays
4. Construct a 4-bit binary counter using the 7493 integrated circuit
5. Construct a 4-bit decade counter using the 7490 integrated circuit
6. Study the effects of the preset and clear inputs with respect to the clock
7. Change the counter modulus using full or partial decoding

Materials List:

♦ Max+plus II software by Altera Corporation
♦ University board with CPLD (optional)
♦ Computer requirements:
    Minimum 486/66 with 8 MB RAM
♦ Floppy disk

Discussion:

J-K flip-flops with preset and clear inputs can be cascaded to create an *n*-bit binary or BCD counter.

The method of clocking each stage within the counter determines if the counter is asynchronously or synchronously clocked. Asynchronous clocking implies that each stage does *not* share the same clock, nor toggle at the same time, as the other flip-flops in the counter. Each flip-flop in an asynchronous counter is clocked by the Q output of the previous flip-flop. If the first stage toggles, it may cause the second stage to toggle, which in turn may cause the third stage to toggle, and so forth. Asynchronous counters, often called ripple counters, are the focus of this lab.

Synchronous counters are designed with all flip-flops responding to the same clock pulse, simultaneously. Synchronous counters are the focus of Lab 18.

The time it takes the Q output of the flip-flop to change with respect to a trigger event on the clock input is called the propagation delay time, t_p. For asynchronous counters, all propagation delay times for each stage are additive. For instance, if a binary counter has the count of 1111_2, it will change to 0000_2 on the next clock, and the delay for the output to change from a logic-HIGH to a logic-LOW will be 25 ns. Then the delay time for the counter to go from the Fh count to 0h count will be 100 ns.

The inherent characteristics of a J-K flip-flop wired in the toggle mode produces a square wave output frequency one-half the clock frequency. Several toggle flip-flops cascaded in asynchronous mode will create a 2^N frequency divider, where N represents the number of flip-flops, as illustrated in Figure 1. In the Figure 1 example, the total frequency division is $2^N = 2^3 = 8$.

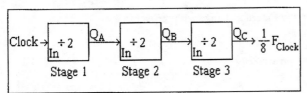

Figure 1

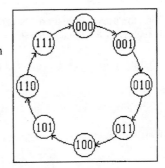

Figure 2

Figure 2 represents the state transition diagram for the circuit illustrated in Figure 1 assuming an up count sequence.

The state transition diagram shows the previous and next state of the counter based on the current value. The modulus may be altered by using a decoder gate (AND or NAND) and wiring its output back to the clear inputs of each flip-flop. Since the clear input is asynchronous, or clock independent, the number the decoder is wired to decode will *not* be seen as part of the counter count sequence.

Part 1   Procedure

1.   Open the Max+plus II software. Assign the project name **counter1** and MAX7000S as the device family.

2.   Open a new Graphic Editor and create the 3-bit counter shown in Figure 1 using JKFF symbols.

3.   Open a new Waveform Editor, set Grid Size to 50 ns, and create input and output waveforms shown in Figure 2.

4.   Compile and simulate the circuit. Assuming zero errors, draw the resulting output waveforms in the area provided in Figure 2.

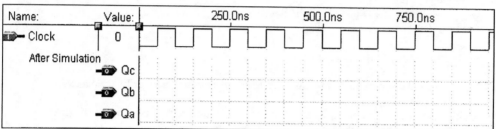

Figure 2

Time Segment	Qc Qb Qa (Bits 0 or 1)	Octal Value
100 – 150 ns	___ ___ ___	_____
200 – 250 ns	___ ___ ___	_____
300 – 350 ns	___ ___ ___	_____
400 – 450 ns	___ ___ ___	_____
500 – 550 ns	___ ___ ___	_____
600 – 650 ns	___ ___ ___	_____
700 – 750 ns	___ ___ ___	_____
800 – 850 ns	___ ___ ___	_____

Table 1

5.   Copy the binary bit pattern for each time segment in Figure 2 into the respective cell block in Table 1, then convert the binary bit pattern to its octal equivalent.

6.   What direction does the circuit in Figure 1 count?   (Up/Down)

7.   Based on your observation, the Q outputs of the circuit in Figure 2 change with respect to the (leading/trailing) edge of the clock applied to the circuit.

8.   Sketch a state transition diagram for the 3-bit counter constructed.

Asynchronous Counters

436

9. Turn off the Snap to Grid feature in the Options menu.

10. Click the Zoom-in button (the magnifying glass with a plus sign icon in the Draw toolbar) several times to magnify the waveforms to view only the time segment from 50 ns to 100 ns. Reposition the horizontal scroll bar as necessary to view this segment of the waveform.

11. Position the cursor on the 50 ns mark in the Waveform Editor. When you click the 50 ns time, a vertical blue line appears, and the **Ref:** box in the Waveform Editor (see Figure 3) shows 50 ns. The **Time:** box in the Waveform Editor shows the position of the mouse as the mouse is moved around the Waveform Editor.

counter1.scf - Waveform Editor				
Ref: 50.0ns	◄ ►	Time: 52.2ns	Interval:	2.2ns

Figure 3

12. Position the mouse pointer right on the blue vertical line on top of the Qa waveform, then click and hold the left mouse button down as you drag the mouse to the right. The section of the waveform you are dragging the mouse across will be highlighted (white waveform on black background) and the **Interval:** box will show the horizontal time of the highlighted area. Release the mouse button when the mouse pointer just touches the rising edge of the Qa waveform.

13. Record the propagation delay time it takes Qa to go from a logic-LOW to a logic-HIGH, T_{PLH}, with respect to the positive edge of the clock transition.

Qa delay at 50 ns: T_{PLH} = _____

14. Repeat Step 11 to determine the delay times for Qb and Qc with respect to the clock. Record the results below.

Qb delay at 50 ns: T_{PLH} = _____
Qc delay at 50 ns: T_{PLH} = _____

15. Position the cursor at 450 ns and determine the delay times for each waveform with respect to the clock transition.

Qa delay at 450 ns: T_{PLH} = _____
Qb delay at 450 ns: T_{PLH} = _____
Qc delay at 450 ns: T_{PLH} = _____

Figure 4

16. As you may have suspected, there is an easier method to determine delay times. Select the Max+plus II option in the main menu, then select the Timing Analyzer option (Figure 4).

17. Click the Start button in the Timing Analyzer.

18. Click the OK button when the timing analysis is completed.

19. Maximize the Delay Matrix and record the delay times in Table 2.

	Qa	Qb	Qc
Clock			

Table 2

20. During the compilation, a report is generated and placed on your diskette. The report may be accessed using a word processor; however, at this time, you will be using the default text editor to view this report.

Asynchronous Counters

21. Recompile your **counter1** file. When finished, an icon labeled **rpt** appears directly below the Fitter box in the Compiler window. Double click on this **rpt** icon (see Figure 5). You must have the Compiler window maximized to see the details within the compiler.

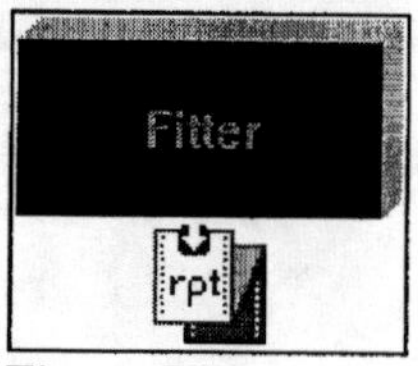

Figure 5

22. Scroll through the report file and answer the following questions.

    a.   What pin was assigned to the clock input? _____

    b.   How many input pins were used for your circuit? _____

    c.   How many output pins were used for your circuit? _____

    d.   How much was the IC utilized for the circuit of Figure 2? _____

    e.   How many VCCIO pins were assigned to the chip? _____

    f.   What is the acceptable voltage range for the VCCIO pins? _____

    g.   What voltage is to be applied to the VCCINT pins? _____

    h.   What name was assigned to the unused pins of the IC? _____

    i.   What pins were labeled GND? _____

    j.   What pin was Qa assigned? _____

    k.   What pin was Qb assigned? _____

    l.   What pin was Qc assigned? _____

    m.   What was the total compilation time for this circuit? _____

23. Based on the waveforms sketched for Figure 2, the frequency of the clock was _____.

24. Based on the waveforms sketched for Figure 2, the frequency of Qa was _____.

25. Based on the waveforms sketched for Figure 2, the frequency of Qb was _____.

26. Based on the waveforms sketched for Figure 2, the frequency of Qc was _____.

27. Write a statement commenting on the frequency relationships of the outputs Qa, Qb, and Qc with respect to the clock frequency.

_____

_____

28. Save all files to Drive A as **counter1**, then exit the Graphic and Waveform Editors.

Part 2   Procedure

1. Open the Max+plus II software. Assign the project name **7493ctra**.

2. Open a new Graphic Editor and construct the circuit shown in Figure 6.

3. Open a new Waveform Editor, set Grid Size to 30 ns, and then create the waveforms shown in Figure 7.

4. Compile and simulate the circuit, then neatly draw the output waveforms in the space provided in Figure 7.

5. The 7493 counter counts (up/down) from _____ to _____.

6. The 7493 counter advances count on the (leading/trailing) edge of the clock signal.

7. Set the clear input to a logic-HIGH from 600 ns to 1 µs.

Asynchronous Counters

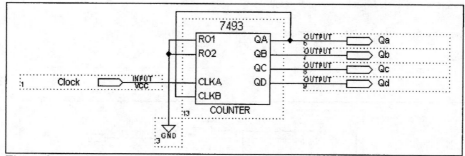

Figure 6

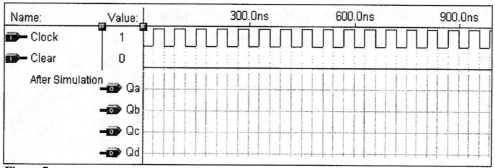

Figure 7

8.   Resimulate the circuit and describe the effects of the clear input on the Q outputs.

_____

9.   Based on your observation of the effects of the clear input, the Clear input on the 7493 is _____ (asynchronous/synchronous).

10. Sketch a state transition diagram for the 4-bit counter constructed using the 7493 macrofunction.

11. Save all files to Drive A as **7493ctra**, then exit both Graphic and Waveform Editors.

Part 3   Procedure

1.   Open the Max+plus II software. Assign the project name **7493ctrb**.

2.   Open a new Graphic Editor and construct the circuit shown in Figure 8.

3.   Open a new Waveform Editor, set Grid Size to 30 ns, and create the waveforms shown in Figure 9.

4.   Draw the output waveform generated by the software after compilation and simulation.

5.   The 7493 counter as wired in Figure 8 counts (up/down) from _____ to _____.

Asynchronous Counters

6. What count was detected by the decoder gate? _____

7. Describe what action took place when the decoder output was "active."

_____

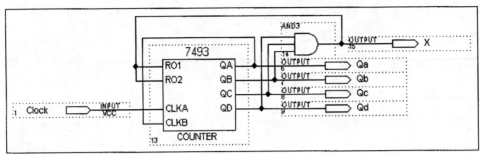

Figure 8

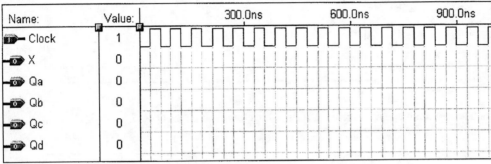

Figure 9

8. What is the natural modulus of the 7493? _____

9. What is the modulus of the circuit shown in Figure 8? _____

10. Sketch a state transition diagram for the 4-bit counter constructed in Figure 8. Include all count values but only the count sequence should appear in the basic loop. Shade the temporary state that is decoded and use dotted lines from the previous to next state.

11. Save all files to Drive A as **7493ctrb**, then exit both Graphic and Waveform Editors.

Part 4   Procedure

1. Open the Max+plus II software. Assign the project name **7493ctrc**.

Asynchronous Counters

440

2. Open a new Graphic Editor. Use the 7493 counter and 74154 decoder to create a Mod 10 counter that gives a BCD count sequence.

3. Open a new Waveform Editor and create a set of waveforms similar to Figure 9.

4. Compile and simulate the circuit.

5. Assuming zero errors, demonstrate the operational Mod 10 counter to the instructor. Obtain the signature of approval directly on the answer page for this lab.

6. Obtain a hard copy of the Graphic and Waveform Editors. Label these hard copies **Part 4, Step 6a** and **Part 4, Step 6b**, respectively.

7. Sketch a state transition diagram for the Mod 10 counter constructed. Include all count values but only the count sequence should appear in the basic loop. Shade the temporary state that is decoded and use dotted lines from the previous state to the next state.

8. Save all files to Drive A as **7493ctrc**, then exit both Graphic and Waveform Editors.

9. Write a 1- to 2-page summary pertaining to the results obtained from this lab. Include at least one embedded graphic with corresponding waveforms after compilation and simulation.

10. Staple all papers for this lab in the following sequence, then submit the lab to your instructor for grading.
    ◆ Cover page
    ◆ Typed summary
    ◆ The completed answer page for this lab
    ◆ Hard copy of the Graphic Editor, **Part 4, Step 6a**
    ◆ Hard copy of the Waveform Editor, **Part 4, Step 6b**

Asynchronous Counters

Asynchronous Counters Answer Pages   Name:_____

Part 1

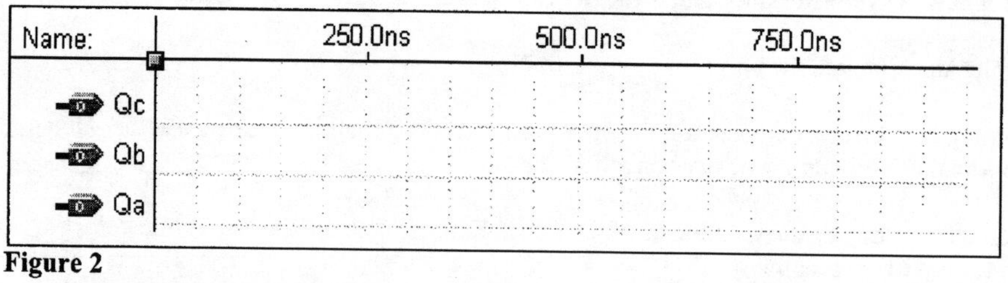

Name:		250.0ns	500.0ns	750.0ns
Qc				
Qb				
Qa				

Figure 2

Time Segment	Qc Qb Qa (Bits 0 or 1)	Octal Value
100 – 150 ns	__ __ __	____
200 – 250 ns	__ __ __	____
300 – 350 ns	__ __ __	____
400 – 450 ns	__ __ __	____
500 – 550 ns	__ __ __	____
600 – 650 ns	__ __ __	____
700 – 750 ns	__ __ __	____
800 – 850 ns	__ __ __	____

Table 1

6. (up/down)   7. (leading/trailing)

8. Sketch the state transition diagram

13. Qa delay at 50 ns: T_{PLH} = _____

14. Qb delay at 50 ns: T_{PLH} = _____   Qc delay at 50 ns: T_{PLH} = _____

15. Delay at 450 ns Qa: T_{PLH} = _____ Qb: T_{PLH} = _____ Qc: T_{PLH} = _____

	Qa	Qb	Qc
Clock			

Table 2

22. A. _____   B. _____   C. _____   D. _____

E. _____   F. _____   G. _____   H. _____

I. _____   J. _____   K. _____

L. _____   M. _____

23. _____   24. _____   25. _____   26. _____

27. _____

_____

Part 2

5. (up/down)   from _____ to _____   6. (leading/trailing)

8. _____   9. (asynchronous/synchronous)

Asynchronous Counters

442

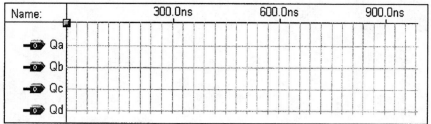

Figure 7

10. Sketch the state transition diagram

Part 3

5. (up/down) from _____ to _____   6. _____

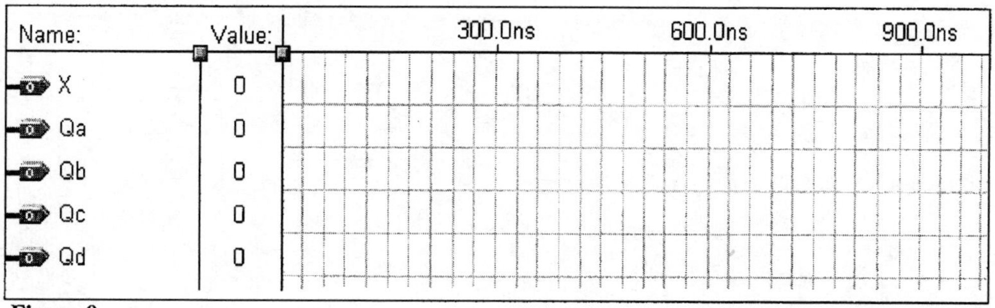

Name:	Value:	300.0ns	600.0ns	900.0ns
X	0			
Qa	0			
Qb	0			
Qc	0			
Qd	0			

Figure 9

7. _____

8. _____   9. _____   10. Sketch the state transition diagram

Part 4

5. Demonstrated to: _____

   Date: _____

7. Sketch the state transition diagram

Grade: _____

Asynchronous Counters

ASYNCHRONOUS COUNTERS - PART II

OBJECTIVES:

[ ] Construct a MOD-8 ripple counter
[ ] Construct a BCD counter with seven-segment display
[ ] Construct a MOD-5 down-counter and observe waveforms on oscilloscope
[ ] Construct a MOD-16 ripple counter with a 74LS93 chip
[ ] Design and build a MOD-10 ripple counter

MATERIALS:

[ ]   TTL Signal Generator
[ ]   Dual Trace Oscilloscope
[ ]   +5 Volt DC Supply
[2]   74LS76 J-K Flip-Flops
[1]   74LS32 Quad Positive OR/Negative AND
[1]   74LS00 Quad NAND
[1]   74LS93 Counter
[1]   74LS47 BCD to Seven-Segment Decoder
[1]   74LS04 Hex Inverter
[1]   Seven-Segment Display
[7]   330 Ohm Resistors
[1]   1K Ohm Resistor
[1]   .1uF Capacitor

INFORMATION:

One application of the flip-flop is as a counter. All sequential circuits operate in a predetermined timing arrangement and are triggered by a timing pulse or clock. The counter is necessary for these timing sequences, as well as in many other applications. There are two basic types of counters, synchronous and asynchronous. This experiment will concentrate on the asynchronous, or ripple counter.

To more fully understand counter operation, we will first construct some ripple counters using individual flip-flops, and then examine construction of counters with counter chips such as the 74LS93.

Counters can be made to count up or down, and to stop at any point and recycle to the beginning. Normal recycling counters are labeled by their number of different binary states, or modulus. A MOD-4 counter, for example, has four states: 00, 01, 10, 11, and then recycles back to 00. A MOD-8 counter would count zero through 7 (or seven through zero if it were a down-counter).

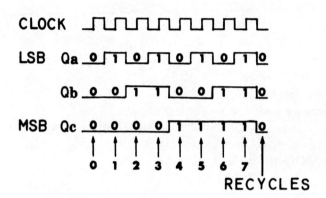

Figure 1

Applications of the various types of counters will be examined in later experiments. The frequency counter project, for example, uses counters for a number of purposes, from timing to actual counting.

Another circuit we will use in this and following experiments is the Power-on-reset or Power-on-preset circuit. This circuit consists only of an RC network connected to the reset or preset pin of a flip-flop or counter (Figure 2). If, for instance, it is necessary to start the count at zero, the RC network will momentarily hold the reset voltage LOW when power is applied. This resets the Q outputs to zero. When the capacitor charges to Vcc, the reset is rendered inactive, allowing the counter to perform its nominal count. If down-counting, this circuit could be attached to the preset pin, thereby setting all Q outputs to 1 when power is turned on!

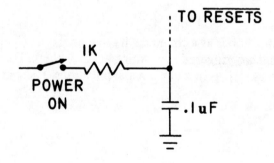

Figure 2

PROCEDURE:

1.   Construct the MOD-8 counter of Figure 3. Using a 1 Hz TTL clock or a debounced switch step through the count and record it in the table provided.

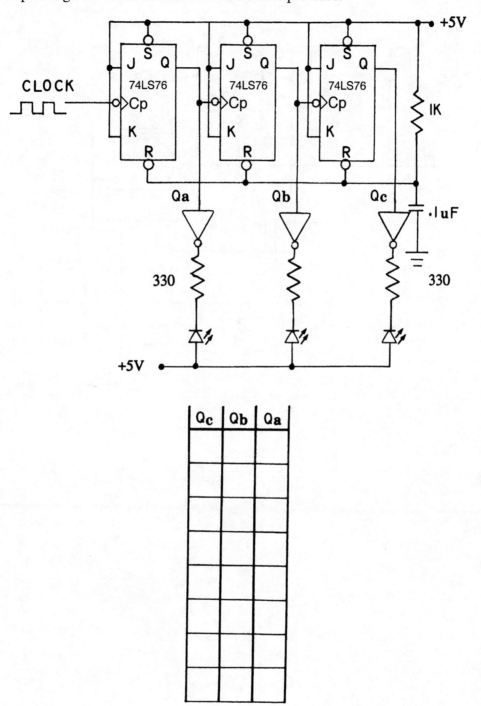

Figure 3

Qc	Qb	Qa

2.   Construct the BCD counter of Figure 4. Also, connect the decoder and seven-segment display. Clocking may be done with either a debounced DC switch or a TTL square wave at a very low frequency (1 Hertz).

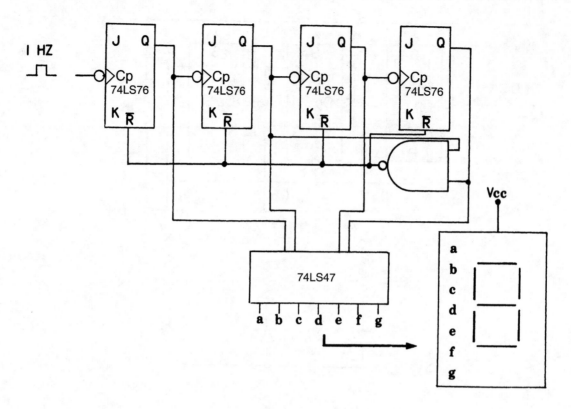

Figure 4

3. The next circuit is a MOD-5 Down-counter. Complete the schematic by drawing in the necessary connections for the 74LS47 decoder and the seven-segment display in Figure 5. Notice that only three inputs are going into the decoder. What should be done with the fourth input pin?

Again, test the counter by clocking it with either a debounced switch or a 1 Hz TTL square-wave.

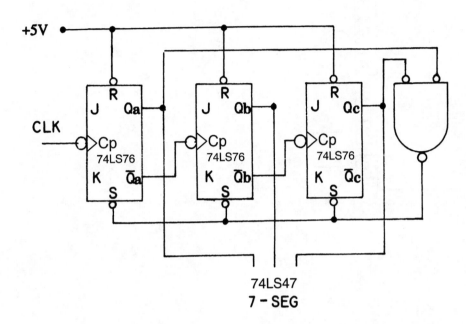

Figure 5

4.   Complete the pin function diagram for the 74LS93 chip in Figure 6. Give a brief description of the chip.

FUNCTION DIAGRAM   DESCRIPTION

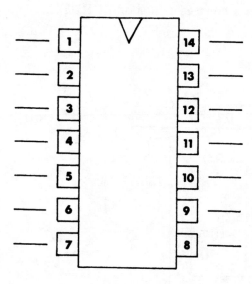

Figure 6

5.   Construct the MOD-16 counter of Figure 7 and hook up a 200KHz TTL signal to CP0. Use the oscilloscope to display the waveforms two at a time and carefully complete the wave-form chart. Extreme care must be taken to get the correct time relationship between the clock and Q1, Q1 and Q2, and so on. Check the count sequence using the waveforms. Do the wave-forms indicate that it is working correctly as a MOD-16 up-counter?

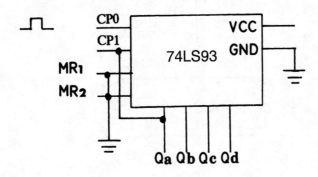

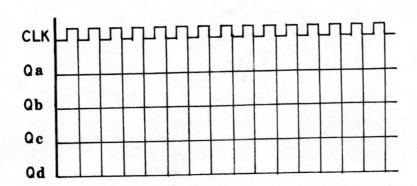

Figure 7

6.   Using the 74LS93 counter, design a MOD-10 up-counter. Draw the complete schematic. Follow logic through the counter to verify the design. Now construct the circuit and check its count sequence.

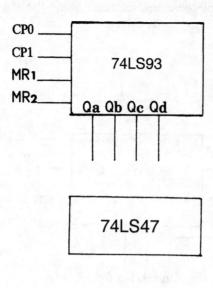

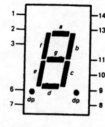

Figure 8

TROUBLESHOOTING:

1.   Assume a 74LS93 wired for MOD 16 with the input clock connected to CP0. What would happen if Qb was connected to CP1 (instead of the normal connection of Qa to CP1)?

2.   What symptom would be observed if MR1 and MR2 were left "floating"?

3.   What MOD would a 74LS93 count if the input clock is fed to CP0, Qa is fed to CP1, Qb is fed to MR1, and Qc is fed to MR2?

QUESTIONS:

1.   What is meant by "ripple counter"?

2.   Show the wiring necessary to connect the 74LS193 counter as a BCD up-counter.

Design of Synchronous Counters

Objectives

After completing this experiment, you will be able to

- Design a synchronous counter with up to 16 states in any selected order.
- Construct and test the counter. Determine the state diagram of the counter.

Materials Needed

Two 74LS76 dual J-K flip-flops
7408 quad AND gate or other SSI IC determined by student

For Further Investigation:
74LS139A dual 2-to-4 line decoder
Six LEDs

Summary of Theory

The design of a synchronous counter begins with a description of the state diagram that specifies the required sequence. All states in the main sequence should be shown; states that are not in the main sequence should be shown only if the design requires these unused states to return to the main sequence in a specified way. If the sequence can be obtained from already existing IC, this is almost always more economical and simpler than designing a special sequence.

From the state diagram, a next state table is constructed. This procedure is illustrated with the example in Figure 1 for a simple counter and again in Figure 4 for a more complicated design. Notice in Figure 1 that the next state table is just another way of showing the information contained in the state diagram. The advantage of the table is that the changes made by each flip-flop going from one state to the next state are clearly seen.

The third step is to observe the transitions (changes) in each state. The required logic to force these changes will be mapped onto a Karnaugh map. In this case, the Karnaugh map takes on a different meaning than it did in combinational logic but it is read the same way.* Each square on the map represents a state of the counter. In effect, the counter sequence is just moving from square to square on the Karnaugh map at each clock pulse. To find the logic that will force the necessary change in the flip-flop outputs, look at the transition table for the J-K flip-flop, shown as Table 1. Notice that all possible output *transitions* are listed first; then the inputs that cause these changes are given. The transition table contains a number of X's (don't cares) because of the versatility of the J-K flip-flop, as explained in the text. The data from the transition table are entered onto the Karnaugh maps as illustrated.

---

*This type of Karnaugh map may be more properly termed a Karnaugh state map.

From *Experiments in Digital Fundamentals,* Sixth Edition, David Buchla. Copyright © 2003 by Pearson Education, Inc. All rights reserved.

Assume you need to design a counter that counts 0–1–3–2 and stays in state 2 until a reset button is pressed. Two flip-flops are required. Let Q_B = MSB and Q_A = LSB. Use a J-K flip-flop.

Step 1: Draw a state diagram.

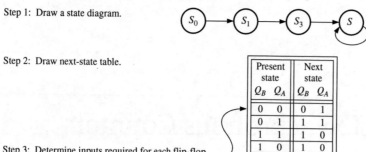

Step 2: Draw next-state table.

Present state		Next state	
Q_B	Q_A	Q_B	Q_A
0	0	0	1
0	1	1	1
1	1	1	0
1	0	1	0

Step 3: Determine inputs required for each flip-flop.
   (a) Read present state 00 on next-state table.
   (b) Note that Q_B does not change $0 \rightarrow 0$ (present to next state) and Q_A changes from $0 \rightarrow 1$.
   (c) Read the required inputs to cause these results from transition Table 1.
   (d) Map each input from transition table onto Karnaugh map.

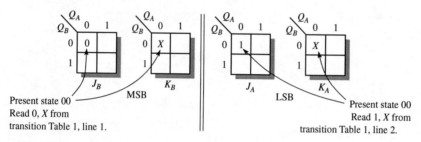

Present state 00
Read 0, X from
transition Table 1, line 1.

MSB   LSB

Present state 00
Read 1, X from
transition Table 1, line 2.

   (e) Complete maps.

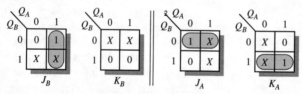

   (f) Read minimum logic from each map.

$$J_B = Q_A, \qquad K_B = 0, \qquad J_A = \overline{Q_B}, \qquad K_A = Q_B$$

Step 4: Draw circuit and check.

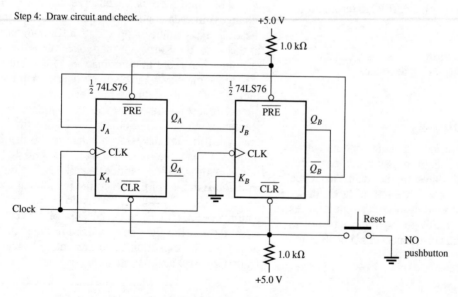

FIGURE 1

456

TABLE 1
Transition table for J-K flip-flop.

Output Transitions		Inputs	
Q_N	Q_{N+1}	J_N	K_N
0 → 0		0	X
0 → 1		1	X
1 → 0		X	1
1 → 1		X	0

Q_N = output before clock

Q_{N+1} = output after clock

J_N, K_N = inputs required to cause transition

X = don't care

When the maps are completed, the logic can be read from the map. This logic is then used to set up the circuit as shown in Step 4. It is a good idea to check the design by verifying that the count sequence is correct and that there are no lock-up states. (A lock-up state is one that does not return to the main sequence of the counter.) The design check can be done by completing a table such as Table 2, on the next page.

The design procedure just described can be extended to more complicated designs. The counter shown below (Figure 2) generates the required waveforms for half-stepping a stepper motor. This counter produces the state sequence shown in Figure 3(a). This sequence can be drawn as a series of four waveforms required by the stepper motor as shown in Figure 3(b).

The design method described here is not the only way to obtain the desired sequence, but it does lead to a fairly straightforward design. Figure 4 illustrates the detailed procedure for designing this circuit. Note that only the main sequence is shown

in the state diagram and on the next-state table. The reason for this is that the unused states will show up as extra "don't cares" in the logic, making the design simpler. All unused states are entered on the maps as "don't cares." After reading the logic equations for the inputs to each flip-flop, the design is checked for lock-up problems. Corrections are made to prevent lock up by examining the "don't-care" logic and changing it if required. The maps for the A and B flip-flops are not shown in Figure 4, but left as a student exercise in Question 1 of the Evaluation and Review Questions.

As you can see in Figure 4, the steps for the more complicated counter are basically the same as those used in Figure 1. The unused states allow the counter to be designed with a minimum of additional logic. The completed design is shown in Figure 2.

Procedure

1. A Gray code synchronous counter is often used in state machine design. This problem requires a six-state Gray code counter. The usual Gray code sequence is not used because the sixth state would not be "Gray" when the counter returns to zero. Instead, the sequence shown in Figure 5 is required. There are two unused states: state 5 and state 7. For the initial design, these states are not shown. Complete the next-state table in the report for the main sequence shown here.

2. Using the transition table for the J-K flip-flop, complete the Karnaugh maps shown in the report. The J-K transition table (Table 1) is repeated in the report for convenience.

3. Read the required logic expressions from each map that you completed in step 2. Check that the unused states return to the main sequence. If they do not, modify the design to assure that they do

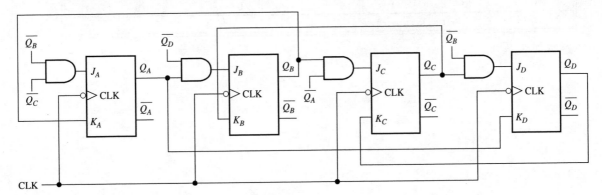

FIGURE 2
Synchronous counter with irregular sequence used for half-stepping a stepper motor.

TABLE 2
Analysis of synchronous counter shown in Figure 2.

Outputs				Inputs							
Q_D	Q_C	Q_B	Q_A	$J_D = \overline{Q_B} \cdot Q_C$	$K_D = Q_A$	$J_C = \overline{Q_A} \cdot Q_B$	$K_C = Q_D$	$J_B = Q_A \cdot \overline{Q_D}$	$K_B = Q_C$	$J_A = \overline{Q_B} \cdot \overline{Q_C}$	$K_A = Q_B$
0	0	0	0	0	0	0	0	0	0	1	0
0	0	0	1								

Step 2 → (0 0 0 0 row)
Step 4 → (0 0 0 1 row)
Step 3 (under K_D / J_C)
Step 1 (under J_B / J_A)

(a) Steps in filling out the table

Outputs				Inputs							
Q_D	Q_C	Q_B	Q_A	$J_D = \overline{Q_B} \cdot Q_C$	$K_D = Q_A$	$J_C = \overline{Q_A} \cdot Q_B$	$K_C = Q_D$	$J_B = Q_A \cdot \overline{Q_D}$	$K_B = Q_C$	$J_A = \overline{Q_B} \cdot \overline{Q_C}$	$K_A = Q_B$
0	0	0	0	0	0	0	0	0	0	1	0
0	0	0	1	0	1	0	0	1	0	1	0
0	0	1	1	0	1	0	0	1	0	0	1
0	0	1	0	0	0	1	0	0	0	0	1
0	1	1	0	0	0	1	0	0	1	0	1
0	1	0	0	1	0	0	0	0	1	0	0
1	1	0	0	1	0	0	1	0	1	0	0
1	0	0	0	0	0	0	1	0	0	1	0
1	0	0	1	0	1	0	1	0	0	1	0
0	0	0	1	At this step, a repeated pattern is noted.							
1	1	0	1	1	1	0	1	0	1	0	0
0	0	0	1	Returns to main sequence							
0	1	0	1	1	1	0	0	1	1	0	0
1	1	1	1	0	1	0	1	0	1	0	1
0	0	0	0	Returns to previously tested state (0000)							
0	1	1	1	0	1	0	0	1	1	0	1
0	1	0	1	Returns to previously tested state (0101)							
1	0	1	0	0	0	1	1	0	0	0	1
1	1	1	0	0	0	1	1	0	1	0	1
1	0	0	0	Returns to main sequence							
1	0	1	1	0	1	0	1	0	0	0	1
0	0	1	0	Returns to main sequence							

Main sequence (rows 0000 through 1001)
Account for all other states (rows 0001 onward)

(b) Completed table

458

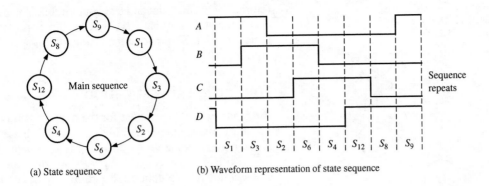

(a) State sequence   (b) Waveform representation of state sequence

FIGURE 3

Step 1: Draw the required state diagram. (Note that only the main sequence is shown as the unused states are not important in this problem.)

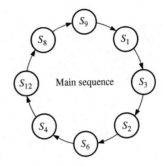

Step 2: Draw the next-state table. Four flip-flops are required because of the number of bits used in the sequence.

Present state				Next state			
Q_D	Q_C	Q_B	Q_A	Q_D	Q_C	Q_B	Q_A
0	0	0	1	0	0	1	1
0	0	1	1	0	0	1	0
0	0	1	0	0	1	1	0
0	1	1	0	0	1	0	0
0	1	0	0	1	1	0	0
1	1	0	0	1	0	0	0
1	0	0	0	1	0	0	1
1	0	0	1	0	0	0	1

Step 3: Using the next-state and transition tables, draw the Karnaugh maps for each flip-flop. For example, in state 1, note that Q_D and Q_C do not change in going to the next state. The transition is $0 \rightarrow 0$. From the transition table, a $0 \rightarrow 0$ transition requires $J = 0$ and $K = X$. These values are entered onto the maps for the D and C counters in the square that represents state 1. Unused states are mapped as Xs. Only the D and C maps are shown in this example.

(Note: Q_B and Q_A are positioned to make the map below easier to read.)

$$J_D = \overline{Q_B}Q_C \qquad K_D = Q_A \qquad J_C = \overline{Q_A}Q_B \qquad K_C = Q_D$$

FIGURE 4

459

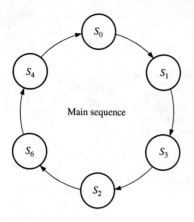

FIGURE 5
Required sequence for Gray code counter.

return. Then, construct and test your circuit. You can check the state sequence with an oscilloscope or a logic analyzer. Summarize the results of your test in your report.

For Further Investigation

A decoded output is needed for the counter you designed. Unfortunately, the only decoder IC that engineering has available for decoding is a 2-line to 4-line 74LS139A decoder! Show how you could connect this IC to obtain full decoding of the output. Then construct the circuit and put a separate LED on each output so that only one LED lights as the counter goes around. (*Hint:* Consider how you could use the enable inputs of the 74LS139A.)

Report for "Design of Synchronous Counters" Experiment

Name: _____ **Date:** _____ **Class:** _____

Objectives:

☐ Design a synchronous counter with up to 16 states in any selected order.
☐ Construct and test the counter. Determine the state diagram of the counter.

Data and Observations:

Present State			Next State		
Q_C	Q_B	Q_A	Q_C	Q_B	Q_A
0	0	0			
0	0	1			
0	1	1			
0	1	0			
1	1	0			
1	0	0			

TABLE 1
Transition table for J-K flip-flop (repeated for reference).

Output Transitions			Inputs	
Q_N		Q_{N+1}	J_N	K_N
0	→	0	0	X
0	→	1	1	X
1	→	0	X	1
1	→	1	X	0

Q_N = output before clock
Q_{N+1} = output after clock
J_N, K_N = inputs required to cause transition
X = don't care

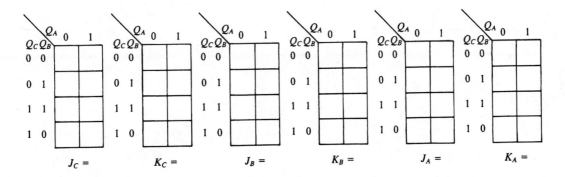

$J_C =$ $K_C =$ $J_B =$ $K_B =$ $J_A =$ $K_A =$

Circuit Design:

Results and Conclusion:

Further Investigation Results:

Evaluation and Review Questions

1. Complete the design of the sequential counter in Figure 4 by constructing Karnaugh maps for the B and A flip-flops. Read the maps. As a check, you can compare your result with the circuit drawn in Figure 2.

2. Describe the logic necessary to add a seven-segment display to the circuit you designed in this experiment to enable the display to show the state of the counter.

3. Assume you wanted to make the sequential circuit you designed in this experiment start in state 6 if a reset pushbutton is pressed. Describe how you would modify the circuit to incorporate this feature.

4. Assume you wanted to change the circuit from this experiment to be able to reverse the sequence. How would you go about this?

5. Assume you wanted to trigger a one-shot (74121) whenever the circuit you designed went into state 2 or state 4. Explain how you could do this.

6. a. Draw the transition table for a D flip-flop. Start by showing all possible output transitions (as in the J-K case) and consider what input must be placed on D in order to force the transition.

b. Why is the J-K flip-flop more versatile for designing synchronous counters with irregular sequences?

One-Shots and Astable Multivibrators

Objectives

After completing this experiment, you will be able to

- Specify components and trigger logic for a 74121 one-shot to produce a specified pulse and trigger mode.
- Measure the frequency and duty cycle of a 555 timer configured as an astable multivibrator.
- Specify components for a 555 timer configured as an astable multivibrator and test your design.

Materials Needed

74121 one-shot
7474 dual flip-flop
555 timer
Two 0.01 μF capacitors
Signal diode (1N914 or equivalent)
Resistors: 10 kΩ, 7.5 kΩ
Other components determined by student

Summary of Theory

There are three types of multivibrators: the bistable, the monostable (or *one-shot*), and the astable. The name of each type refers to the number of stable states. The bistable is simply a latch or flip-flop that can be either set or reset and will remain in either state indefinitely. The one-shot has one stable (or inactive) state and one active state, which requires an input trigger to assert. When triggered, the one-shot enters the active state for a precise length of time and returns to the stable state to await another trigger. Finally, the astable multivibrator has no stable state and alternates (or "flip-flops") between HIGH and LOW by itself. It frequently functions as a clock generator, since its output is a constant stream of pulses. Many systems require one-shot or astable multivibrators. The traffic light control system,* requires two one-shots and an astable multivibrator as a clock. In this experiment, you will specify the components for the astable multivibrator and test the frequency and duty cycle. In the For Further Investigation section, you will design the one-shots.

Most applications for one-shots can be met with either an IC timer or an IC one-shot. A timer is a general-purpose IC that can operate as an astable or as a one-shot. As a one-shot, the timer is limited to pulse widths of not less than about 10 μs or frequencies not greater than 100 kHz. For more stringent applications, the IC one-shot takes over. The 74121, which you will test in this experiment, can provide pulses as short as 30 ns. In addition, integrated circuit one-shots often have special features, such as both leading and trailing edge-triggering

---

*See Floyd's text "Digital System Application" for Chapter 6.

and multiple inputs that can allow triggering only for specific logic combinations. As you will see later, these can be extremely useful features. The logic circuit and function table for the 74121 are shown in Figure 1. The circuit is triggered by a rising pulse on the output of the Schmitt AND gate. The purpose of the Schmitt AND gate is to allow slow rise-time signals to trigger the one-shot. In order for B to trigger it, the input must be a rising pulse, and either A_1 or A_2 must be held LOW, as shown in the last two lines of the function table. If B is held HIGH, then a trailing edge trigger on either A_1 or A_2 will trigger the one-shot provided the other A input is HIGH. Other combinations can be used to inhibit triggering.

This experiment includes an introduction to the 555 timer, the first and still the most popular timer. It is not a TTL device but can operate on +5.0 V (and up to +18 V), so it can be TTL- or CMOS-compatible. This timer is extremely versatile but has limited triggering logic. Some applications include accurate time-delay generation, pulse generation, missing pulse detectors, and voltage-controlled oscillators (VCOs).

Procedure

Monostable Multivibrator Using the 74121

1. The 74121 contains an internal timing resistor of 2.0 kΩ. You can select the internal resistor for the timing resistor by connecting R_{INT} to V_{CC}, or you can select an external resistor. To use an external timing resistor, connect it as shown in Figure 1 with R_{INT} (pin 9) left open. The capacitor is an external component but can be eliminated for very short pulses. (See the manufacturer's data sheet.)

The equation that gives the approximate pulse width t_W is

$$t_W = 0.7 C_{EXT} R_T$$

where R_T is the appropriate timing resistor, either internal or external. C_{EXT} is in pF, R_T is in kΩ, and t_W is in ns. Using a 0.01 μF capacitor, calculate the required timing resistor to obtain a 50 μs pulse width. Obtain a resistor near the calculated value. Measure its resistance and measure the capacitance C_{EXT}. Record the computed R_T and the measured values of R_T and C_{EXT} in Table 1 of the report.

2. Using the measured values of R_T and C_{EXT}, compute the expected pulse width, t_W. Record the computed value in Table 1.

3. Assume that you need to trigger the one-shot using a leading-edge trigger from the pulse generator. Determine the required connections for A_1, A_2, and B. List the input logic levels and the generator connection in your report. Build the circuit. One-shots are susceptible to noise pickup, so you should install a 0.01 μF bypass capacitor from V_{CC} to ground as close as possible to the 74121.

4. Apply a 10 kHz TTL-compatible signal from the pulse generator to the selected trigger input. Look at the pulse from the generator on channel 1 of a two-channel oscilloscope and the Q

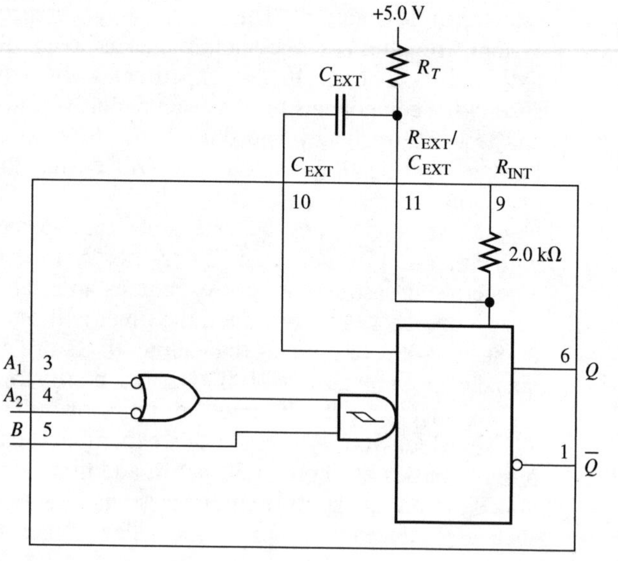

(a) Logic circuit

Inputs			Outputs	
A_1	A_2	B	Q	$\bar{Q}$
L	X	H	L	H
X	L	H	L	H
X	X	L	L	H
H	H	X	L	H
H	↓	H	⊓	⊔
↓	H	H	⊓	⊔
↓	↓	H	⊓	⊔
L	X	↑	⊓	⊔
X	L	↑	⊓	⊔

H = high logic level
L = low logic level
X = can be either low or high
↑ = positive going transition
↓ = negative going transition
⊓ = a positive pulse
⊔ = a negative pulse

(b) Function table

FIGURE 1

output on channel 2. Measure the pulse width and compare it with the expected pulse width from Step 1. (You may need to adjust R.) Record the measured pulse width in Table 1.

5. Increase the frequency slowly to 50 kHz while viewing the output on the scope. What evidence do you see that the 74121 is not retriggerable? Describe your observations.

The 555 Timer as an Astable Multivibrator

6. One of the requirements for many circuits is a clock, a series of pulses used to synchronize the various circuit elements of a digital system. In the astable mode, a 555 timer can serve as a clock generator.

A basic astable circuit is shown in Figure 2. There are two timing resistors. The capacitor is charged through both but is discharged only through R_2. The duty cycle, which is the ratio of the output HIGH time t_H divided by the total time T, and the frequency f are found by the following equations:

$$\text{Duty cycle} = \frac{t_H}{T} = \frac{R_1 + R_2}{R_1 + 2R_2}$$

$$f = \frac{1.44}{(R_1 + 2R_2)C_1}$$

Measure the value of two resistors R_1 and R_2 and capacitor C_1 with listed values as shown in Table 2. Record the measured values of the components in Table 2. Using the equations, compute the expected frequency and duty cycle for the 555 astable multivibrator circuit shown in Figure 2. Enter the computed frequency and duty cycle in Table 2.

7. Construct the astable multivibrator circuit shown in Figure 2. Using an oscilloscope, measure

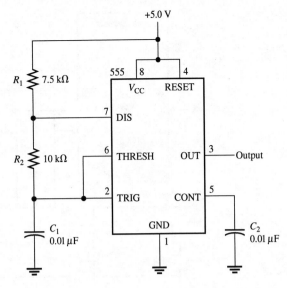

FIGURE 2

the frequency and duty cycle of the circuit and record it in Table 2.

8. With the oscilloscope, observe the waveforms across capacitor C_1 and the output waveform at the same time. On Plot 1, sketch the observed waveforms.

9. While observing the waveforms from Step 8, try placing a short across R_2. Remove the short and write your observations in space provided in the report.

10. A clock oscillator signal, generated from an astable multivibrator, is required for the traffic-light control system. The specified oscillator frequency is 10 kHz. The circuit in Figure 2 oscillates at too low a frequency. Modify the design of this circuit so that it oscillates at 10 kHz (the duty cycle is not critical). Show the circuit in the space provided in the report.

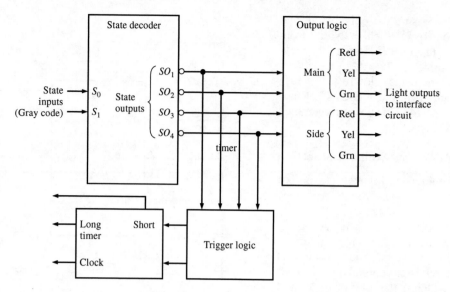

FIGURE 3
Block diagram of the state decoding and output logic.

For Further Investigation

The traffic light control system requires two one-shots, shown in the system as the *short timer* and the *long timer* (Figure 3). When the state decoder changes from LOW to HIGH, it causes the trigger logic to change from HIGH to LOW (trailing edge). It is this HIGH-to-LOW transition (trailing edge) that is used to trigger the timers. The short timer must have a 4 s positive pulse and the long timer must have a 25 s positive pulse. Check the manufacturer's maximum values of R_T and C_{EXT} for the 74121.* Then design and build the circuits. An LED (with 330 Ω current-limiting resistor) can be used as an indicator. Test your design to see that the pulse width is approximately correct. Draw the circuits in the report and indicate your test results.

---

*See Appendix.

Report for "One-Shots and Astable Multivibrators" Experiment

Name: _____ Date: _____ Class: _____

Objectives:

☐ Specify components and trigger logic for a 74121 one-shot to produce a specified pulse and trigger mode.
☐ Measure the frequency and duty cycle of a 555 timer configured as an astable multivibrator.
☐ Specify components for a 555 timer configured as an astable multivibrator and test your design.

Data and Observations:

TABLE 1
Data for 74121 monostable multivibrator.

Quantity	Computed Value	Measured Value
Timing Resistor, R_T		
External Capacitor, C_{EXT}	0.01 μF	
Pulse Width, t_W		

Step 3. Input logic levels and generator connection:

Step 5. Observations as frequency is raised to 50 kHz:

TABLE 2
Data for 555 timer as an astable multivibrator.

Quantity	Computed Value	Measured Value
Resistor, R_1	7.5 kΩ	
Resistor, R_2	10.0 kΩ	
Capacitor, C_1	0.01 μF	
Frequency		
Duty Cycle		

Step 8:

Capacitor waveform:

Output waveform:

PLOT 1

Step 9. Observations with a short across R_2:

Step 10. Circuit for a 10 kHz oscillator for traffic-light controller:

Results and Conclusion:

Further Investigation Results:

Evaluation and Review Questions

1. What does the term *nonretriggerable* mean for a monostable multivibrator?

2. a. For the 74121 monostable multivibrator circuit, compute the value of the capacitor for a pulse width of 50 μs using the internal resistor.

   b. What change to the circuit is required to cause the output to be variable from 50 μs to 250 μs?

3. From the data sheet for the 74121, determine the largest timing resistor and capacitor recommended by the manufacturer. What pulse width would you predict if these values were chosen for the circuit in Figure 1?

$$t_W = \underline{\hspace{3cm}}$$

4. Compute the duty cycle and frequency for a 555 astable multivibrator if $R_1 = 1.0$ kΩ, $R_2 = 180$ kΩ, and $C_1 = 0.01$ μF.

5. For the 555 astable multivibrator, determine R_1 and R_2 necessary for a period of 12 s if $C_1 = 10$ μF and the required duty cycle is 0.60.

$$R_1 = \underline{\hspace{3cm}}$$

$$R_2 = \underline{\hspace{3cm}}$$

6. Assume the 555 astable multivibrator in Figure 2 is operating from +15 V. What voltage range do you expect to see across capacitor C_1?

The ADC0804 Analog-to-Digital Converter

Objectives:

After performing this experiment, you will be able to:

1. Construct an analog to digital converter circuit using an ADC0804 operating in free-running mode. Calibrate the step width and check the transfer function for a few steps.
2. Describe the basic signals in and from the ADC0804.
3. Determine the binary output pattern for a particular input voltage.
4. Interface an LM335 Kelvin temperature sensor to an ADC0804 and calibrate it to read Centigrade temperatures.

Summary of Theory:

Most physical quantities originate in analog (continuous) form. These quantities can be converted into an electrical parameter (typically voltage) by a transducer. Before processing with a digital computer, it is necessary to convert the electrical analog quantity to a number. An analog-to-digital converter (ADC) is a circuit that performs this conversion.

Conversion is a sampling process that produces an error between the actual input and the digitized representation. Several factors, discussed in the text, contribute to this error. Two critical considerations in choosing a particular ADC are the amount of error that can be tolerated in the digitized result and the conversion speed. Other considerations include the range of the input voltage, the format of the output, and power supply requirements.

The ADC0804 is a widely used 8-bit successive approximation type with parallel outputs that can be latched or put into a high impedance state for direct interfacing with a computer data bus. The ADC0804 operates on a nominal +5.0 V supply voltage. Frequently, the analog voltage of interest is less than 0 V to +5.0 V so the *span* (actual range of the input voltage) needs to be reduced. This is accomplished by a separate dc input to the ADC0804. In addition to a variable range, the ADC0804 can also accommodate different full-scale input voltages.

The sequence for the conversion process is shown in four steps in Figure 36-1. First, the internal latches are reset by making both the $\overline{WR}$ (write) input and the $\overline{CS}$ (chip select) input lines low. Conversion begins within 1 to 8 clock cycles after $\overline{WR}$ or $\overline{CS}$ makes a low to high (0 to 1) transition. Because the ADC0804 is a successive approximation ADC, it requires a clock. An internal clock can be selected that is configured by an external resistor and a capacitor or an external system clock can be used. After a maximum of 64 clock cycles, conversion is complete, signaled by the $\overline{INT}$ (interrupt) line from the ADC0804 going low. If the data is sent to a computer, the computer checks the $\overline{INT}$ line for this low and, if ready,

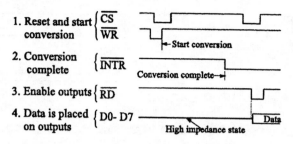

Figure 36-1 Timing for the ADC0804.

issues a $\overline{CS}$ followed by a $\overline{RD}$ (read) input. These two signals are required to be low to enable the output latches and place the data on the data bus.

The ADC0804 can operate in a free-running mode. In the free-running mode, it can be set up without any other ICs in the circuit and can display the output binary code with LEDs. In the first part of this experiment, you will test an ADC0804 using the free-running mode and observe the signals. National Semiconductor advises that a momentary low on the $\overline{WR}$ line will assure start-up during the first power-up cycle. This is done by a normally open pushbutton switch.

A concern with ADCs is noise and glitches (switching "spikes"). An ADC resolves the input signal in the millivolt and microvolt range. Any noise can have an adverse effect on the conversion accuracy as the internal comparator can respond to the noise. National Semiconductor recommends that a 1 μF (or better) tantalum (low inductance) capacitor be connected between the V_{cc} pin and ground. Another concern is assuring that the converter's ground line is not sharing high currents from other parts of the circuit; high currents create unwanted conduction noise that can affect the 0 V level for the converter. Ground currents can be reduced by using fairly high-value current-limiting resistors in series with the LED indicators.

In this experiment, you are introduced to an IC temperature transducer, the LM335 (drawn as an "adjustable" zener diode). The LM335 is internally calibrated for an output of 10 mV per Kelvin degree[1]. Related devices are the LM34 and LM35 designed for measuring positive Fahrenheit and Centigrade temperatures, respectively. At 0° C, the LM335 should have an output of 2730 mV (273 x 10 mV) whereas the the LM35 will have a 0 V output (representing 0° C). The LM335 can be used to read either Fahrenheit or Centigrade temperatures at the output of the ADC0804 as you will see. This process will give you experience with controlling the span and offset for a measurement.

Materials Needed:
Resistors: one 1.0 kΩ, eight 1.2 kΩ, one 2.2 kΩ, one 10 kΩ
Potentiometers: one 1 kΩ (ten-turn), two 10 kΩ
Capacitors: one 150 pF, one 0.1 μF, one 1.0 μF (or larger) tantalum
One ADC0804 analog-to-digital converter
One N.O. pushbutton switch
Eight light-emitting diodes (LEDs)
One LM335 IC temperature sensor
One 1N4619 3.0 V zener diode

---

[1] The Kelvin scale uses the same size degree units as the Celsius scale and is based on the coldest possible temperature as 0 K. Equivalent temperatures are 273° larger than those on the Celsius scale.

Procedure:

1. Construct the circuit shown in Figure 36-2. Generally the power supply voltage is set to +5.0 V; however, it is shown here as +5.12 V to make the output steps exactly 20 mV. (5.12 V / 256 steps = 20 mV/ step). The $V_{ref}/2$ voltage is set internally to one-half the supply voltage unless an external reference voltage is connected to this pin. For this test circuit, an external 10 kΩ potentiometer sets the reference. The 3.0 V zener diode is added to ensure this point is fixed regardless of any power supply fluctuations.

   R_2 is a ten-turn potentiometer used to set a precise analog input between 0 and 5.12 V. If you do not have a ten-turn potentiometer, a regular one-turn potentiometer can be substituted (but with reduced precision for setting the voltages).

   C_3 is a 1.0 μF (or larger) tantalum bypass capacitor that should be connected close to the V_{CC} of the ADC0804. If you experience noise problems, try increasing this capacitor.

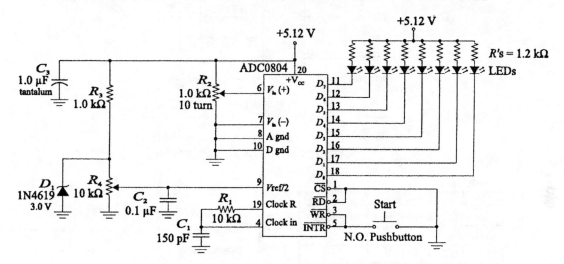

Figure 36-2 Free-running ADC circuit.

2. Adjust the power supply to +5.12 V and momentarily push the Start pushbutton. The ADC should be operating. The internal clock speed is controlled by R_1 and C_1.

   Set the R_2 potentiometer to its lowest resistance setting (0 V) and observe the LEDs. They should all be on. Slowly increase the analog input voltage to maximum. You should observe that the pattern in the LEDs changes as the input voltage is increased until they are all off. Notice that an LED that is *on* represents a binary 0 and an LED that is *off* represents a binary 1. If you do not observe the changing pattern described, troubleshoot the circuit to see that it was wired correctly.

Testing the output

3. This step "fine tunes" the threshold voltages and sets the steps to 20 mV per step, except for the very last step which is 30 mV wide. The adjustments required should be small.

   Adjust R_2 for an input voltage ($V_{in}(+)$) of 5.09 V. This represents 1.5 steps (30 mV) *less* than the full scale of 5.12 V for the last step. At this point, all LEDs except D_0 should be off. (D_0 may be either on or off.) While observing the D_0 LED, readjust the $V_{ref}/2$ voltage using potentiometer R_4 so that the output is *just* changing between 0 and 1. This setting of R_4 should be left for remaining tests.

4. In this step, you will check several steps in the transfer function. The transfer function is a plot of the analog input as a function of the digital output. An ideal transfer function is shown in Figure 36-3 for the first 4 steps (out of a possible 256 steps) for the free-running ADC circuit. Notice that the output ideally switches at points 1/2 between the least significant bit step value.

   Set the R_2 for minimum (0 V). All the LEDs should be on. Adjust R_2 until the D_0 LED just goes out (representing a binary 1). Measure the voltage on the (V_{in}(+)) input. This represents the first threshold voltage. Ideally it should be 10 mV, but it may be slightly larger due to current in the resistance of the ground conductor of the protoboard. Record the measured value in the first space of Table 36-1.

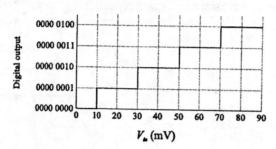

Figure 36-3 Ideal transfer function showing the first four steps for the ADC in Figure 36-1.

Table 36-1

Digital number	Ideal threshold	Measured threshold
0000 0001	10 mV	
0000 0010	30 mV	
0000 0011	50 mV	
0000 0100	70 mV	

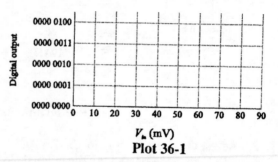

V_{in} (mV)

Plot 36-1

5. Raise the input voltage and observe the point where the binary code switches to 0000 0010. Record this threshold in Table 36-1. Repeat for the next two codes in the sequence. Plot the transfer function for the first four steps of your circuit in Plot 36-1.

6. Starting from the least significant position, each binary bit position represents twice the value of the preceding bit. For example, if the least significant bit represents 20 mV, the second position represents 40 mV, the third represents 80 mV and so forth. In this step you will test the input voltage required to turn off a single LED.

   Adjust R_2 carefully for 20 mV. Record the observed binary output in Table 36-2. Remember that an LED that is off is a binary 1.

7. Repeat step 6 for each of the input voltages listed in Table 36-2. Set the input voltage as accurately as possible and record the binary pattern in Table 36-2.

Table 36-2

Input voltage	Binary output
20 mV	
40 mV	
80 mV	
160 mV	
320 mV	
640 mV	
1.28 V	
2.56 V	

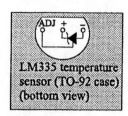

LM335 temperature sensor (TO-92 case) (bottom view)

Figure 36-4

Forming a digital thermometer

8. An analog temperature transducer is the LM335, described in the Summary of Theory. The pinout is shown in Figure 36-4. Replace the input circuitry for pins 6 and 7 on the ADC as shown in Figure 36-5 to accommodate the LM335.

   The ADC circuit you have been testing has 20 mV steps. Once V_{CC} is set, these steps are determined by the voltage on the $V_{ref}/2$ input. Since the LM335 has 10 mV/°C output, change the ADC to 10 mV/step also. You can change the ADC to 10 mV/step by changing the voltage on the $V_{ref}/2$ input to 1.28 V (one-half the desired full-scale range).

   Another adjustment will convert the output of the ADC to represent a Celsius temperature scale. In order to force the output to represent 0° C when the temperature in Kelvin is 273 K, a voltage of 2.73 V is placed on the inverting input (pin 7) of the ADC0804 using the ten-turn potentiometer to set the voltage.

   Can you read the temperature of the room? Try holding the temperature sensor between your fingers. Test the circuit and describe your results:

   _____

   _____

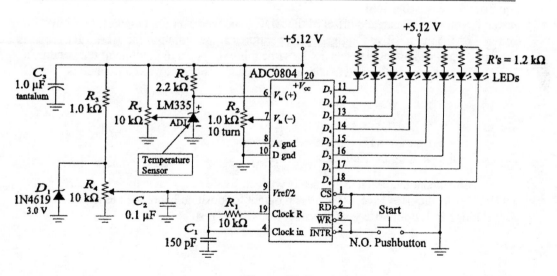

Figure 36-5

477

Conclusion:

Evaluation and Review Questions:

1. What binary output would you expect if the input to the circuit in Figure 36-2 was 800 mV?

2. If the binary output in Figure 36-2 is 1010 0000, what *input* voltage ($V_{in(+)}$) would you expect to observe?

3. In step 8, you were instructed to change the $V_{ref}/2$ input to 1.28 V. Explain how this setting produces a 10 mV/step output.

4. In step 8, what temperature is represented by an output of 1111 1111?

5. What is the purpose of the $\overline{WR}$ line on the ADC0804?

For Further Investigation:

In step 8, you set the span and offset of the ADC to convert Kelvin temperatures above 273 K from the LM335 to positive Centigrade temperatures at the output of the ADC. By properly setting the span and offset, you can do the same thing for positive Fahrenheit temperatures.

The equation that is used to convert Centigrade temperature to Fahrenheit is:

$$F = \frac{9}{5}C + 32°$$

where:

F = temperature in Fahrenheit
C = temperature in Centigrade

Think about the problem and see if you can figure out what setting of R_2, R_4, and R_5 will enable the circuit to have a 10 mV/step output for positive Fahrenheit temperatures. Test your settings and summarize your procedures and your results.

The Traffic Light Controller

Objectives

After completing this experiment, you will be able to
- Complete the design of a sequential counter that is controlled by input variables.
- Construct and test the circuit from the first objective.

Materials Needed

7408 quad AND gate
7474 dual D flip-flop
74121 one-shot
74LS153 dual data selector
One 150 μF capacitor
Two LEDs
Resistors: two 330 Ω, six 1.0 kΩ, one to be determined by student

Summary of Theory

A synchronous counter forms the heart of many small digital systems. In such systems, a small synchronous counter can be used to represent each of the possible "states" that the output can take. Here the state of the counter in the traffic light controller is determined by three input variables and two state variables. When certain conditions of these variables are met, the counter advances to the next state. The three input variables are defined as follows:

Vehicle on side street $= V_s$

25 s timer (long timer) is on $= T_L$

4 s timer (short timer) is on $= T_S$

The use of complemented variables indicates the opposite conditions. A state diagram, introduced in the text, is repeated in Figure 1 for reference. Based on this state diagram, the sequential operation is described as follows:

1st state: The counter shows the Gray code 00, representing main-green, side-red. It will stay in the first state if the long timer is on *or* if there is no vehicle on the side street $(T_L + \overline{V}_s)$. It will go to the second state if the long timer is off *and* there is a vehicle on the side street $(\overline{T}_L V_s)$.

2nd state: The counter shows 01, representing main-yellow, side-red. It will stay in the second state if the short timer is on (T_S). It will go to the third state if the short timer is off $(\overline{T}_S)$.

3rd state: The counter shows 11, representing main-red, side-green. It will stay in the third state if the long timer is on *and* there is a vehicle on the side street $(T_L V_s)$. It will go to the fourth state if the long timer is off *or* there is no vehicle on the side street $(\overline{T}_L + \overline{V}_s)$.

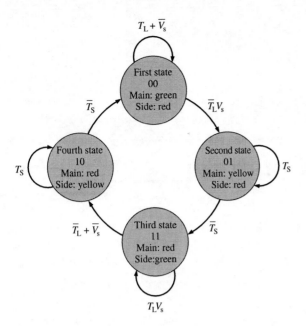

FIGURE 1
State diagram.

4th state: The counter shows 10, representing main-red, side-yellow. It will stay in the fourth state if the short timer is on (T_S). It will go to first state if the short timer is off ($\overline{T}_S$).

The block diagram in Figure 2 further defines the sequential logic. The input logic block consists of two data selectors to route the three input variables (V_s, T_L, and T_S) to the flip-flops. This is shown in more detail in the partially completed schematic shown in the report as Figure 4. The data selectors (DS-0 and DS-1) are the 74LS153 chips. The line selected (C_0 through C_3) is determined by the present state (because the flip-flop outputs are connected to the select inputs).

In this experiment, you will design and construct a portion of the system. To make our simula-

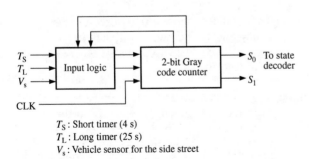

T_S: Short timer (4 s)
T_L: Long timer (25 s)
V_s: Vehicle sensor for the side street

FIGURE 2
Block diagram of the sequential logic.

tion more realistic, it will be helpful to have the short timer working. The short timer can be constructed from a 74121 one-shot. From the next-state table, it can be seen that the short timer should be ON in the second and fourth states (Gray codes 01 and 10). Triggering will be set up so that the short timer will trigger on the trailing edge of the clock, causing it to start in any state. This won't matter for this experiment, but later, we may trigger the short timer only when the traffic light enters the second state (Gray code 01) or the fourth state (Gray code 10) (yellow light). The trailing edge is used for triggering the short timer because the outputs change on the leading edge. This avoids a "race" condition where the clock and states change together. The triggering for this experiment is shown in Figure 3.

The present state–next state table with input conditions is shown in Table 1 of the report. Each pair of lines in Table 1 represents the two possible states that the counter could assume. For example, on the first pair of lines, the counter is in the first state (Gray code 00) and could either stay in the first state (Gray code 00) or go to the second state (Gray code 01), depending on the long timer and vehicle sensor inputs. Notice that in the first state

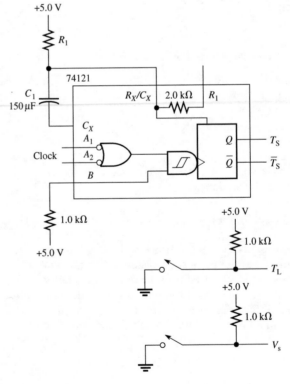

FIGURE 3

480

(Gray code 00), the next state for Q_1 requires that it remain a 0 *no matter what the inputs do,* so a 0 is entered for the product term for data selector-1 (DS-1). On the other hand, Q_0 will be a 1 *only* if the long timer is LOW (timed out) *and* the vehicle sensor is HIGH (vehicle waiting). Thus, the input product term for DS-0 is $\overline{T}_L V_s$. As one more example, notice that in the second state (Gray code 01), the next state for Q_0 will be a 1 *no matter what the inputs do,* so a 1 is entered in the table.

Procedure

1. Review the Summary of Theory to be sure you understand the idea for the circuit. The present state–next state table with input conditions is shown in Table 1 of the report. Three of the inputs for the data selectors are completed as an example. Decide what to do with the remaining inputs and complete the remaining five inputs in Table 1.

2. From the inputs determined in Step 1, complete the schematic shown in Figure 4 of the report. Show the inputs to each data selector and the enable. Note that the select lines of the data selectors are connected to the outputs of the flip-flops.

3. Construct the short timer shown in Figure 3. You will need to compute the value of R_1 in order to make a 4 s timer. The triggering of the short timer is different than in the full system for reasons of simplicity. The long timer and vehicle sensor are made from SPST switches as shown in Figure 3. A "NOTed" variable, such as $\overline{T}_L$, is asserted when the switch is closed.

4. On the same protoboard as the short timer and the switches representing the long timer and vehicle sensor, add the sequential logic in Figure 4. The LEDs serve as state indicators. Connect all inputs in accordance with your design in Step 1. Set the pulse generator to 10 kHz.

5. The state diagram (Figure 1) will guide you through the inputs required for the sequence in order to test the circuit. Start by opening the long timer and vehicle sensor switches (both HIGH). Place the counter in the first state (Gray code 00) by placing a momentary ground on the $\overline{CLR}$ inputs. In this condition, a vehicle is assumed to be on the side street (because V_s is HIGH) but the long timer has not finished the cycle on the main street. Close the long timer switch. This should immediately cause the circuit to go into the second state (Gray code 01), and the 4 s short timer should take over. While the 4 s timer is on, open the long timer switch again. The circuit should switch by itself (after 4 s) to the third state (Gray code 11).

6. If you successfully arrived in the fourth state (Gray code 10), look at the state diagram and decide what steps need to be taken to return to the first state and remain there. Then, use the switches to move back to the first state. Summarize your results in the report.

For Further Investigation

Assume your boss wonders, "Can you simplify the traffic light controller if you eliminate the short timer and make the clock (pulse generator) operate at a period of 4 s? Does this have any advantages? Also, as a second idea, I noticed you triggered the short timer without using trigger logic, just the clock. Could you also trigger the long timer this way?"

Consider both of these ideas (after all, you shouldn't ignore the boss). Indicate the circuit modifications you would suggest in order to accomplish each. Try putting the first idea into effect by modifying the circuit and testing it again. Then write a short summary to the boss stating what you think of her idea.

Report for "The Traffic Light Controller" Experiment

Name: _____ Date: _____ Class: _____

Objectives:

- ☐ Complete the design of a sequential counter that is controlled by input variables.
- ☐ Construct and test the circuit from the first objective.

Data and Observations:

TABLE 1

Present State		Next State		Input Conditions	Input Product Term for Data Selector-1	Input Product Term for Data Selector-0
Q_1	Q_0	Q_1	Q_0			
0	0	0	0	$T_L + \overline{V}_s$		
0	0	0	1	$\overline{T}_L V_s$	0	$\overline{T}_L V_s$
0	1	0	1	T_s		
0	1	1	1	$\overline{T}_s$		1
1	1	1	1	$T_L V_s$		
1	1	1	0	$\overline{T}_L + \overline{V}_s$		
1	0	1	0	T_s		
1	0	0	0	$\overline{T}_s$		

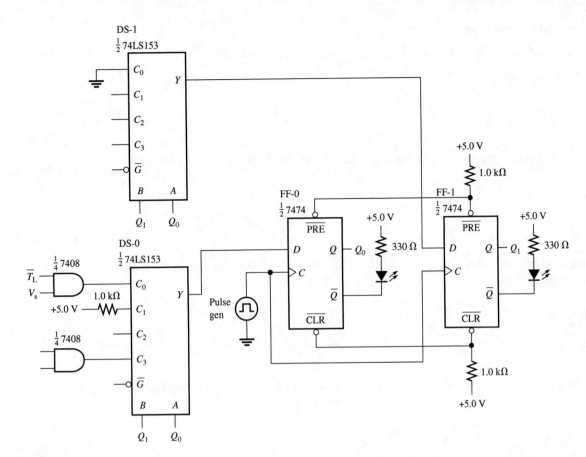

FIGURE 4

Results and Conclusion:

Further Investigation Results:

Evaluation and Review Questions

1. Why was Gray code selected for the design of the traffic light controller?

2. What two conditions are required for the counter to stay in the third state (Gray code 11)?

3. Explain what modifications would be needed to make the traffic light controller cycle through eight states instead of four states.

4. Suppose you want to build the traffic light controller using J-K flip-flops instead of D flip-flops. How should the J and K inputs be connected to allow this change?

5. The B input of the 74121 (Figure 3) was connected to a HIGH. Explain.

6. Assume the traffic-light controller is "locked-up" in the first state (Gray code 00). The light never cycles to the side street even when a vehicle is present, causing drivers to become extremely annoyed. You test the vehicle sensor and find that it is HIGH at the input to the 7408 AND gate. Describe the troubleshooting procedure you would use to identify the problem.

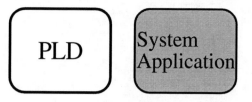

Traffic Light Controller with a PLD

Objectives

After completing this experiment, you will be able to
☐ Using ABEL software, enter the input source listing for a sequential traffic light controller circuit and compile the file.
☐ Using a PLD programmer, program a PLD for the traffic light problem in the first objective.
☐ Complete the schematic for the circuit; then construct and test it.

Materials Needed

Computer and ABEL software for programming a PLD (software available from Lattice Semiconductor. See Preface for directions for obtaining software.)
PLD Programmer (Hi-Lo Systems model ALL-07* and ACCESS software or equivalent)
One Lattice GAL16V8 PLD
    (order part GAL16V8D)
Two 74121 monostable multivibrators

One 1-position DIP switch (wire may be substituted)
Resistors: six 330 Ω, three 1.0 kΩ, two 39 kΩ
Six LEDs: two red, two yellow, two green to represent traffic lights
Capacitors: two each; values to be determined by student

Summary of Theory

Programmable logic devices (PLDs) were introduced in Chapter 1 of Floyd's text and in the Code Conversion with a PLD Experiment. The code converter in that experiment was an example of combinational logic; that is, the output was only a function of the present inputs. No memory is involved in combinational logic.

Sequential logic circuits are basically combinational circuits with the addition of memory. Circuits that have the ability to change their outputs based on the inputs and past history are called state machines. The heart of a state machine is a counter that represents the "states" of the circuit. We will use the same state diagram introduced in The Traffic Light Controller Experiment that programmed a four-state traffic light. This time, you will program a PLD to do all but the timer functions. Before proceeding, you should review the description of the state machine described in that experiment (please consult your instructor). In this experiment, the same design is accomplished by writing equations for ABEL, forming the JEDEC file, and programming a PLD. The circuit

*Available from Jameco Electronics, 1355 Shoreway Rd., Belmont, CA 94002-4100. Internet address: www.jameco.com

is then constructed with just three ICs: two timers and the PLD!

The circuit in this experiment is a little different from the circuit in the text. It will "fit" into one of the devices supported by the educational version of ABEL. The main difference is the triggering of the short and long timers. The GAL16V8 does not support enough output functions to provide the needed logic as well as the timer triggers, so a different technique is used for triggering the timers. The clocking for the timers will be discussed in the procedure. In addition, clocking problems can occur with state machine design because outputs can change on the clock pulse *following* the one that caused the state to change (causing the machine to ignore the necessary inputs). To prevent this, and cause the outputs to change *with* the state, the WITH statement is used in the ABEL equations.

Procedure

Part 1: Running ispDesignEXPERT Program under Windows 95, Windows 98, or later version

1. The problem for this experiment is to program a PLD to simulate a very basic traffic light at an intersection with a main street and a side street as described in the text. The state diagram for the light is shown in Figure 1 and represents a Moore state machine in which the outputs are solely a function of the present state. Notice in Figure 2 that the states are given names that relate to the output for that state (for instance MGSR is the first state and the outputs are *Main Green, Side Red*). Likewise, the inputs and outputs are named for their function. Inputs are vehicle sensor, (VS), short timer (TS), and long timer (TL). Outputs are Main red (MR), main yellow (MY), main green (MG), side red (SR), side yellow (SY), and side green (SG). A zero is the active level for all outputs.

The procedure for the traffic light project is very similar to the one given in the Code Conversion with a PLD Experiment for the binary to Gray conversion problem. Pin assignments are left for the software to choose and will be given to you in the document file.

a. Open the program titled ispDesignEXPERT to start the program. This will open the ispDesign-EXPERT Project Navigator screen.

b. Under the File menu, select New Project. This will open a new window titled "Create New Project". Choose a name for your project with

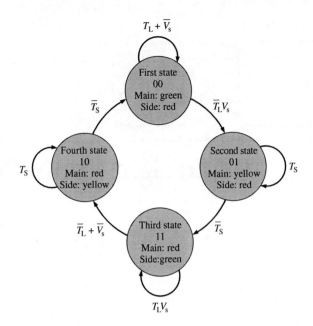

FIGURE 1
State diagram.

the default extension of .syn. On the line labeled Project Type, choose Schematic/ABEL from the dropdown list. Then click $\boxed{\text{Sav}}$.

c. Select the Source menu; click New and select the ABEL-HDL module. Give the module a name. For this example, the module name is *traffic*. This will be the name assigned to the document file. Use the same name for the file name. The Title block can be added as Traffic Light Control System. When you have assigned these names, press $\boxed{\text{OK}}$; the "Text Editor" window will open automatically.

d. Type the source file into the text editor exactly as shown in Figure 2. Save the file; then close the Text Editor window. (Exception: the open quotation mark ["] by itself indicates the beginning of a comment to clarify the listing. Comments are ignored by the ABEL compiler and may be omitted).

e. On the left side of the Project Navigator window, double-click on the part number ispLS15256VE-165LF256. This will open a new window called "Device Selector". The Device Family should default to a GAL. Under Device:, scroll down to GAL16V8D and select it. (*Note: the D suffix indicates a DIP configuration*). Under Part name:, choose a GAL16V8-15QP. Under Package:, select 20PDIP. Then click $\boxed{\text{OK}}$.

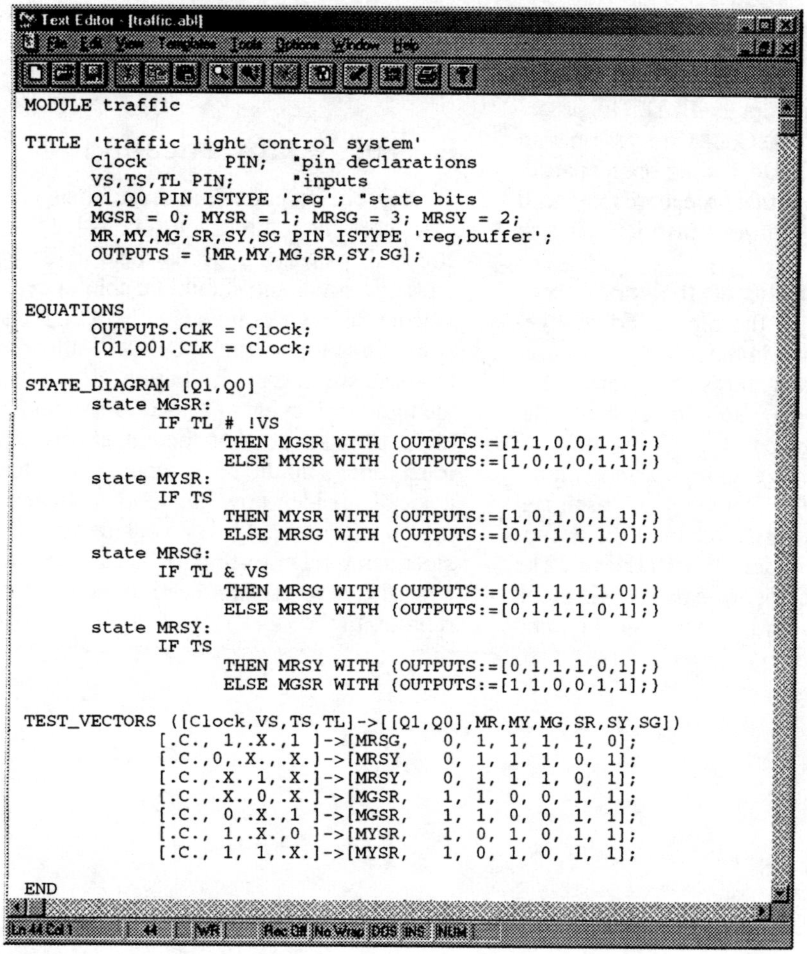

```
Text Editor - [traffic.abl]
File Edit View Templates Tools Options Window Help

MODULE traffic

TITLE 'traffic light control system'
        Clock        PIN;    "pin declarations
        VS,TS,TL PIN;        "inputs
        Q1,Q0 PIN ISTYPE 'reg'; "state bits
        MGSR = 0; MYSR = 1; MRSG = 3; MRSY = 2;
        MR,MY,MG,SR,SY,SG PIN ISTYPE 'reg,buffer';
        OUTPUTS = [MR,MY,MG,SR,SY,SG];


EQUATIONS
        OUTPUTS.CLK = Clock;
        [Q1,Q0].CLK = Clock;

STATE_DIAGRAM [Q1,Q0]
        state MGSR:
            IF TL # !VS
                THEN MGSR WITH {OUTPUTS:=[1,1,0,0,1,1];}
                ELSE MYSR WITH {OUTPUTS:=[1,0,1,0,1,1];}
        state MYSR:
            IF TS
                THEN MYSR WITH {OUTPUTS:=[1,0,1,0,1,1];}
                ELSE MRSG WITH {OUTPUTS:=[0,1,1,1,1,0];}
        state MRSG:
            IF TL & VS
                THEN MRSG WITH {OUTPUTS:=[0,1,1,1,1,0];}
                ELSE MRSY WITH {OUTPUTS:=[0,1,1,1,0,1];}
        state MRSY:
            IF TS
                THEN MRSY WITH {OUTPUTS:=[0,1,1,1,0,1];}
                ELSE MGSR WITH {OUTPUTS:=[1,1,0,0,1,1];}

TEST_VECTORS ([Clock,VS,TS,TL]->[[Q1,Q0],MR,MY,MG,SR,SY,SG])
        [.C., 1,.X.,1 ]->[MRSG,  0, 1, 1, 1, 1, 0];
        [.C.,0,.X.,.X.]->[MRSY,  0, 1, 1, 1, 0, 1];
        [.C.,.X.,1,.X.]->[MRSY,  0, 1, 1, 1, 0, 1];
        [.C.,.X.,0,.X.]->[MGSR,  1, 1, 0, 0, 1, 1];
        [.C., 0,.X.,1 ]->[MGSR,  1, 1, 0, 0, 1, 1];
        [.C., 1,.X.,0 ]->[MYSR,  1, 0, 1, 0, 1, 1];
        [.C., 1, 1,.X.]->[MYSR,  1, 0, 1, 0, 1, 1];

END

Ln 44 Col 1        44      WR      Rec Off No Wrap DOS INS NUM
```

FIGURE 2

f. You will see the ispLS15256VE-165LF256 device has been replaced by the GAL16V8-15QP. You will be asked to confirm the change. Select Yes.

g. Highlight the .abl file on the left side of the Project Navigator window. Then highlight Compile Logic on the right side of this window. With the Compile Logic highlighted, click the Properties button on the lower right. In the menu that appears, select ABEL Compatibility. Double-click this item until it shows "Implied Logic"; then close the window.

h. In the right-hand window of the Project Navigator box, click the ○ Compile Logic (top) menu item. The compilation should proceed. If successful, a green check mark will appear to the left of the ○ Compile Logic item. If not successful, you will need to correct the error before proceeding.

i. Continue down the list of items in the right-hand window of the Project Navigator. You should get a green check mark for each item listed. If not, stop and correct the problem before proceeding.

j. Go to the left window of the Project Navigator and select the vector file traffic-vectors. Double-click the processes listed on the right side except skip the Functional Simulation, the JEDEC Simulation Waveform, and the Timing Simulation.

k. Select GAL16V8D-15QP in the left side of the Project Navigator window. You can select and print any report that you want from the right-hand window. The Chip Report will contain a diagram of the assigned pins for the PLD. At this point, you will have the JEDEC file on the hard disk, which you use to program the PLD.

487

Part 2: Programming the PLD and Constructing the Circuit

2. You can now program the PLD. The procedure for this was given in the Code Conversion with a PLD Experiment, Part 3. Depending on the particular programmer you have, that procedure may need to be modified; check with your instructor if you aren't sure.

3. A partial schematic of the traffic controller circuit is shown in the report. For convenience, the pins are shown in the actual configuration of the ICs. Notice how the timers are triggered. The trigger signals come from the named outputs of the PLD. Complete the schematic by showing where all inputs and outputs are connected to the PLD, showing the assigned pins. The CLOCK input signal for the PLD is supplied by a pulse generator set for a TTL level. The frequency of the clock is not critical; a 1 kHz clock is fine. You will need to find the values for C_1 and C_2 for the timers based on the equations given on the data sheet for the 74121. Summarize your results in the report.

For Further Investigation

Oh no! The requirements have changed! A pedestrian crossing button must be added to the side street. A pedestrian needs the full 25 seconds to cross the street and should be able to cycle the light whether or not a vehicle is present on the side street. A modification of the circuit will allow you to add this pedestrian crossing button. When it is pressed, the lights will cycle to the side street and only return to the main street when the longer timer expires; the long timer should be extended *only* for the next cycle. Consider how to do this, then show your design in the report. Try your design! (*Hint:* Consider using a D flip-flop to "latch" the presence of a pedestrian. You do not need to modify the timers or reprogram the PLD!)

Report for "Traffic Light Controller with a PLD" Experiment

Name: _____ Date: _____ Class: _____

Objectives:

☐ Using ABEL software, enter the input source listing for a sequential traffic light controller circuit and compile the file.

☐ Using a PLD programmer, program a PLD for the traffic light problem in the first objective.

☐ Complete the schematic for the circuit; then construct and test it.

Data and Observations:

Schematic of Traffic Controller

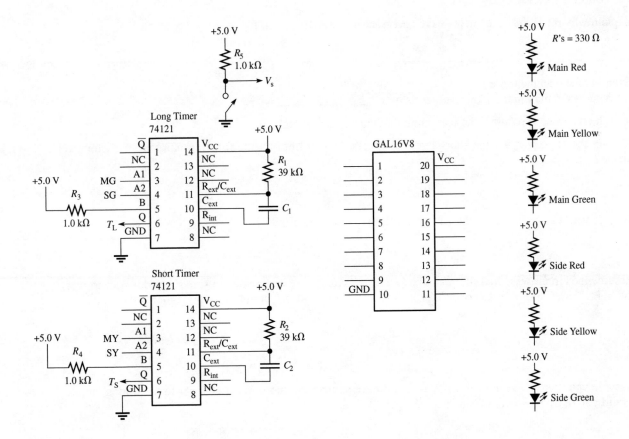

Results and Conclusion:

Further Investigation Results:

Evaluation and Review Questions

1. Explain why the WITH statements were necessary in the ABEL input file.

2. Examine the document file.
   a. What is the maximum number of terms used? _____
   b. Which output(s) required the maximum number? _____

3. Explain the triggering for the short and long timers. Which lines on the function table are used for the timers?

4. Why doesn't the frequency of the CLOCK affect the circuit operation?

5. Assume the circuit was "locked up" in the first state (MGSR). A vehicle on the side street does not trigger the light. Name at least three possible problems with the circuit that could cause this other than a bad IC.

6. Assume you didn't have any 74121 ICs but did have some 555 timers. What changes to the timing circuit would you make to accommodate the 555 timers?

Name:_____

Date:_____

Course and Section:_____

Instructor:_____

Methods of Analysis

OBJECTIVES

1. Validate the branch-current-analysis technique through experimental measurements.
2. Test the mesh- (loop-) analysis approach with experimental measurements.
3. Demonstrate the validity of the nodal-analysis technique through experimental measurements.

EQUIPMENT REQUIRED

Resistors

1—1.0-kΩ, 1.2-kΩ (1/4-W)

2—2.2-kΩ, 3.3-kΩ (1/4-W)

Instruments

1—DMM

2*—dc Power supplies

---

*The unavailability of two supplies will simply mean that two groups must work together.

EQUIPMENT ISSUED

RÉSUMÉ OF THEORY

The branch-, mesh-, and nodal-analysis techniques are used to solve complex networks with a single source or networks with more than one source that are not in series or parallel.

The branch- and mesh-analysis techniques will determine the currents of the network, while the nodal-analysis approach will provide the potential levels of the nodes of the network with respect to some reference.

The application of each technique follows a sequence of steps, each of which will result in a set of equations with the desired unknowns. It is then only a matter of solving these equations for the various variables, whether they be current or voltage.

PROCEDURE

Part 1   Branch-current Analysis

(a)   Construct the network of Fig. 1 and insert the measured values of the resistors in the spaces provided.

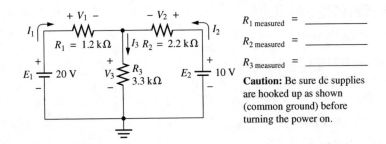

$R_{1\text{ measured}}$ = _____

$R_{2\text{ measured}}$ = _____

$R_{3\text{ measured}}$ = _____

Caution: Be sure dc supplies are hooked up as shown (common ground) before turning the power on.

FIG. 1

(b)   Using branch-current analysis, *calculate* the current through each branch of the network of Fig. 1 and insert in Table 2. Use the measured resistor values and assume the current directions shown in the figure. Show all your calculations in the space provided and be neat!

TABLE 2

Current	Calculated	Measured	% Difference
I_1			
I_2			
I_3			

(c) Measure the voltages V_1, V_2, and V_3 and enter below with a minus sign for any polarity that is opposite to that in Fig. 1.

$V_1 = $ _____ , $V_2 = $ _____ , $V_3 = $ _____

Calculate the currents I_1, I_2, and I_3 using the measured resistor values and insert in Table 2 as the measured values. Be sure to include a minus sign if the current direction is opposite to that appearing in Fig. 1. Show all work.

How do the calculated and measured results compare? Determine the percent difference for each current in Table 2 using the equation:

$$\% \text{ Difference} = \left| \frac{\text{Measured} - \text{Calculated}}{\text{Measured}} \right| \times 100\% \qquad \textbf{(1)}$$

Part 2   Mesh Analysis

(a)   Construct the network of Fig. 2 and insert the measured values of the resistors in the spaces provided.

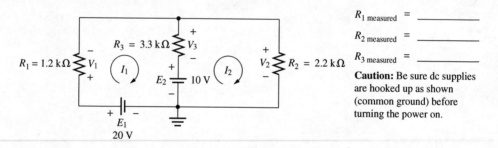

$R_{1 \text{ measured}}$ = _____

$R_{2 \text{ measured}}$ = _____

$R_{3 \text{ measured}}$ = _____

Caution: Be sure dc supplies are hooked up as shown (common ground) before turning the power on.

FIG. 2

(b)   Using mesh analysis, *calculate* the mesh currents I_1 and I_2 of the network. Use the measured resistor values and the indicated directions for the mesh currents. Then determine the current through each resistor and insert in Table 3 in the "Calculated" column. Include all your calculations and organize your work.

Mesh currents (calculated): $I_1 = \underline{\hspace{2cm}}$
$I_2 = \underline{\hspace{2cm}}$

TABLE 3

Current	Calculated	Measured	% Difference
$I_{R_1} = I_1$			
$I_{R_2} = I_2$			
$I_{R_3} = I_1 - I_2$			

(c) Measure the voltages V_1, V_2, and V_3 and enter here with a minus sign for any polarity that is opposite to that in Fig. 2.

$V_1 = \underline{\hspace{2cm}}$, $V_2 = \underline{\hspace{2cm}}$, $V_3 = \underline{\hspace{2cm}}$

Calculate the currents I_{R_1}, I_{R_2}, and I_{R_3} using the measured voltage and resistor values and insert in Table 3 as the measured values. Be sure to include a minus sign if the current direction is opposite to that defined by the polarity of the voltage across the resistor.

How do the calculated and measured results compare? Determine the percent difference for each current of Table 3.

Part 3　Nodal Analysis

(a) Construct the network of Fig. 3 and insert the measured resistor values.

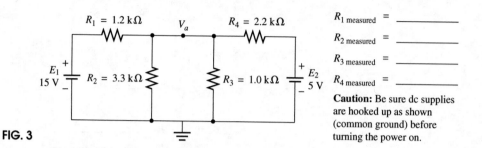

R_1 measured = _____

R_2 measured = _____

R_3 measured = _____

R_4 measured = _____

Caution: Be sure dc supplies are hooked up as shown (common ground) before turning the power on.

FIG. 3

Calculations:

(b) Using measured resistor values, determine V_a using nodal analysis. Show all work and be neat!

V_a (calculated) = _____

496

    (c) Using V_a, calculate the currents I_{R_1} and I_{R_3} using measured resistor values and insert in Table 4.

TABLE 4

Current	Calculated	Measured	% Difference
I_{R_1}			
I_{R_3}			

Measurements:

    (d) Energize the network and measure the voltage V_a. Compare with the result of part 3(b).

        V_a(measured) = _____

    (e) Using V_a(measured), calculate the currents I_{R_1} and I_{R_3} using measured resistor values and insert in Table 4 as the measured results.

(f) How do the calculated and measured results for I_{R_1} and I_{R_3} compare? Determine the percent differences for each current in Table 4.

Part 4 Bridge Network

(a) Construct the network of Fig. 4. Insert the measured resistor values.

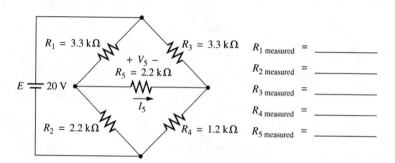

R_1 measured $=$ _____

R_2 measured $=$ _____

R_3 measured $=$ _____

R_4 measured $=$ _____

R_5 measured $=$ _____

FIG. 4

(b) Using any one of the three techniques examined in this experiment, calculate the voltage V_5 and the current I_5. Use the measured resistor values.

V_5(calculated) $=$ _____, I_5(calculated) $=$ _____

(c) Measure the voltage V_5 and insert below with a minus sign if the polarity is different from that appearing in Fig. 4.

V_5(measured) = _____

(d) Calculate the percent difference between the two values of V_5.

% Difference = _____

(e) Calculate the current I_5 using the measured value of V_5 and the measured value of the resistor R_5.

I_5(measured) = _____

How does the measured value of I_5 compare with the calculated value of part 4(b)? Determine the percent difference.

% Difference = _____

QUESTION

Many times one is faced with the question of which method to use in a particular problem. The laboratory activity does not prepare one to make such choices but only shows that the methods work and are solid. From your experience in this activity, summarize in your own words which method you prefer and why you chose the method you did for the analysis of part 4.

The Superposition Theorem

Name _____
Date _____
Class _____

OBJECTIVES
After performing this experiment, you will be able to:
1.   Apply the superposition theorem to linear circuits with more than one voltage source.
2.   Construct a circuit with two voltage sources, solve for the currents and voltages throughout the circuit, and verify your computation by measurement.

MATERIALS NEEDED
Resistors:
    One 4.7 kΩ, one 6.8 kΩ, one 10.0 kΩ

SUMMARY OF THEORY
To superimpose something means to lay one thing on top of another. The superposition theorem is a means by which we can solve circuits that have more than one independent voltage source. Each source is taken, one at a time, as if it were the only source in the circuit. All other sources are replaced with their internal resistance. (The internal resistance of a dc power supply or battery can be considered to be zero.) The currents and voltages for the first source are computed. The results are marked on the schematic, and the process is repeated for each source in the circuit. When all sources have been taken, the overall circuit can be solved. The algebraic sum of the superimposed currents and voltages is computed. Currents that are in the same direction are added; those that are in opposing directions are subtracted with the sign of the larger applied to the result. Voltages are treated in a like manner.

    The superposition theorem will work for any number of sources *as long as you are consistent in accounting for the direction of currents and the polarity of voltages.* One way to keep the accounting straightforward is to assign a polarity, right or wrong, to each component. Tabulate any current which is in the same direction as the assignment as a positive current and any current which opposes the assigned direction as a negative current. When the final algebraic sum is completed, positive currents are in the assigned direction; negative currents are in the opposite direction of the assignment. In the process of replacing a voltage source with its zero internal resistance, you may completely short out a resistor in the circuit. If this occurs, there will be no current in that resistor for this part of the calculation. The final sum will still have the correct current.

PROCEDURE

1. Obtain the resistors listed in Table 1. Measure each resistor and record the measured value in Table 1.

2. Construct the circuit shown in Figure 1. This circuit has two voltage sources connected to a common reference ground.

Table 1

	Listed Value	Measured Value
R_1	4.7 kΩ	
R_2	6.8 kΩ	
R_3	10.0 kΩ	

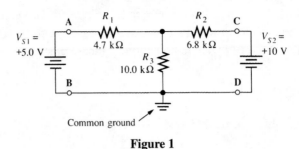

Figure 1

3. Remove the 10 V source and place a jumper between the points labeled **C** and **D,** as shown in Figure 2. This jumper represents the internal resistance of the 10 V power supply.

Figure 2

4. Compute the total resistance, R_T, seen by the +5.0 V source. Then temporarily remove the +5.0 V source and measure the resistance between points **A** and **B** to confirm your calculation. Record the computed and measured values in Table 2.

Table 2 Computed and measured resistances.

	Quantity	Computed	Measured
Step 4	R_T (V_{S1} operating alone)		
Step 7	R_T (V_{S2} operating alone)		

5. Use the source voltage, V_{S1}, and the total resistance to compute the total current, I_T, from the +5.0 V source. This current is through R_1, so record it as I_1 in Table 3. Use the current divider rule to determine the currents in R_2 and R_3. The current divider rule for I_2 and I_3 is:

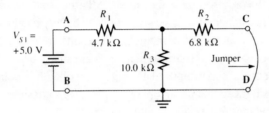

$$I_2 = I_T\left(\frac{R_3}{R_2 + R_3}\right) \qquad I_3 = I_T\left(\frac{R_2}{R_2 + R_3}\right)$$

Table 3 Computed and measured current and voltage.

	Computed Current			Computed Voltage			Measured Voltage		
	I_1	I_2	I_3	V_1	V_2	V_3	V_1	V_2	V_3
Step 5									
Step 6									
Step 8									
Step 9									
Step 10 (totals)									

Record all three currents as *positive* values in Table 3. This will be the assigned direction of current. Mark the magnitude and direction of the current in Figure 2. Note that the current divider rules shown in this step are only valid for this particular circuit.

6. Use the currents computed in step 5 and the measured resistances to calculate the expected voltage across each resistor of Figure 2. Then connect the +5.0 V power supply and measure the actual voltages present in this circuit. Record the computed and measured voltages in Table 3. Since all currents in step 5 were considered *positive,* all voltages in this step are also *positive.*

7. Remove the +5.0 V source from the circuit and move the jumper from between points **C** and **D** to between points **A** and **B.** Compute the total resistance between points **C** and **D.** Measure the resistance to confirm your calculation. Record the computed and measured resistance in Table 2.

8. Compute the current through each resistor in Figure 3. Note that this time the total current is through R_2 and divides between R_1 and R_3. Mark the magnitude and direction of the current on Figure 3. *Important:* Record the current as a *positive* current if it is in the same direction as recorded in step 5 and as a *negative* current if it is in the opposite direction as in step 4. Record the computed currents in Table 3.

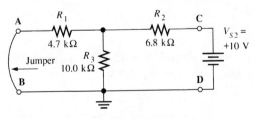

Figure 3

9. Use the currents computed in step 8 and the measured resistances to compute the voltage drops across each resistor. Record the computed voltage drops in Table 3. If the current through a resistor was a *positive* current, record the resistor's voltage as a *positive* voltage. If a current was a *negative* current, record the voltage as a *negative* voltage. Then connect the +10 V source as illustrated in Figure 3, measure, and record the voltages. The measured voltages should confirm your calculation.

10. Compute the algebraic sum of the currents and voltages listed in Table 3. Enter the computed sums in Table 3. Then replace the jumper between **A** and **B** with the +5.0 V source, as shown in the original circuit in Figure 1. Measure the voltage across each resistor in this circuit. The measured voltages should agree with the algebraic sums. Record the measured results in Table 3.

CONCLUSION

EVALUATION AND REVIEW QUESTIONS

1.   (a)   Prove that Kirchhoff's voltage law is valid for the circuit in Figure 1. Do this by substituting the measured algebraic sums from Table 3 into a loop equation written around the outside loop of the circuit.

       (b)   Prove Kirchhoff's current law is valid for the circuit of Figure 1 by writing an equation showing the currents entering a junction are equal to the currents leaving the junction. Keep the assigned direction of current from step 5 and use the signed currents computed in step 10.

2.   If an algebraic sum in Table 3 is negative, what does this indicate?

3.   What would be the effect on the final result if you had been directed to record all currents in step 5 as negative currents instead of positive currents?

4. In your own words, list the steps required to apply the superposition theorem.

5. Use the superposition theorem to find the current in R_2 in Figure 4.

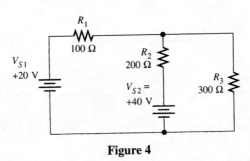

Figure 4

FOR FURTHER INVESTIGATION
Compute the power dissipated in each resistor in the circuits shown in Figures 1, 2, and 3. Using the computed results, find out if the superposition theorem is valid for power. Summarize your computations and conclusion.

MULTISIM TROUBLESHOOTING

This experiment has four Multisim files on the CD. Three of the four files contain a simulated "fault"; one has "no fault". The file with no fault is named EXP11-1-nf.msm. You may want to open this file to compare your results with the computer simulation. Then open each of the files with faults. Use the simulated instruments to investigate the circuit and determine the problem. The following are the filenames for circuits with troubleshooting problems for this experiment.

EXP11-1-f1.msm
    Fault: _____

EXP11-1-f2.msm
    Fault: _____

EXP11-1-f3.msm
    Fault: _____

Name: _____

Date: _____

Course and Section: _____

Instructor: _____

Thevenin's Theorem and Maximum Power Transfer

OBJECTIVES

1. Verify Thevenin's theorem through experimental measurements.
2. Become acutely aware of the differences between applying Thevenin's theorem to an ac network as compared to a dc system.
3. Demonstrate the validity of the conditions for maximum power transfer in an ac network.

EQUIPMENT REQUIRED

Resistors

1—10-Ω, 470-Ω, 1-kΩ, 1.2-kΩ, 2.2-kΩ, 3.3-kΩ, 6.8-kΩ (1/4-W)

1—0–1-kΩ potentiometer

Capacitors

1—0.0047-μF, 0.01-μF, 0.02-μF, 0.047-μF, 0.1-μF, 1-μF

2—0.02-μF

Inductors

1—10-mH

Instruments

1—DMM

1—Oscilloscope

1—Audio oscillator or function generator

1—Frequency counter (if available)

EQUIPMENT ISSUED

TABLE 1

Item	Manufacturer and Model No.	Laboratory Serial No.
DMM		
Oscilloscope		
Audio oscillator or function generator		
Frequency counter		

RÉSUMÉ OF THEORY

Thevenin's theorem states that any two-terminal linear ac network can be replaced by an equivalent circuit consisting of a voltage source in series with an impedance. To apply this theorem, follow these simple steps:

1. Remove the portion of the network across which the Thevenin equivalent circuit is found.
2. Replace all voltage sources by a short-circuit equivalent and all current sources by an open-circuit equivalent.
3. Calculate Z_{Th} across the two terminals in question.
4. Replace all sources.
5. Calculate E_{Th}, which is the voltage across the terminals in question.
6. Draw the Thevenin equivalent circuit and replace the portion of the circuit originally removed.
7. Solve for the voltage or current originally desired.

EXAMPLE   Using Thevenin's theorem, find the current through R in Fig. 1.

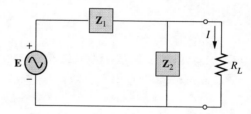

FIG. 1

Solution

Step 1:   Remove R. See Fig. 2(a).
Step 2:   Replace E by a short-circuit equivalent. See Fig. 2(a).
Step 3:   Solve for Z_{Th}. In this case, $Z_{Th} = Z_1 \| Z_2$. See Fig. 2(a).
Step 4:   Replace E. See Fig. 2(b).
Step 5:   Calculate E_{Th} from

$$E_{Th} = \frac{Z_2}{Z_1 + Z_2} E$$

See Fig. 2(b).

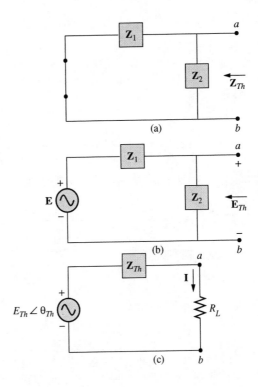

FIG. 2

Step 6: Draw the equivalent circuit and replace R. See Fig. 2(c).

Step 7: Calculate **I** from

$$\mathbf{I} = \frac{\mathbf{E}_{Th}}{\mathbf{Z}_{Th} + \mathbf{Z}_{R_L}}$$

MAXIMUM POWER TRANSFER THEOREM

The maximum power transfer theorem states that for circuits with ac sources, maximum power will be transferred to a load when the load impedance is the conjugate of the Thevenin impedance across its terminals. See Fig. 3.

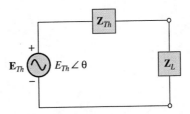

FIG. 3

For maximum power transfer, if

$$\mathbf{Z}_{Th} = |\mathbf{Z}_{Th}| \angle\theta$$

then

$$\mathbf{Z}_L = |\mathbf{Z}_{Th}| \angle-\theta$$

PROCEDURE
Part 1

(a) Construct the network of Fig. 4. Insert the measured values of R_L, R_1, and R_2 in Fig. 4.

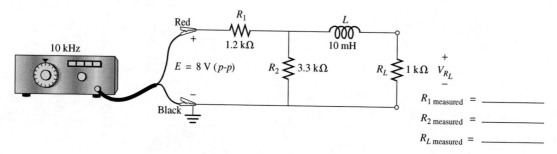

$R_{1 \text{ measured}}$ = _____

$R_{2 \text{ measured}}$ = _____

$R_{L \text{ measured}}$ = _____

FIG. 4

(b) With E set at 8 V (p-p), measure $V_{R_{L(p-p)}}$ with the oscilloscope.

$V_{R_{L(p-p)}}$ = _____

(c) Remove the resistor R_L and measure the open-circuit voltage across the resulting terminals with the oscilloscope. This is the magnitude of $\mathbf{E}_{Th}$.

$|\mathbf{E}_{Th}|_{p-p}$ = _____

(d) Using the measured resistance levels, calculate the magnitude of $\mathbf{E}_{Th}$ and its associated angle. Assume that $\mathbf{E} = E \angle 0° = 8$ V (p-p) $\angle 0°$. Show all work! Organize your presentation.

$\mathbf{E}_{Th}$ = _____

How does the magnitude of the calculated value compare with the measured value of part 1(c)?

(e) Calculate $\mathbf{Z}_{Th}$ (magnitude and angle) using the measured resistor values and the nameplate inductor level of 10 mH. The applied frequency is 10 kHz.

$\mathbf{Z}_{Th} = $ _____

Determine the resistive and reactive components of $\mathbf{Z}_{Th}$ by converting $\mathbf{Z}_{Th}$ to rectangular form.

$R = $ _____ , $X_L = $ _____

(f) Insert the measured value of $E_{Th(p-p)}$ from part 1(c) in Fig. 5. Set the 1-kΩ potentiometer R of Fig. 5 to the value calculated in part 1(e). Use 10 mH for the inductor, since X_L of part 1(e) is defined solely by the inductor of Fig. 4. The Thevenin equivalent circuit for the network to the left of the resistor R_L of Fig. 4 has now been established in Fig. 5. Turn on the supply, set to the indicated value, and measure the peak-to-peak level of the voltage across the resistor R_L with the oscilloscope.

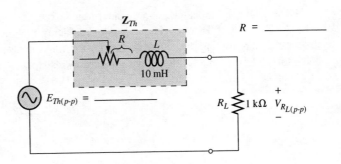

FIG. 5

$V_{RL(p-p)} = $ _____

How does this value compare with the measured level of part 1(b) for the original network? Has the equivalence of the Thevenin circuit been verified?

(g) Change R_L in Fig. 5 to a 6.8-kΩ resistor and calculate the resulting voltage across the new resistance level.

$$V_{R_{L(p-p)}} = \underline{\hspace{3cm}}$$

Change R_L in Fig. 5 to 6.8 kΩ and measure the resulting voltage across the new resistance level using the oscilloscope.

$$V_{R_{L(p-p)}} = \underline{\hspace{3cm}}$$

How do the two levels of $V_{R_{L(p-p)}}$ compare?

Do the preceding measurements verify the fact that the Thevenin equivalent circuit is valid for any level of R_L?

Part 2   Determining Z_{Th} Experimentally

The Thevenin impedance can be determined experimentally following the procedure outlined in the Résumé of Theory. The process of replacing the source by a short-circuit equivalent is the same as removing the source and reconstructing the network, as shown in Fig. 6. By applying a source to the load terminals with a sensing resistor, the magnitude of the Thevenin impedance can be determined from

$$|Z_{Th}| = \frac{E_{p-p}}{I_{p-p}} \tag{1}$$

with

$$I_{p-p} = \frac{V_{R_{s(p-p)}}}{R_{s(measured)}}$$

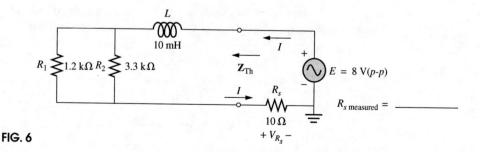

FIG. 6

512

The angle associated with the Thevenin impedance can be determined by finding the phase angle between $\mathbf{E}$ and $\mathbf{I}$ (same phase angle as $\mathbf{V}_{R_s}$) using the oscilloscope.

(a) Construct the network of Fig. 6. Insert the measured value of R_s.

(b) Set E to 8 V (p-p) with the oscilloscope and measure the voltage V_{R_s} with the oscilloscope.

$$V_{R_{s(p\text{-}p)}} = \underline{\hspace{2in}}$$

Calculate the peak-to-peak value of the current I using Ohm's law.

$$I_{p\text{-}p} = \underline{\hspace{2in}}$$

Determine the magnitude of Z_{Th} using Eq. (1) and ignoring the effects of R_s.

$$Z_{Th} = \underline{\hspace{2in}}$$

(c) Determine the phase angle between $\mathbf{E}$ and $\mathbf{V}_{R_s}$ (same as $\mathbf{I}$) using the oscilloscope. Show all calculations. The angle between $\mathbf{E}$ and $\mathbf{I}$ is the same one associated with the Thevenin impedance.

$$D_1 = \underline{\hspace{1.5in}}, D_2 = \underline{\hspace{1.5in}}$$

$$\theta = \underline{\hspace{1.5in}}$$

(d) Using the results of parts 2(b) and 2(c), write the Thevenin impedance in polar form.

$$\mathbf{Z}_{Th} = \underline{\hspace{1.5in}}$$

Convert to the rectangular form to define the levels of R and X_L.

$$R = \underline{\hspace{1.5in}}, X_L = \underline{\hspace{1.5in}}$$

(e) How do the levels of R and X_L determined here compare with those of part 1(e)?

Part 3   Maximum Power Transfer

(a) Construct the circuit of Fig. 7. Include the measured resistor values.

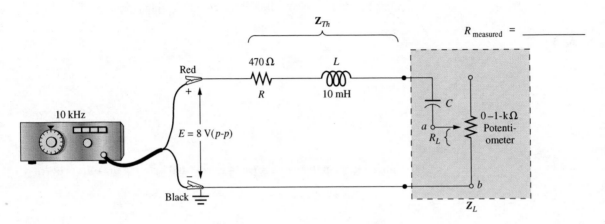

FIG. 7

(b) Set the 0–1-kΩ potentiometer to $R_L = R_{\text{measured}}$, as required for maximum power transfer. Place this value in each row of Table 2.

$$R_L = R_{\text{measured}} = \underline{\hspace{3cm}}$$

TABLE 2

R_L	X_L	$|Z_{Th}|$	$C*$	X_C	$|Z_L|$	$V_{ab(p\text{-}p)}$	$P_L = (V_{ab(p\text{-}p)})^2/8R_L$
			0.0047 μF				
			0.01 μF				
			0.0147 μF				
			0.0247 μF				
			0.047 μF				
			0.1 μF				
			1 μF				

$C*$: some capacitance levels are the result of placing the given capacitors in parallel.

(c) For $f = 10$ kHz, calculate X_L and insert (the same value) in each row of Table 2.

(d) Using the results of parts 2(b) and 2(c), calculate the magnitude of the Thevenin impedance Z_{Th} and insert (the same value) in each row of Table 2.

(e) For each value of C, calculate X_C at $f = 10$ kHz and insert in Table 2.

514

(f) Calculate the magnitude of $\mathbf{Z}_L$ with $R_L = R_{measured}$ and insert in each row of Table 2.

(g) Energize the network and, for each capacitance value, measure the peak-to-peak value of V_{ab} with the oscilloscope and insert in Table 2. (Note that 0.0247 μF = 0.02 μF + 0.0047 μF.) To save time, use the dual-trace capability of your oscilloscope to measure $V_{ab(p\text{-}p)}$ and maintain E at 8 V $(p\text{-}p)$.

(h) Calculate the power delivered to the load using $P_L = (V_{ab(p\text{-}p)})^2/8R_L$ derived from

$$P_L = \frac{V_{ab(\text{rms})}{}^2}{R_L} = \frac{\left(\frac{1}{\sqrt{2}}\left(\frac{V_{ab(p\text{-}p)}}{2}\right)\right)^2}{R_L} = \frac{\left(\frac{V_{ab(p\text{-}p)}{}^2}{8}\right)}{R_L} = \frac{(V_{ab(p\text{-}p)})^2}{8R_L} \tag{2}$$

(i) Plot P_L versus X_C on Graph 1. Finish off the plot as well as you can with the data you have.

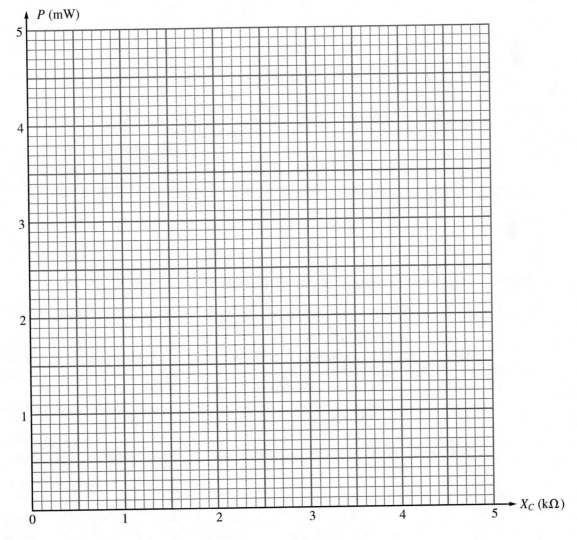

GRAPH 1

(j) Using Graph 1, determine X_C when the power to the load is a maximum. How does it compare to the level of X_L of the second column of Table 2?

$X_C =$ _____

(k) Maximum power transfer requires that $X_C = X_L$. Has this condition been verified by the experimental data?

The theory also requires that $|Z_L| = |Z_{Th}|$ for maximum power transfer to the load. Has this condition also been met when P_L is a maximum?

(l) Assuming that L is exactly 10 mH, what value of capacitance will ensure that $X_C = X_L$ at $f = 10$ kHz? How close do we come to this value in Table 2?

$C =$ _____

Part 4 Maximum Power Transfer (The Resistive Component)

(a) Reconstruct the network of Fig. 7 with C set to the value that resulted in maximum power transfer in part 2. Record the value of C to be used in Table 3.

(b) In this part of the experiment we will determine whether maximum power to the load is, in fact, delivered when $R_L = R_{Th}$ by varying the load resistance. Set R_L to the values listed in Table 3 and measure the voltage $V_{ab(p-p)}$ with the oscilloscope. For each row of Table 3, insert $V_{ab(p-p)}$ and calculate the power to the load.

(c) Plot P_L versus R_L on Graph 2, clearly indicating each plot point and labeling the curve. Finish off the curve as well as you can with the data you have.

(d) At what value (using Graph 2) of R_L is maximum power delivered to the load? How does this value compare to the total resistance $R_T = R$? Should they be close in value?

R_L (Graph 2) = _____ , $R_T = R_{measured} =$ _____

THEVENIN'S THEOREM AND MAXIMUM POWER TRANSFER

TABLE 3 $C =$ _____

R_L	$V_{ab(p\text{-}p)}$	$P_L = V_{ab(p\text{-}p)}^2/8R_L$
100 Ω		
300 Ω		
400 Ω		
500 Ω		
600 Ω		
800 Ω		
1000 Ω		
$R_L = R_{Th} =$ _____		

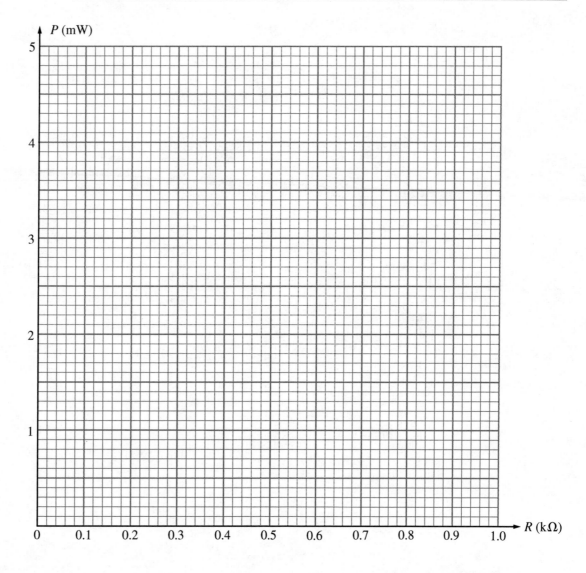

GRAPH 2

Name:_____

Date:_____

Course and Section:_____

Instructor:_____

Thevenin's Theorem and Maximum Power Transfer

OBJECTIVES

1. **Validate Thevenin's theorem through experimental measurements.**
2. **Become aware of an experimental procedure to determine E_{Th} and R_{Th}.**
3. **Demonstrate that maximum power transfer to a load is defined by the condition $R_L = R_{Th}$.**

EQUIPMENT REQUIRED

Resistors

1—91-Ω, 220-Ω, 330-Ω, 470-Ω, 1-kΩ, 2.2-kΩ, 3.3-kΩ (1/4-W)

1—0–1-kΩ potentiometer, 0–10-kΩ potentiometer

Instruments

1—DMM

1—dc Power supply

EQUIPMENT ISSUED

RÉSUMÉ OF THEORY

Through the use of Thevenin's theorem, a complex two-terminal, linear, multisource dc network can be replaced by one having a single source and resistor.

The Thevenin equivalent circuit consists of a single dc source referred to as the *Thevenin voltage* and a single fixed resistor called the *Thevenin resistance*. The Thevenin voltage is the open-circuit voltage across the terminals in question (Fig. 1). The Thevenin resistance is the resistance between these terminals with all of the voltage and current sources replaced by their internal resistances (Fig. 1).

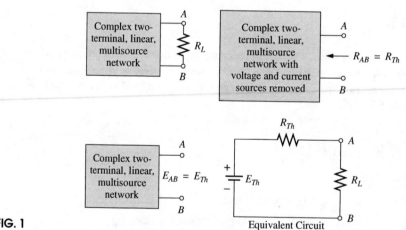

FIG. 1

Equivalent Circuit

If a dc voltage source is to deliver maximum power to a resistor, the resistor must have a value equal to the internal resistance of the source. In a complex network, maximum power transfer to a load will occur when the load resistance is equal to the Thevenin resistance "seen" by the load. For this value, the voltage across the load will be one-half of the Thevenin voltage. In equation form,

$$R_L = R_{Th}, \qquad V_L = \frac{E_{Th}}{2}, \quad \text{and} \quad P_{\max} = \frac{E_{Th}^2}{4R_{Th}}$$

(1)

PROCEDURE

Part 1   Thevenin's Theorem

Calculations:

(a)   Construct the network of Fig. 2. Calculate the Thevenin voltage and resistance for the network to the left of points a–a' using measured resistor values. Show all work!

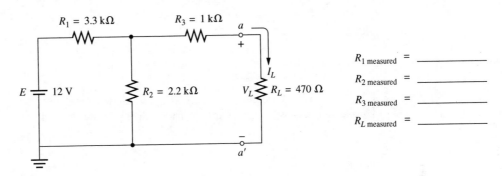

$R_{1\,measured}$ = _____

$R_{2\,measured}$ = _____

$R_{3\,measured}$ = _____

$R_{L\,measured}$ = _____

FIG. 2

E_{Th} = _____ , R_{Th} = _____. Enter these values in column 1 of Table 2.

TABLE 2

Calculated Values of E_{Th} and R_{Th} [Part 1(a)]	Measured Values of E_{Th} and R_{Th} [Parts 1(e) and 1(f)]	% Difference
E_{Th} = _____	E_{Th} = _____ [part 1(f)]	
R_{Th} = _____	R_{Th} = _____ [part 1(e)]	

(b) Insert the values of E_{Th} and R_{Th} in Fig. 3 and calculate I_L.

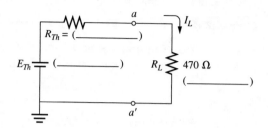

FIG. 3

$I_L = $ _____.

(c) Calculate the current I_L in the original network of Fig. 2 using series-parallel techniques (use measured resistor values). Show all work!

$I_L = $ _____.

How does this calculated value of I_L compare to the value of part 1(b)?

Measurements:

(d) Turn on the 12-V supply of Fig. 2 and measure the voltage V_L. Using the measured value of R_L, calculate the current I_L.

V_L(measured) = _____, I_L(calculated from V_L) = _____

How does this measured value of I_L compare with the calculated levels of parts 1(b) and 1(c)?

Determining R_{Th}:

(e) Determine R_{Th} by constructing the network of Fig. 4 and measuring the resistance between points a–a' with R_L removed.

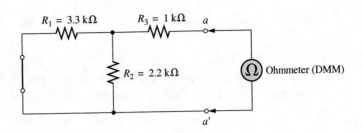

FIG. 4

$R_{Th} =$ _____. Enter this value in column 2 of Table 2.

Determining E_{Th}:

(f) Determine E_{Th} by constructing the network of Fig. 5 and measuring the open-circuit voltage between points a–a'.

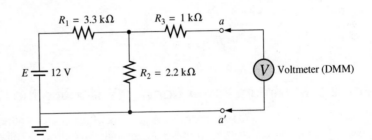

FIG. 5

E_{Th} (measured) = _____. Enter this value in column 2 of Table 2.

Thevenin Network:

(g) Construct the network of Fig. 6 and set the values obtained for the measured values of E_{Th} and R_{Th} in parts 1(e) and 1(f), respectively. Use the ohmmeter section of your meter to set the potentiometer properly. Then measure the voltage V_L and calculate the current I_L using the measured value of R_L.

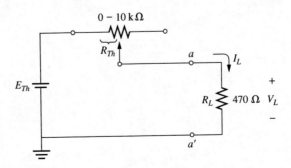

FIG. 6

V_L(measured) = _____, I_L(calculated from V_L) = _____

How does this value of I_L compare with the calculated level of part 1(b)?

How do the calculated and measured values of E_{Th} and R_{Th} compare? Insert the magnitude of the percent difference in the third column of Table 2 using the equations:

$$\% \text{ Difference} = \left| \frac{\text{Measured} - \text{Calculated}}{\text{Measured}} \right| \times 100\% \qquad (2)$$

Noting the overall results of Table 2, has Thevenin's theorem been verified?

Part 2 Maximum Power Transfer (Validating the Condition $R_L = R_{Th}$)

(a) Construct the network of Fig. 7 and set the potentiometer to 50 Ω. Measure the voltage across R_L as you vary R_L through the following values: 50, 100, 200, 300, 330, 400, 600, 800, and 1000 Ω. Be sure to set the resistance with the ohmmeter section of your meter before each reading. Remember to turn off the dc supply and disconnect one terminal of the potentiometer when setting the resistance level. Complete Table 3 and plot P_L versus R_L on Graph 1.

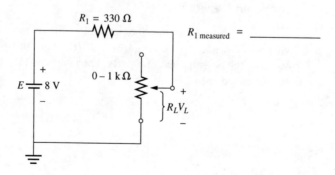

FIG. 7

TABLE 3

R_L	V_L	$P = \dfrac{V_L^2}{R_L}$ (mW)
0 Ω	0 V	0 mW
50 Ω		
100 Ω		
200 Ω		
300 Ω		
$R_{1_{measured}} =$ _____		
400 Ω		
600 Ω		
800 Ω		
1000 Ω		

(b) Theoretically, for the network of Fig. 7, what value of R_L should result in maximum power to R_L?

$R_L =$ _____

Referring to the plot of Graph 1, what value of R_L resulted in maximum power transfer to R_L?

$R_L =$ _____

How do the theoretical and measured values of R_L compare?

(c) Under maximum power transfer conditions, how are the voltages V_L and E related? Why?

Based on the preceding conclusion, determine V_L for maximum power transfer to R_L.

$V_L =$ _____

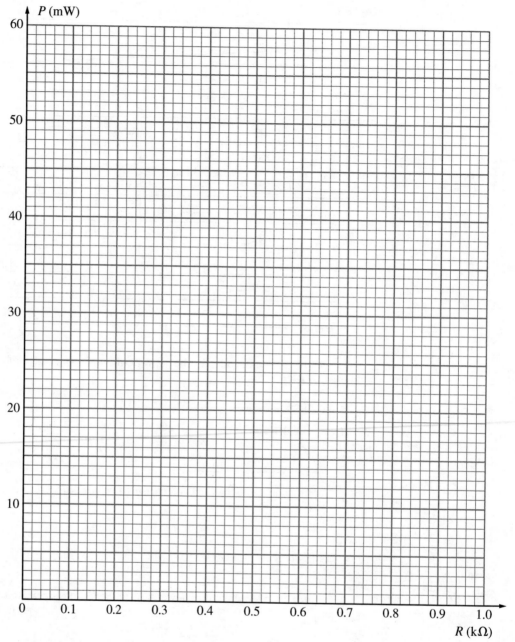

GRAPH 1

Set the potentiometer to the resistance R_L that resulted in maximum power transfer on Graph 1 and measure the resulting voltage across R_L.

$V_L = $ _____

How does the measured value compare to the expected theoretical level?

Part 3 Maximum Power Transfer (Experimental Approach)

(a) Construct the network of Fig. 8. Insert the measured value of each resistor.

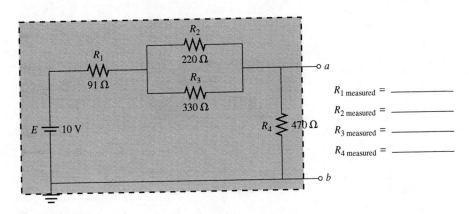

R_1 measured = —————

R_2 measured = —————

R_3 measured = —————

R_4 measured = —————

FIG. 8

(b) The Thevenin equivalent circuit will now be determined for the network to the left of the terminals a–b without disturbing the structure of the network. All the measurements will be made at the terminals a–b.

E_{Th}:

Determine E_{Th} by turning on the supply and measuring the open-circuit voltage V_{ab}.

$$E_{Th} = V_{ab} = \text{—————}$$

R_{Th}:

Introduce the 1-kΩ potentiometer to the network of Fig. 8, as shown in Fig. 9.

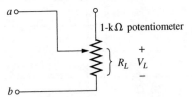

1-kΩ potentiometer

R_L V_L

FIG. 9

Turn on the supply and adjust the potentiometer until the voltage V_L is $E_{Th}/2$, a condition that must exist if $R_L = R_{Th}$. Then turn off the supply and remove the potentiometer from the network without disturbing the position of the wiper arm. Measure the resistance between the two terminals connected to a–b and record as R_{Th}.

$$R_{Th} = R_L = \text{—————}$$

527

(c) Now we need to check our measured results against a theoretical solution. Calculate R_{Th} and E_{Th} for the network to the left of terminals a–b of Fig. 8. Use measured resistor values.

$$R_{Th} = \underline{\hspace{3cm}}, E_{Th} = \underline{\hspace{3cm}}$$

How do the calculated and measured values compare?

(d) Let us now plot P_L and V_L versus R_L to confirm once more that the conditions for maximum power transfer to a load are that $R_L = R_{Th}$ and $V_L = E_{Th}/2$.

Leave the potentiometer as connected in Fig. 9 and measure V_L for all the values of R_L appearing in Table 4*. Then calculate the resulting power to the load and complete the table. Finally, plot both P_L and V_L versus R_L on Graphs 2 and 3, respectively.

TABLE 4

R_L	V_L(measured)	$P_L = V_L^2/R_L$ (calculated)
0 Ω	0 V	0 mW
25 Ω		
50 Ω		
100 Ω		
150 Ω		
200 Ω		
250 Ω		
300 Ω		
350 Ω		
400 Ω		
450 Ω		
500 Ω		

*Be sure to remove the potentiometer from the network when setting each value of R_L. At the very least, disconnect one side of the potentiometer when making the setting.

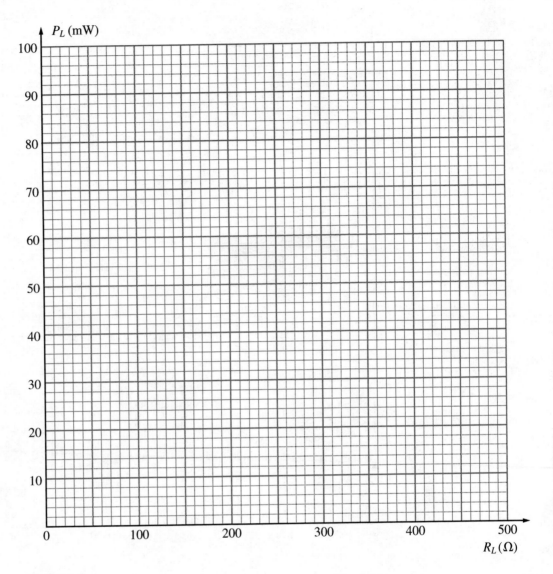

GRAPH 2

Reviewing Graph 2, did maximum power transfer to the load occur when $R_L = R_{Th}$? What conclusion can be drawn from the results?

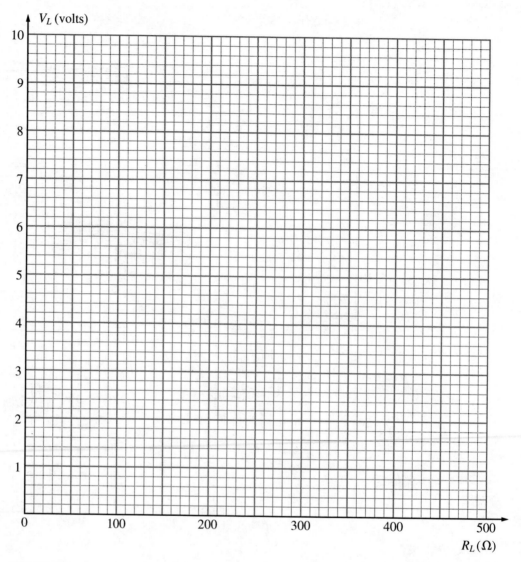

GRAPH 3

Noting Graph 3, does $V_L = E_{Th}/2$ when $R_L = R_{Th}$? Comment accordingly.

PROBLEMS

For the network of Fig. 10:

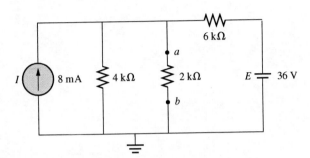

FIG. 10

(a) Determine R_{Th} and E_{Th} for the network external to the 2-kΩ resistor.

$R_{Th} =$ _____ , $E_{Th} =$ _____

(b) Determine the power delivered to the 2-kΩ resistor using the Thevenin equivalent circuit.

(c) Is the power determined in part (b) the maximum power that could be delivered to a resistor between terminals a and b? If not, what is the maximum power?

Name:_____

Date:_____

Course and Section:_____

Instructor:_____

Norton's Theorem and Source Conversions

OBJECTIVES

1. Validate Norton's theorem through experimental measurements.
2. Become aware of an experimental procedure to determine I_N and R_N.
3. Demonstrate how a current source can be constructed (for a limited load range) using a voltage source.

EQUIPMENT REQUIRED

Resistors

1—10-Ω, 47-Ω, 100-Ω, 220-Ω, 330-Ω, 3.3-kΩ, 10-kΩ (1/4-W)

1—0–1-kΩ potentiometer

Instruments

1—DMM

1—dc Power supply

EQUIPMENT ISSUED

TABLE 1

Item	Manufacturer and Model No.	Laboratory Serial No.
DMM		
Power supply		

RÉSUMÉ OF THEORY

Through the use of Thevenin's or Norton's theorem, a complex two-terminal, linear, multisource dc network can be replaced by a single source and resistor.

The Norton equivalent circuit is a single dc current source in parallel with a resistor. The *Norton current (I_N)* is the short-circuit current between the terminals in question. The *Norton resistance (R_N)* is the resistance between these terminals with all voltage and current sources replaced by their internal resistances.

The theory of source conversion dictates that the Norton and Thevenin circuits be terminally equivalent and related as follows:

$$R_N = R_{Th} \qquad E_{Th} = I_N R_N \qquad I_N = \frac{E_{Th}}{R_{Th}} \tag{1}$$

A current source of some practical value can be constructed using a voltage source if the source resistance (R_s), as shown in Fig. 1(a), is much greater than the range of the load resistance R_L.

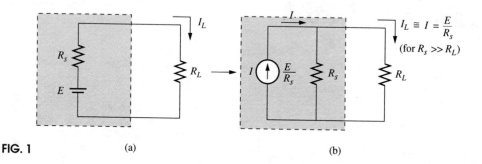

FIG. 1 (a) (b)

For Fig. 1(a)

$$I_L = \frac{E}{R_s + R_L}$$

If $R_s >> R_L$, $R_s + R_L \cong R_s$ and

$$I_L \cong \frac{E}{R_s}$$

demonstrating that the current I_L of the load is essentially unaffected by changes in R_L as long as $R_s >> R_L$. The equivalent current source for $R_s >> R_L$ appears in Fig. 1(b).

PROCEDURE

Part 1 Designing a 1-mA Current Source

(a) Construct the network of Fig. 2. Insert the measured resistor values.

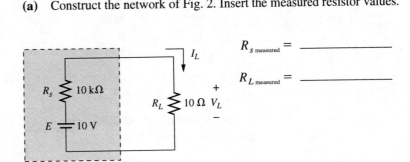

$R_{s\,measured} = $ _____

$R_{L\,measured} = $ _____

FIG. 2

(b) Using measured resistor values, calculate the current I_L.

$I_L = $ _____

(c) Turn on the supply and measure the voltage V_L. Then calculate the current I_L using the measured resistor value.

$V_L = $ _____

$I_L = $ _____

(d) Turn off the supply and change R_L to 47 Ω and then calculate the resulting current I_L using measured resistor values.

$R_{L\,measured} = $ _____

$I_L = $ _____

(e) Turn on the supply and measure the voltage V_L. Then calculate the current I_L using the measured resistor value.

$V_L = $ _____

$I_L = $ _____

(f) Increase R_L to 100 Ω and measure the voltage V_L. Then calculate the current I_L using the measured resistor value.

$V_L =$ _____ $R_{L\,measured} =$ _____

$I_L =$ _____

(g) Finally, increase R_L to 220 Ω and measure the voltage V_L. Then calculate the current I_L using the measured resistor value.

$V_L =$ _____ $R_{L\,measured} =$ _____

$I_L =$ _____

(h) Plot I_L (from measured V_L) versus R_L on Graph 1 for the values of R_L chosen in parts 1(a) through 1(g).

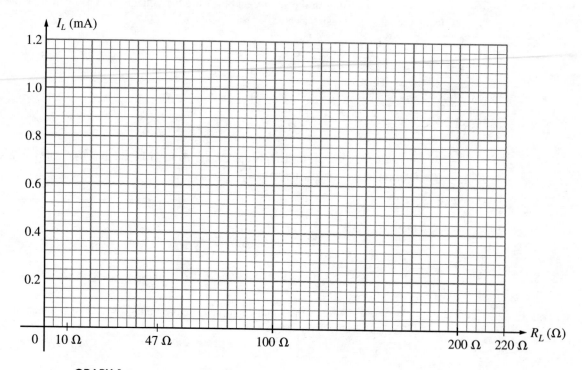

GRAPH 1

(i) Does the plot of Graph 1 reveal that I_L is fairly constant for the range of chosen R_L values?

(j) Would you consider the network of Fig. 3 a good equivalent to the configuration of Fig. 2? Make any appropriate comments.

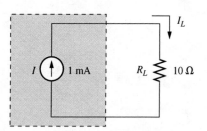

FIG. 3

Part 2   Determining R_N and I_N

(a) Construct the network of Fig. 4(a). Insert the measured value of each resistor.

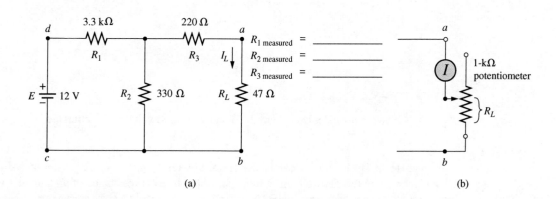

FIG. 4

(b) Using measured resistor values, calculate the levels of R_N and I_N for the network to the left of the 47-Ω resistor.

$$R_N = \text{\underline{\hspace{3cm}}} \, , I_N = \text{\underline{\hspace{3cm}}}$$

(c) Using the Norton equivalent circuit calculated in part 2(b), calculate the current I_L for a load of 47 Ω.

$$I_L = \text{\underline{\hspace{3cm}}}$$

(d) Turn on the supply and measure the voltage V_{ab}. Then calculate the current I_L using the measured resistor value.

$$V_{ab} = \text{\underline{\hspace{3cm}}}$$

$$I_L = \text{\underline{\hspace{3cm}}}$$

How do the calculated (part 2(c)) and measured values of I_L compare?

(e) The level of I_N can be determined by replacing the 47-Ω resistor by a short circuit and measuring the short-circuit current. Since the internal resistance of an ammeter is relatively low, all this can be accomplished by simply removing the 47-Ω resistor and replacing it by the ammeter section of the DMM. Since the current level is unknown, start with the highest scale and work down to the scale that provides the highest degree of accuracy. Record the level of I_N.

$$I_N = \text{\underline{\hspace{3cm}}}$$

How does the calculated value of I_N from part 2(b) compare with this measured value of I_N?

(f) R_N is now determined experimentally by first calculating $I_N/2$ using the measured value from part 2(e). For the Norton equivalent circuit with $R_L = R_N$, $I_L = I_N/2$.

$$\frac{I_N}{2} = \underline{\hspace{3cm}}$$

Connect the 1-kΩ potentiometer and ammeter in a series configuration between points a and b, as shown in Fig. 4(b). Turn on the supply and vary the potentiometer until the ammeter reading is $I_N/2$. Then remove the potentiometer and measure R_N.

$$R_N = \underline{\hspace{3cm}}$$

How does the calculated value of R_N from part 2(b) compare with this measured value of R_N?

(g) We will now construct the Norton equivalent circuit defined by the calculated levels of R_N and I_N from part 2(b).

First construct the network of Fig. 5.

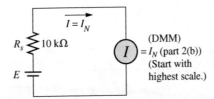

FIG. 5

Then vary the supply voltage until the DMM indicates the value I_N from part 2(b). Record the values of E and I_N in Fig. 6(b). Next remove the DMM and, using it as an ohmmeter, set the 0–1-kΩ potentiometer to the value of R_N from part 2(b). Now insert the 0–1-kΩ potentiometer in the circuit of Fig. 6(b).

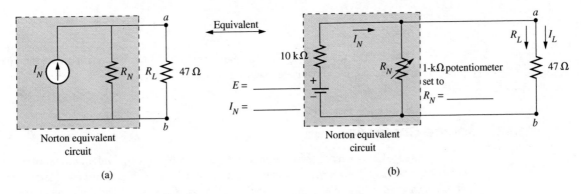

(a)

(b)

FIG. 6

The network of Fig. 6(b) is the Norton equivalent circuit. The 0–1-kΩ potentiometer is equivalent to R_N, and the 10-kΩ resistor in series with the power supply is the equivalent current source. The 10-kΩ resistor was chosen to ensure minimum sensitivity on the part of I_N to the smaller resistor values connected in parallel in Fig. 6(b). In other words, $I_N = E/(10 \text{ k}\Omega + R_{network}) \cong E/10 \text{ k}\Omega$ and, therefore, approximates an ideal current source.

Measure the voltage V_{ab} and compute I_L using the measured resistor value.

$V_{ab} =$ _____

$I_L =$ _____

How does the level of I_L determined here compare with the calculated level of part 2(c)? Has the Norton equivalent circuit been verified?

(h) Replace the 47-Ω resistor of Fig. 6(b) by a 100-Ω resistor and measure the voltage V_{ab}. Then calculate the resulting current I_L using the measured resistor value.

$V_{ab} =$ _____

$I_L =$ _____

Reconstruct the network of Fig. 4 with $R_L = 100 \ \Omega$ and measure the voltage V_{ab}. Then calculate the current I_L using the measured resistor value.

$V_{ab} =$ _____

$I_L =$ _____

How do the levels of I_L for this part compare? Have we verified that the Norton equivalent circuit is valid for changing loads across its terminals?

Part 3   Source Conversion

(a) Using source conversion techniques, the Norton equivalent circuit of Fig. 6(b) can be converted to a Thevenin equivalent circuit. Further, if the circuits are completely equivalent, the measured values of V_{ab} and I_L should be the same as before. The conversion can be accomplished by first calculating the Thevenin voltage E_{Th}. Determine E_{Th} using the conversion equation $E_{Th} = I_N R_N$ and the parameters of Fig. 6(b).

$E_{Th} =$ _____

Since $R_{Th} = R_N$, the Thevenin equivalent circuit can now be constructed.

(b) Construct the Thevenin equivalent circuit of Fig. 7:

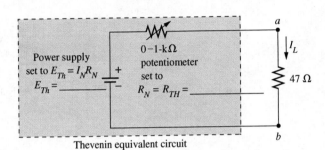

FIG. 7   Thevenin equivalent circuit

Now measure the voltage V_{ab} and again compute I_L. (Use the measured value of the 47-Ω resistor.)

$V_{ab} =$ _____ , $I_L =$ _____

How do V_{ab} and I_L compare to those in part 2(d)? Calculate the percent difference from

$$\% \text{ Difference} = \frac{|\text{Part 2(d)} - \text{Part 3(b)}|}{\text{Part 2(d)}} \times 100\%$$

$\%$ Difference $(I) =$ _____ , $\%$ Difference $(V_{ab}) =$ _____

Do the results verify the source conversion theory?

PROBLEMS

For the network of Fig. 8:

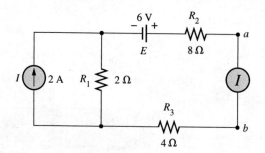

FIG. 8

(a) Find I_N by determining the reading of an ammeter placed between points a and b.

$I_N =$ _____

(b) Find R_N by determining the load resistor R_L that must be placed between points a and b to establish $I_L = I_N/2$.

$R_N =$ _____